D1612601

BOSCOMBE DOWN 1939-45

A MOST SECRET PLACE

BOSCOMBE DOWN 1939-45

Brian Johnson
& Terry Heffernan

A MOST SECRET PLACE

JANE'S

Computer typesetting by
D. P. Media Limited, Hitchin, Hertfordshire

Printed in Great Britain by
Mackays of Chatham

CONTENTS

A record of the order moving the Aeroplane and Armament Experimental Establishment from Martlesham Heath to Boscombe Down at the outbreak of the Second World War.

See instructions for use of this form in K.R. and A.C.I., para 2319 and War Manual, Pt. II, chapter XX, and notes in R.A.F. Pocket Book.

OPERATIONS RECORD BOOK

ORIGINAL.
R.A.F. Form 540
No. of pages used for day...........

of (Unit or Formation) .... Aeroplane & Armament Experimental Establishment.

Place.	Date.	Time.	Summary of Events.	References to Appendices.
Martlesham Heath.	1-9-39.		General Mobilization ordered.	
"	2-9-39		Married quarters surrendered in accordance with pre-arranged plan.	
{Initial Position} compt	3-9-39		Ultimatum delivered to German Government to remove all his troops from Poland or else a state of war would exist between the U.K. and Germany. This ultimatum to expire at 1100 hrs.	
"	"	1100	State of War declared to exist between the United Kingdom and Germany only. (Air Ministry signal A.34 3/9 1115) The Prime minister - The Right Hon Neville Chamberlain gave the news in a broadcast message to the Empire.	Appendix 2.
Martlesham Heath.	"		In accordance with Operation order N°1, A & A.E.E commenced to move from Martlesham Heath to Boscombe Down. 51 aircraft departed hm.	Appendix 3.
"	4/9/39.		Continued to move from Martlesham Heath — Boscombe Down. 19 aircraft departed.	
Several aircraft	"	1200	Message from H.M. the King to the Secretary of State for Air — the Rt Hon Sir Kingsley Wood M.P. (received from Air Ministry) and reply thereto.	Appendix 4.
Martlesham Heath	3/9/39 5 4/9/39 C 7/9/39		Aircraft rear personnel of D flight detailed to field.	
	7/9/39		Remainder of air party A.& A.E.E. to Boscombe Down.	
	8/3/39		Last rail & road party A & A E E to Boscombe Down.	
	9/9/39	.	Second rail party A. & A. E. E. to Boscombe Down.	

PREFACE

The A&AEE, Aeroplane and Armament Experimental Establishment, was officially granted that title in 1924 though much of the work had been carried out under different names for some years previously. The airfield from which the A&AEE tested the aircraft and their armaments between the wars was Martlesham Heath, a bleak, windswept site near Woodbridge, Suffolk.

Between the wars, the work of the Establishment progressed from the early fabric-covered biplanes to the new generation of metal monoplanes which included the Spitfire and Hurricane. When, after the 1938 Munich crisis, it was clear that war with Germany was inevitable, plans were laid to evacuate the A&AEE from its vulnerable site on the east coast to Boscombe Down, near Salisbury. Boscombe Down started as an RFC airfield in 1917 but lay derelict after the First World War until 1930, when the first stages of the expansion of the RAF caused it to re-open, as a bomber station. On the outbreak of the Second World War on 3 September 1939, the A&AEE moved, lock, stock and barrel, to Boscombe Down, where it remains to this day.

The function of the A&AEE was, and still is, the evaluation of aircraft, their armament and other equipment for the Services.

Broadly speaking, the A&AEE was only concerned with the suitability of the aircraft for their intended Service role: naturally there was considerable interchange and co-operation with the manufacturers and the Royal Aircraft Establishment, Farnborough. During the Second World War, every aircraft type which entered squadron service with the RAF and Fleet Air Arm (and a good many which did not) was tested at Boscombe Down; a glance at the 'aircraft on charge' in the Appendix will reveal the diversity of types.

The present volume reflects the nature of this arduous and often dangerous work; all the accounts are based on the official contemporary reports; many quoted at length. These reports were written under pressure at a time of severe national crisis; where obvious typing errors have occurred and the original meaning is clear, these have been corrected. The reports used Imperial units of speed, height and measurement; these are retained: it would have compromised the accuracy of the reports to change them and would have been tedious to include the metric equivalents.

When possible the original photographs – many unpublished – are reproduced though it should be pointed out that, with very few exceptions, the negatives are lost and the surviving prints are now over 40 years old. However, it was considered that readers would rather have a faded original than a well-known substitute.

The A&AEE reports are held at Boscombe Down which is, for obvious reasons, closed to the public; the serious student of aviation history will, however, find many of the files duplicated under AIR/AVIA lists at the Public Record Office, London.

My co-author, Terry Heffernan, witnessed and, indeed, participated in some of the test flights reported. I, as an outsider, can only wonder, as doubtless will the reader, at the courage and dedication of the test flight crews, Service and civilian, some of whom gave their lives to ensure that the Services got the best possible aircraft – a goal which remains at Boscombe Down, that 'Most Secret Place'.

Terry Heffernan and I are indebted to the Commandant A&AEE for help extended and The Controller, Her Majesty's Stationery Office, for permission to reproduce Crown Copyright material. My wife, Sybil, typed (and retyped) the manuscript which was skilfully edited by Michael Stevens of Jane's.

BRIAN JOHNSON
London, August 1982

CHAPTER ONE

A&AEE Report No. 760

The Case of the Disappearing Halifaxes

Handley Page Limited, of Cricklewood, London, had been designing and producing heavy bombers for the RAF since its inception in April 1918; even before
that, the Handley Page O/400 had been the largest aircraft in the Royal Flying
Corps. Its successor, the four-engined V/1500, had been the largest aircraft built
in Britain during the First World War; it had been designed to bomb Berlin but
the war ended before the type became operational. Other Handley Page bombers
that equipped RAF squadrons between the wars were the Hyderabad, Hinaidi,
Heyford and the monoplane Harrow which, though ordered as a bomber, was
never to be used as such, being employed on training and transport duties.

With such a background, the Handley Page Company was, not surprisingly,
one of the contractors tendering for the B.13/36 prototypes which were to be
powered by the then new Rolls-Royce Vultures – this being the same
specification that resulted in the ill-fated Avro Manchester.

The Air Ministry contract for two prototypes, L7244 and L7245, to B.13/36
was signed by the Handley Page Company in April 1937, the aircraft then being
known as Type H.P.56. The design team, led by G. R. Volkert, had been at work
for only a month or two when it was rumoured that there could be a possible
shortage of Vulture engines – that, at any rate, is one version of the story; it may
be, however, that the Handley Page team had heard of the very considerable
'teething' troubles that the Rolls-Royce X-24 engine was suffering from, to the
extent that the engine was in danger of being, at the very least, delayed in
production. A. V. Roe pressed on with their Manchester, but there could
well have been disquiet at the Air Ministry about the ultimate future of the
Vulture so, possibly to hedge the bets, Handley Page Ltd were officially encour-
aged to revise their design while it was still on the Cricklewood drawing boards to
take four Rolls-Royce Merlins – unlike Avro's, who had eventually to modify
substantially (under pressure of war) an actual aircraft. The Handley Page team
was able to effect a considerable revision at the cost of only the paper; the result
was a very much enlarged and far heavier aircraft than the original, the gross
weight rising from 26,300 lb for the twin to around 40,000 lb for the revised
four-engined bomber.

Two prototypes, known simply as Type H.P.57, were constructed at Cricklewood, work commencing in January 1938. The first prototype, L7244 (the
original service serials allocated for the two Vulture engined aircraft were
retained), was transported by road to RAF Bicester and flew from that grass
airfield for the first time on 25 October 1939 with Handley Page Company's chief

1

test pilot, Major Cordes, in command. The prototype was powered by four Rolls-Royce Merlin Xs, each offering 1,075 hp for take-off. On the first flight the prototype was not fitted with armament or turrets but it still tipped the scale at 55,000 lb. The flight was uneventful, which was just as well since the type had been 'ordered off the drawing board' in September 1937, when contracts for 100 Type H.P.57s were issued. This was later increased; the Air Staff envisaging 500 Handley Page Halifaxes, as the new bomber had been named, in RAF service by April 1942. (The plan had also called for 1,500 Manchesters by the same date.) The second prototype flew for the first time on 17 August 1940, by which time production was well under way, the first Halifax I (L9485) flying on 11 October 1940.

By the time the Mk I production aircraft were flying, the maximum take-off weight was 55,000 lb. Maximum speed of the Mk Is was 265 mph at 17,500 ft, with 2,242 Imperial gallons of fuel and a normal bomb load of 5,800 lb. Range was 1,860 statute miles; operational ceiling 22,800 ft. The standard armament consisted of two .303-inch guns in the nose turret and four .303-inch guns in the rear turret. A number of Mk I aircraft also had two single-beam .303 guns on either side of the fuselage.

On the night of 10–11 March 1941, six Halifax Is of No. 35 Squadron, based at Linton-on-Ouse, made the first operational sortie of the type: an attack on targets at Le Havre. A daylight raid was made on the German naval base at Kiel on 30 June 1941, followed by further daylight attacks on the battleship *Scharnhorst*, lying at the French Biscay port of La Pallice. Further daylight sorties followed, culminating in an attack on the battleships *Scharnhorst* and *Gneisenau*, then at Brest. This was to be the last major daylight bombing raid by Halifaxes; mounting losses, due to increasingly effective Luftwaffe fighters, caused Bomber Command to change to a policy of night bombing. (The Luftwaffe had come to the same decision, following unacceptably heavy losses of bombers during the Battle of Britain in the summer of 1940.)

An appreciation, following the introduction of the Halifax I into Bomber Command's Order of Battle, was that the aircraft was to some extent underpowered and, certainly on daylight sorties against well defended targets, underarmed. To remedy the latter shortcoming, the Handley Page design staff proposed an increase in the defensive armament. The first production Halifax I, L9485, was extensively tested at Boscombe Down, with ventral and dorsal turrets. After the tests, the ventral turret (and beam guns) were deleted but the dorsal turret became standard for B.Mk II production aircraft. The turret chosen (made by Boulton and Paul) was a somewhat bulbous affair, mounting twin .303s, and essentially the same as was then fitted to Coastal Command's Lockheed Hudsons, for which reason the turret, when fitted to Halifaxes, was usually referred to as the 'Hudson' turret.

The gross weight of production Halifaxes had by now risen to 60,000 lb, necessitating more powerful engines, these being, on early B.Mk II series Is, 1,390 hp Rolls-Royce Merlin XXs. The higher all-up weight, together with the drag of the 'Hudson' turret and a power wasting, flame-damping exhaust system, correctly considered essential for night operations, caused the already underpowered bomber to become distinctly tricky to fly, to the extent that, when fully loaded, the aircraft was prone to fall into uncontrollable spins. Accidents – many fatal – mounted, causing official alarm and considerable unpopularity among the operational Halifax squadron crews.

In an endeavour to alleviate the problem, a standard production Halifax (R9534) was sent to Boscombe Down where an intensive programme of weight and drag reduction was implemented. The result was the deletion of the nose turret, which service experience had shown was seldom used, particularly at night. A neat Perspex fairing replaced the twin gun turret, though a single, hand-operated Vickers 'K' .303 was mounted in some aircraft, more to encourage the bomb-aimer than seriously to discourage enemy fighters. The bomb-aiming 'chin' was replaced by an optically flat panel, which in itself must have considerably reduced drag. The large dorsal turret gave way to a much shallower type, similar to that fitted to the two-seater, single-engined Defiant night fighter. The engine cowlings were cleaned up aerodynamically, mainly by redesigning the radiators, and the power-consuming exhaust flame-dampers were removed. A good deal of unnecessary internal equipment was jettisoned; the tail-wheel was made semi-retractable; radio and D/F aerials were revised. Other detail modifications included redesigned bomb-doors and fuel jettison pipes. All these, together with still further uprated engines, Rolls-Royce Merlin XXIIs, were to enable the subsequent production Halifax B.Mk II Series IA to show a ten per cent increase in performance over the earlier marks. (Pending the supply of the new production Mk II, early aircraft were retrospectively modified to incorporate most of the A&AEE (Aeroplane and Armament Experimental Establishment) recommendations. These aircraft were then known as B.Mk II Series I (Special).)

When the Mk II Halifaxes entered squadron service, the increased performance was welcomed, but unfortunately the number of Halifax losses continued to mount steadily, to the point where the Air Ministry Departments CI (Accidents) and S4 (Statistics), on analysing the reports, came to the inescapable conclusion that the numbers of Halifaxes missing over enemy territory were more than could be ascribed solely to battle losses. There had, in addition, been a number of inexplicable accidents – all fatal – over the UK; one, which occurred on 7 June 1942, was to have a serious effect on the radar war. The most secret prototype H_2S centimetric radar was being tested in Halifax V9977, which had taken off from the Telecommunications Research Establishment (TRE) airfield at Defford, with practically the entire H_2S development team on board, including the brilliant scientist A. D. Blumlein. V9977 did not return: it had crashed from unknown causes into a field near Ross-on-Wye, killing all the occupants. Further Halifax crashes followed, none of the aircrews surviving to give an account as to the cause. Minute inspection of squadron aircraft or sifting through the remains of Halifaxes which had crashed in the UK revealed no clues, though some form of structural failure was naturally suspected.

As part of a separate investigation into the performance of Halifax IIs, a representative aircraft had been acquired from an operational squadron in the summer of 1942. This aircraft, DG221, when flown by A&AEE test pilots, showed with stark reality the narrow margins which operational pilots and aircrews unwittingly accepted.

The A&AEE report[1] noted that the aircraft had been flown direct from an operational squadron 'in the condition in which it had been operating'. The report continued:

This aeroplane [DG221] . . . showed evidence of bad workmanship and poor servicing, and had also been treated with a particularly rough brand of special night black finish. . . .

This particular aircraft had completed nine operational sorties; its poor servicing was reflected in the fitting of an odd propeller: the starboard inner had a Rotol R7/35/55 but the three remaining engines drove Rotol R7/35/54s. The carburettor hot air shutters were found to be working loose and had to be wired permanently in the cold air position.

The handling test of this aircraft revealed from the outset a marginal performance, as the report reveals:[2]

> *Take off.* The aeroplane had a poor take-off performance . . . the take-off run on a warm day became critical. On the final flight, with the ground temperature at 25°C, a take-off run of 42 seconds was registered. On this occasion the aerodrome boundary was cleared with difficulty after two previous attempts had been made to lift the aeroplane off the ground. It was obvious that the slightest faltering on the part of any engine or on the part of the pilot would have been disastrous.
>
> It was intended to test this aeroplane in the worst operational conditions, i.e. with exhaust shrouds [flame-dampers] and 2/4,000 lb bombs fitted. In view of the poor performance at take-off and at altitude these tests were cancelled. We consider this aeroplane so loaded to be unairworthy on a hot summer's day.

The poor performance at altitude was frankly reported on:[3]

> *Operation at Altitude.* Finally it is interesting to record flight experience on this aeroplane [DG221] at altitude in hot weather (approximately 10°C above standard). The aeroplane was flown with exhaust shrouds on and with bomb doors closed.
>
> At 18,000 ft a speed of 150 mph A.S.I. (Cruising threshold) was just maintained using maximum all-out level power. At 15,000 ft the aeroplane would just maintain height at maximum weak mixture cruising power (M.S. gear) at 142 mph A.S.I., a speed which is far too low either for comfort or emergency. These observations were made at an all-up weight (in flight) in the neighbourhood of 57,000 lb.
>
> In this condition of flight a minor emergency did in fact occur, the starboard outer engine boiled and the pilot immediately throttled back the engine slightly. The right wing dropped sharply, followed by the nose.

The A&AEE discovered that the performance of DG221, a representative squadron aircraft which had, as stated above, already completed nine operations, could not maintain 15,000 ft in normal weak mixture cruise and that in hot weather 13,000 ft was, to all intents and purposes, the operational ceiling of the aircraft and that even then:

> when flying in these conditions [i.e. the 'cruising threshold'] it is impossible to take sudden violent evasive action or carry out any quick manoeuvres because this may lead to the aeroplane falling out of control.

Although the performance of DG221 was poor,[4] it did not, in itself, explain the mounting losses of Halifaxes. The A&AEE began to suspect that rudder overbalance could be a contributory cause and an investigation was decided upon.

The A&AEE was requested to investigate the possible causes of the mounting accidents.

The first step was to examine the reports of the early handling trials which had been made at Boscombe Down on the second prototype, L7245, and also on the first production aircraft, L9485. In the 3rd part of the Report A&AEE/760, dated 21 December 1940, was this significant observation:

Para 4.4   *Response of Controls*
Rudders. At speeds below 120 mph these give little response. They are effective at higher speeds and appear to have sufficient power to cope with engine failure. . . . At speeds below 150 mph there is a tendency for rudders to overbalance with application of rudder trim. This is particularly noticeable when speed is reduced through throttling one engine and application of rudder to prevent yaw. This is being investigated and a modified [trim] tab has been fitted in an attempt to prevent this.

Three weeks later another Halifax handling report had been issued; this, too, contained a significant observation:

4th Part of A&AEE/760 (17 January 1941):
L7245 Airscrew feathering tests
Para 3.2   *Handling*

Further tests were made with both engines on one side throttled back and airscrews feathered. The minimum speed at which the aeroplane could be flown straight and level was determined. . . . [minimum speed with both starboard airscrews feathered was 122 mph and 140 mph with both port engines feathered].

The factor limiting the minimum speed . . . was overbalance of the rudder. If the angle of the rudder trimmer was reduced to avoid overbalance the force on the rudder bar became excessive.

Para 5   *Recommendations*

The rudder overbalance, which is manifest when both port airscrews are feathered, would cause great fatigue to a pilot attempting to keep straight and level under such conditions, and modification action is necessary in order to overcome this defect.

It appeared, in the light of the original A&AEE reports, that rudder overbalance could be a likely lead in the enquiry.

The fins and rudders on the Halifax II were in the form of 'end plate fins'; that is the tailplane terminated in two arrow-shaped fins, each with an interconnected rudder. This form of tail assembly was a common feature of several contemporary multi-engined aircraft – the Lancaster had a similar layout; it was a popular arrangement with designers for it placed the rudders in the slipstream of both the port and starboard inner engines, making the rudders highly effective, particularly on take-off. Take-off with four-engined tail-wheel aircraft, especially with a fully loaded heavy bomber, could be difficult; as the throttles were opened to full take-off power, the aircraft tended to swing off the runway, due to engine torque. As the tail-wheel left the ground, the only directional control was from the rudders which, had they not been in the propeller slipstream, would, at the low air speeds in the early part of the take-off run, have been largely ineffective. (The Stirling had a single large fin and rudder on the aircraft's centre line; as a consequence, it was notoriously prone to 'swing' on take-off, requiring deft differential throttle control when on the ground to keep the bomber straight.)

5

The wartime RAF heavy bombers did not have power-operated controls, the pilot moving them directly. To help ease the considerable manual control loads, the elevators and rudders were aerodynamically balanced; that is, part of the actual control surface projected in front of the hinge line. The air loads on these forward projections acted to oppose the loads on the rest of the control surface, considerably easing the manual force required on the rudder bar. This assistance was necessary if the pilot had to apply large angles of rudder, as when taking evasive action or compensating for an engine failure. Without 'balancing', the rudders on an aircraft the size of the Halifax would be virtually solid at all but very low airspeeds.

Clearly, since the effect of the balancing areas of the rudder depends on the airspeed over the rudders, the size was inevitably a compromise between sufficient power to aid the pilot with the worst case of two dead engines on the same side, and not being over effective and taking over control of the rudders. This last case is the effect of overbalancing – a tendency noted by the A&AEE test pilots when conducting the original type handling trials.

As a result of those trials, a series of additional test flights was undertaken at A&AEE by Sqn. Ldr. W. J. Carr, AFC, and a civilian scientist, J. J. Unwin, MBE, to examine Halifax asymmetric flight characteristics. The tests were conducted with L9515, an early production Halifax I which had been used at Boscombe for previous trials. In their report[5] on the tests, Carr and Unwin recommended a redesign to the leading edges of the rudders, making them bulbous, and a reduction of the total movement of the rudder balance tab.

When the above modifications, which became known as Mod 413, were recommended, it was thought the Halifax II simply had a *tendency* to overbalance; it was not at that time known to be a definite hazard when flying the type, which continued to be used operationally. As the accident rate increased, however, it was decided that further flight trials with a standard service Halifax should be undertaken by A&AEE test pilots and scientists, to ascertain the extent of rudder overbalance and to assess if this was a likely cause of the accidents. As stated above, the original Halifax handling tests at Boscombe Down had been with the first prototype and first production aircraft, which were not representative of subsequent RAF squadron machines. The Carr and Unwin trials were also made with a non-standard aircraft. A standard production Halifax II, W7917, was therefore borrowed from 102 Squadron of No. 4 Group. This aircraft was new; it had flown a total of only 40 hours and was in every way representative of the Halifax IIs then in squadron service with No. 4 Group, Bomber Command.

The test programme began on 4 February 1943, when W7917 took off from Boscombe Down with Unwin on board. The pilot on this latest test flight was Flt. Lt. S. Reiss, a Pole serving with the RAF, who had been with the A&AEE for some time. The crew was completed by the flight engineer, Sgt. J. Fielding.

Reiss was, as one would expect, an experienced pilot; his total hours were in excess of 1,640 and he had, whilst acting as a Boscombe Down test pilot, enjoyed something of a charmed life, surviving two crashes the previous year. The first had been on 17 August 1942, when the nose-wheel of a B-24 Liberator (AL505) collapsed on landing. Three weeks later (6 September) Reiss was involved in a much more serious incident, when a fire broke out in the starboard outer engine of a Stirling III (R9309) which he was flying. The flight engineer found he could not extinguish the blaze, which began to spread alarmingly; Reiss then gave the order for the crew to bale out, which they did without injury, and then Reiss courageously attempted to perform the first duty of a test pilot: to bring the aircraft safely down, if at all possible. Unfortunately, when approaching Boscombe Down, the aircraft became uncontrollable, crashing into a wood on Porton Ridge. Reiss was very lucky to escape with broken ribs.

To return to the flight of Halifax W7917. It took off from Boscombe at a recorded all-up weight of 50,000 lb, with the stated intention of investigating rudder overbalance. Just what happened on the flight is conjecture, for when at an altitude of 12,000 ft, according to the official report,[6] it:

> was seen to dive and [then] pulled out in a shallow turn which terminated in a flat spin in which condition it struck the ground.
>
> The airframe broke into three sections, the front section consisting of the portion forward of the trailing edge of the wings catching fire on impact.
>
> All three occupants were killed immediately.

A full investigation of the wreckage at the crash site, a field two miles north-east of Sutton Scotney, near Winchester, revealed that the top half of one of the rudders had broken away in flight. This was attributed by the investigators to the rudders overbalancing with such force that one had fractured, rendering the aircraft uncontrollable.

As a result of the crash of W7917, witnessed by competent observers on the ground, any lingering doubts as to the reason for the mounting Halifax accidents were now dispelled.

The problem confronting A&AEE and the manufacturers of the Halifax, Handley Page Ltd, was to try to ascertain if a relatively simple alteration to the rudder or fins could be recommended, preferably one that could be applied by the squadrons as a retrospective field modification, rather than a disruptive redesign on the production lines. It was considered by the investigation team at Boscombe that this latter course would probably prove to be the case and that the overbalancing of the rudder was inherent in the original design. As the accident rate was still rising, the problem was assuming major proportions.

As an emergency interim measure, a series of flight tests was to be made to explore more fully the motion of the aircraft subsequent to rudder overbalancing, and it was hoped that a study of this motion might result in a means of reducing the accident rate.[7]

Two Halifax Mk II, Series IA aircraft, HR679 and HR727, both of which had been used for various experiments, were made available for the trials. These machines, though nominally the same Mark, were in fact similar but not identical and both differed from operational RAF Series II bombers in the shape of the nose.

HR679, with a standard production fin and rudder assembly, incorporating the recommended modification 413, was to be used principally to ascertain if it was feasible to make a relatively simple modification to reduce the rudder overbalance by limiting the movement of the rudders. A description of this Halifax was as follows:[8]

HR679

(i) The front turret was removed and the nose of the aircraft was streamlined in Perspex.

(ii) The Gallay coolant radiators were replaced by Morris block type radiators.

This (and [iii] and [v]) were part of the earlier A&AEE recommendations made to 'clean up' the Halifax II; the radiator change enabled a narrower cowling to be used, causing less drag.

(iii)   A Defiant-type [.303] 4-gun turret was fitted in the dorsal position.
(iv)   The inboard engine nacelles were extended beyond the trailing edge of the wings. [This was for another A&AEE trial unconnected with rudder overbalance.]
(v)   The tail-wheel was retractable.
(vi)   A Mk VIII pitot-static head was mounted in the under-nose position but only the pressure head was connected during the major part of the tests, the static pressure being supplied from a static vent situated on the port side of the fuselage near the tail. Toward the end of the tests it was decided to change over to the static side of the Mk VIII head because it was thought this source of static supply gave more reliable readings under conditions of sideslip.
(vii)   The fins and rudders were standard production items embodying Mod. 413.

The second Halifax, HR727, to be used in the tests was, like HR679, a non-standard aircraft, it too having been used for various tests unconnected with the investigation into rudder overbalancing. However, it was to fly with a redesigned rudder and fin which Handley Page Ltd had supplied. For interest, the other differences between the two aircraft, which with the exception of (iv) are irrelevant, are given as they appeared in the original report:[9]

HR727
(i)   Items (i), (ii) and (iii) [of the details of HR679] apply also to this aircraft.
(ii)   The inboard engine nacelles finished flush with the trailing edge of the wings, as on all production [Mk II] Series I aircraft.
(iii)   The tail-wheel is non-retractable. This cannot be classed as a difference from the production Series I.
(iv)   The fins and rudders were further modified [i.e. in addition to Mod. 413] by removing the bulbous noses, setting back the portion of the leading edges forward of the hinge line by 2 in, and by filling in the space with additional fin surface. In addition, the balance tab gearing was increased.
(v)   A Mk VIII pitot static head was mounted in the under-nose position and the static side of this head supplied static pressure to the pilot's airspeed indicator throughout the tests.

The primary role of this second Halifax, HR727, was to determine whether the revised Handley Page rudder/fin assembly would be successful in eliminating the overbalance trouble, assuming – as most of the people concerned with the investigation did – that the simple modification made to the other test Halifax would fail to cure the overbalance.

The first test flight was made on 26 February 1943. This flight was to ascertain the precise nature of the problem and, in effect, reproduce the manoeuvre which had caused the fatal crash to W7917, a fortnight earlier. Unfortunately the surviving A&AEE records at Boscombe Down do not contain the names of the very brave trials crew who conducted this dangerous flight, though even the cold print of the official report[10] cannot mask the supreme skill and coolness of the unknown test pilot. It is here reproduced:

4.1 HR679

4.11 This ... test [was] made to ... determine the subsequent behaviour if
overbalance set in during sideslip.

At 150 mph ASI the pilot attempted to introduce sideslip by applying right aileron
and opposite rudder, but the forces required were too high to make it possible for
more than a very small amount of control to be used. The angle of bank was about
15° and the rudder was heavy with no tendency to overbalance.

At 140 mph ASI the test was repeated and it was possible to apply a little more
bank with more rudder movement, and the results were similar to those obtained
at the higher speed.

At 130 mph ASI it was possible to apply full rudder with again about 15° of bank,
and there was no tendency for the rudder to overbalance.

At 120 mph ASI the pilot moved the rudder bar to approximately ¾ of its travel,
and thereafter the rudders moved of their own accord to the full extent of their
travel. The pilot was unable to centralise the rudder bar. The aircraft went into a
spiral dive in the direction of the applied rudder [to port]. Opening the throttles
fully on the port side failed to produce recovery, but, when the control column
was moved forward the airspeed rose to about 150 mph ASI, the rudder bar could
be returned to central, and straight flight was resumed.

During that test, the Halifax lost 4,000 ft. The reaction of those on board can well
be imagined, especially as, in such a large aircraft in a spiral dive, it would be
virtually impossible to move, due to centrifugal force, making it impossible to
bale out. Having survived a condition of flight that had killed numerous other
crews, the test pilot then climbed the Halifax back to 12,000 ft and tried a further
test, this time at 110 mph indicated airspeed. The same rudder locking occurred,
though this time the pilot was able to assist the recovery by opening up the port
engines to full take-off power: 2,850 rpm + 9 lb of boost.

The report summarizes these first tests:

When rudder locking takes place, the rudder overpowers the ailerons completely and
the aircraft rolls over to the side in which rudder is applied. At the same time, the nose
drops, and the aircraft enters a spiral dive. The recommended method of recovery is
to remove the opposite aileron, move the control column forward until the speed has
increased to at least 150 mph and then, after centralising the rudder, recover from the
resultant dive.

If [the report continues] the pilot pulls the control column back as the aircraft rolls
over and drops its nose (as he would instinctively do) then the controls are set for a spin
and, unless action is taken quickly ... a spin may result. In any case there is a large
height loss of anything up to 4,000 feet during recovery.

The root cause of the many Halifax accidents was now apparent. The trouble was
that the locking of the rudder was occurring at a speed likely to be encountered
just when any spiral or spin would be disastrous; that is when near the ground.
120 mph or less would be the speed of the bombers when approaching to land,
when any coarse operation of the rudders, coupled with a sideslip, could provoke
the fatal rudder locking; a not unlikely eventuality, particularly in making
crosswind landings.

Asymmetric flight, a common enough hazard on operational bombers with one
or more engines inoperative due to enemy action, was another flight condition
which could easily provoke the rudders to lock over; again, a Halifax flying on two
engines would be forced to cruise in the dangerous low speed range. Many

Halifaxes which failed to return from operation could well have spun in, following evasive manoeuvres to escape from the increasingly effective radar-guided German night fighters, particularly when crews resorted to the desperate evasive measure of 'corkscrewing'.

If a rear or upper gunner spotted a night fighter closing on his bomber, he would call on the intercom: 'Corkscrew, Skipper'. The pilot would then slam shut the throttles of the two engines on the same side, at the same time applying full rudder, usually to the left (a fact well known to German night fighter pilots, who reported that nine out of ten heavy bombers broke left on attack). The resultant violent corkscrew usually 'lost' the fighter: it may well have lost a number of Halifax IIs. It was, in any event, a dangerous measure in heavy bombers since they often had sustained structural damage from flak, unknown to the crews, and 'corkscrewing' imposed severe additional strain on the weakened airframes.

As far as the A&AEE were concerned, it was now true that a skilled test pilot had reproduced the conditions that had caused so many fatal Halifax accidents and had further empirically devised a successful recovery technique. However, it was clearly one thing for an experienced test pilot to effect a recovery in daylight with adequate height and the knowledge as to the nature of the problem; for operational squadron pilots, with perhaps as little as 200 hours total time, exhausted, possibly wounded and flying damaged bombers at night on instruments, in bad weather, over enemy territory, it would be quite another case. Merely pinpointing cause and effect and recommending a difficult recovery technique was not going materially to reduce the losses, or indeed commend the Halifax to its crews.

At Boscombe Down, before any further flights were undertaken, a safety measure was introduced on both of the test Halifaxes. It was decided, in the light of the first A&AEE report, to fit a restrictor which was attached to the rudder bar, enabling the pilot to govern the total amount of rudder travel in flight. The nominal maximum travel of a standard production Halifax II's rudder was a minute or two under 20°; the restrictor could be set up – on the ground – to limit the total angular movement to about 12°. In practice, due to losses in the control linkages, hinge play and flexing of the structure, the actual angle at the rudder was more than the nominal permitted by the restrictor. It was found that taking up this play acted as a damper and the rudder could no longer slam hard over, as had apparently happened to W7917. The restrictor on the rudder bar was calibrated in degrees, enabling the test crew to preselect the maximum rudder angle.

After the safety restrictor was fitted, the first proposition considered to prevent the locking of the rudders was a simple one: that of making them so heavy that no pilot could apply sufficient rudder to overbalance them in normal flight, yet leaving enough movement for control on take-off and compensating for asymmetric flight with dead engines. The first attempt to achieve this was a time-honoured method, well known to RAF riggers: 'stringing' or 'cording'.

'Cording' was used in the days of fabric-covered biplanes to adjust for minor rigging anomalies. If a pilot reported that his aircraft was flying, say, left wing low, the airframe riggers, after checking that the aircraft was rigged as accurately as eye and trammels allowed, would dope a short length of cord, of about ⅛ inch diameter, along the trailing edge on top of the left aileron. This cord acted on the airflow over the control, pushing it down, thereby lifting the low wing; by adjusting the length or diameter of the cord, an accurate trim could be obtained.

The practice of cording continued into the era of all-metal monoplanes because many, including the Halifax, still had fabric-covered control surfaces.

The cording of the Halifax was to be on both sides of the trailing edges of the rudders, with the object of making the control sufficiently heavy to prevent the fatal overbalance angle being achieved in flight.

With the cording doped into place, tests were flown with HR679 with rudder restricted firstly to a total left/right travel of 12°, then with 12° left and 15° right. Some unexpected facts emerged from the test flight; the test pilots were surprised to find that, contrary to expectations, the cord made no difference to the rudder 'feel', no additional heaviness being apparent. No rudder overbalance occurred when sideslipping to starboard, even down to 105 mph indicated, at a maximum rudder angle of 14°; but when sideslipping to port, overbalance occurred at a 12° rudder angle, but only at the low speed of 105 mph.

The conclusions drawn from the tests flown with HR679, with the restricted rudder movement and ⅛ inch cord doped to the rudder, did not offer any appreciable hope of solving the problem, though the A&AEE report[11] reveals that the 'cord' was still considered as a possible solution:

... It was still hoped that a condition might be found in which the rudders would be too heavy for the pilot to apply sufficient control to reach the overbalance stage and yet in which the effectiveness of the rudders, when acted upon by the trimming tabs, would be sufficient to cater for the worst asymmetric flight case [i.e. two engines out on the same side].

To this end the ⅛ inch cord was removed from the trailing edges of the rudders and replaced by cord of ³/₁₆ inch diameter, but below the trimming tabs only. At the same time, the angular movement of the rudders was reduced from [a nominal] 20° each way to 17° each way.

Other tests had shown that 17° each way was ample to cover the worst case of asymmetric flight.

Several test flights were made with HR679 in the condition described above. The aircraft was flown by a number of A&AEE pilots, a Handley Page test pilot and an experienced RAF captain from No. 4 Group which operated Halifaxes. The report summarized the tests:

1. The rudders were considered too heavy for general flying.
2. The ... cord did not improve the rudder locking characteristic.
3. The restricted angular movement provided ample rudder control for turns against two engines running at emergency power conditions [2,850 rpm and +9 lb boost] down to a speed of 140 mph ASI.

Since the ³/₁₆ inch cord simply made the rudders unpleasantly heavy in flight, whilst contributing nothing to the central problem of rudder overbalance, the cord was removed and the aircraft test flown with just a restrictor fitted to the rudder bar. The report concluded that:

... It was anticipated that the rudder angle required to cater for two dead engines on the starboard side would be less than that required for the opposite side [due to the effect of engine torque] and, since no cure could be offered to the Service for rudder locking, it was hoped that a further restriction in angular rudder movement to port could be recommended, it being agreed that, provided sufficient rudder movement was left to allow turns to be made against two working engines, the smaller the angular movement available, the less violent would be the behaviour of an aircraft when rudder locking took place.

The tests conducted were to be repeated with the second Halifax, HR727, with the factory modified rudder with the smaller balance areas. The results of the test were disappointing, as the report summarizes:

5.2   HR727   The modified rudders, with reduced aerodynamic balance, are more pleasant for general flying than the standard rudders because they are more effective, but, because they suffer also from overbalance troubles, and because, being more effective they overbalance at smaller angles, they cannot be recommended for fitment to Service aircraft. . . .

The report held out little hope of solving the basic Halifax problem, as stated in the 'Conclusions and Recommendations' of the report:

Since no cure nor palliative can be suggested to stop Halifax rudders locking in Service, it is recommended that all existing rudders be restricted in angular movement to 17° each way. . . . A further restriction of 2° to port could be made if desired, but it is probably safer to keep the movement equal each way. Tests now being carried out at the Royal Aircraft Establishment [RAE Farnborough] should show whether the rudder locking characteristic is due to overbalance, tail stalling, or both. In any case, a cure can almost certainly be effected by the introduction of increased fin area, and it is strongly recommended that a substantial increase of fin area be provided.

Modifications to the rudder limit stops were recommended and, as far as the existing squadron Halifaxes were concerned, that was combined with careful briefing of pilots at the operational training units (OTU) and No. 4 Group as to the possible consequences of inadvertently locking the rudders and the recommended recovery techniques; there the matter for the moment had to rest. However, the number of Halifax accidents did fall.

It was considered at A&AEE that the recommendations were only a palliative and in no way cured the rudder locking, which the RAE traced to complex fin and rudder stalling, due in part to turbulent air from the rather slab-sided Halifax fuselage. The final cure was a redesigned 'D' shaped fin with 40 per cent larger area. The new tail was tested by A&AEE on Halifax III, R9534.

The rudders on the new tail could be moved 20° either way and, though rather heavy, showed no tendency to overbalance in any condition of flight. They were adopted by Handley Page on all future Halifax production.

The A&AEE later tested a production Mk V, DK145 with the new 'D' type rudders and found them satisfactory, concluding that:

The handling qualities of the Halifax II or V are satisfactory with the large D type rudder and fin combination. There is sufficient rudder for flight with two engines dead on one side and turns can be made against the working engines. There is no tendency for the rudders to overbalance when sideslipping down to 120 mph ASI.

The case was now closed.

The Halifax II with the revised 'D' type fins continued in second line service (mainly with training units) until the end of the war; it had been supplanted on the production lines by the B.Mk III, which began its operational career with Bomber Command in February 1944. This bomber variant was the best of the Halifaxes. It was powered by four Bristol Hercules XVIs, fourteen cylinder sleeve valve radials, offering 1,615 hp for take-off which, with an increase of wingspan from the original 98 ft 10 inches to 104 ft 2 inches, substantially improved the operational ceiling of the type.

A final Halifax bomber, the B.Mk VI, was operational by October 1944, but was too late to see extensive service though, had the war in the Pacific continued, the Mk VI would have been used in the Far East.

During the war years, in addition to service with Radio Counter Measure squadrons, Coastal, Transport and Training Commands, Halifaxes of Bomber Command flew on 75,532 sorties, dropping 227,610 tons of bombs.

A single Halifax III of 462 Squadron shared with Mosquitos the distinction of dropping the last bombs on Germany, with a sortie against Flensburg on 2 May 1945.

The total production of 6,176 Halifaxes, which included 1,966 Mk IIs and 2,000 Mk IIIs, were produced by Handley Page, English Electric, Rootes and Fairey Aviation. The last Halifax built, a Mk IX (RT938), left the Handley Page factory at Cricklewood in London on 20 November 1946.

The later Halifaxes, Mks VIII and IX, were used postwar for the training of parachutists and supply dropping and numbers of them remained with the RAF in this role until finally superseded by the Handley Page Hastings in 1948.

The Halifax, in common with many of the aircraft of the fighting powers during the Second World War had its problems, but these were overcome to enable the only bomber produced in Greater London to make a considerable contribution to the RAF's share of victory, in which the scientists and test pilots of the A&AEE played a vital, though hitherto unpublished, role.

CHAPTER TWO

A&AEE Report No. 751

The Manchester

Very few of the hundreds of aircraft types produced by the fighting powers during the Second World War entirely fulfilled the hopes of either their constructors or of the operational crews who flew them in action; but such crews tend to be loyal to their charges, however serious their shortcomings. In point of fact, considering the pressures under which most wartime aircraft were designed and built, there were remarkably few *total* disasters. The German Me210 was one; the American Brewster Buffalo another; Britain contributed the Blackburn Botha and, perhaps the most 'disappointing' of all, the Avro Manchester.

It should be remembered that many of the aircraft of the war years, 1939–1945, were designed, or at least envisaged, during the mid-thirties, at a time when the science and, indeed, art of aerodynamics were undergoing profound changes. The stressed skin, all-metal monoplane had appeared; engine powers were double what had been available in the twenties and early thirties. New concepts of variable pitch airscrews, retractable undercarriages and wing flaps requiring complex use of hydraulic systems; new radio aids and instruments created design problems for the industrial nations at the precise time of universal re-armament.

During the thirties, the rise of the German Luftwaffe and the very real threat posed by the political ambitions of Hitler shook the British Government from the years of complacency to the extent that, in 1934, the long overdue modernisation of the RAF resulted in the issuing of several specifications, two of which were to enable Fighter Command eventually to receive the Spitfire and Hurricane. Bomber Command, which in the mid-thirties was still flying biplane bombers – the Handley Page Heyford was typical – was to have its squadrons re-equipped with modern monoplanes: the Fairey Battles, Bristol Blenheims, Handley Page Hampdens, Armstrong Whitworth Whitleys and Vickers Wellingtons. Most of these types – not in the event all equally successful – were ordered around 1935, at which time a target of 1,000 bombers by March 1939 was set.

Of the above, only the Whitley and Wellington could be considered 'heavies' – a fact soon realised by the Air Ministry Director of Operational Requirements, Group Captain R. D. Oxland who, in May 1936, with considerable foresight, issued Specification B.12/36 which called for a four-engined bomber, and Specification B.13/36 for a twin-engined heavy bomber. These aircraft were to have the then unprecedented capacity to lift up to 12,000 lb of bombs. (For comparison, the Heyford's maximum bomb load was 3,000 lb.)

There were, not surprisingly, objections to these, then, enormous aircraft, not the least of which was the problem of getting them airborne; in 1936, RAF airfields were just that: relatively small grass fields with no hard runways whatsoever. As a consequence, the twin-engined bomber to be built to B.13/36 was to be stressed for 'Frictionless Take-off'; in effect, a large hydro-pneumatic catapult with which the Royal Aircraft Establishment was experimenting.

The firms tendering for the two bomber specifications included Messrs. A. V. Roe, Supermarine, Handley Page and Short Brothers. After the proposals were considered, contracts for prototypes of the four-engined B.12/36 were awarded to Short Brothers and Supermarine, whose chief designer, R. J. Mitchell, had just finished his work on the Spitfire. Mitchell's prototype, the Type 317, which was incidentally the last design he completed, was destroyed in a 1940 air raid; by that time R. J. Mitchell had died and, in view of the company's involvement with the development of the Spitfire, the Supermarine project was dropped. The B.12/36 production contract went to Short Brothers who were to produce it as the Short Stirling.

The second 1936 specification, B.13/36, that for the twin, was to be filled by two prototypes: the Avro 679 and the Handley Page H.P.56. Both types were originally to be powered by the new Rolls-Royce Vulture engines which promised 1,760 hp for take-off. In 1936, 1,760 hp from a single engine was very high power indeed; the Vultures – in effect though not in detail – were two 880 hp Rolls-Royce V-12 Peregrine engines joined to a common crankcase to form an X-24 engine. Handley Page, whether from deep insight or just plain good luck, decided to forego these new complex and untried engines and to opt for four of the more modest 1,030 hp V-12 Rolls-Royce Merlins, which were more or less scaled-up versions of that RAF workhorse, the 550 hp Rolls-Royce Kestrel, which had successfully powered many RAF aircraft for a decade or more. The B.13/36 specification was therefore re-drawn to incorporate the change; the Handley Page prototype became the H.P.57 – eventually to enter RAF service as the Halifax.

A. V. Roe's chief designer, Roy Chadwick, and his team stuck to the twin Vultures and began their detailed design of the Avro 679, later to be named the Manchester. It was, by then, early 1937 and such was the political climate in Europe at that time that the company, while still working on the mock-up, received an order for 200 Vulture powered Manchesters. If there were any celebrations on signing the contracts at Avro's Newton Heath factory, they were to prove distinctly premature.

The original B.13/36 specification was upgraded and a new number, B.19/37, was allocated for two pre-production prototypes. While the prototypes were under construction, two parallel developments were in hand. Rolls-Royce acquired two Hawker Henley aircraft from the makers, K5115 (the Henley prototype) and K3302, to act as flying testbeds for the Vulture engines which were proving troublesome. The second development was under way at Harwell (then an RAF airfield, but better known today as the Atomic Energy Research Establishment), where the RAE's 'Frictionless Take-off' catapult was being constructed. This, too, was proving to be a difficult proposition.

In July 1939, the first prototype Manchester, L7246, was complete and stood at A. V. Roe's factory airfield at Ringway (now Manchester Airport) awaiting its first test flight. It was an impressive enough aircraft and, by the standards of the day, enormous, with an all-up weight in excess of twenty tons. The fuselage was 70 ft in length and stood 19 ft 6 in on its retractable tail-wheel undercarriage.

Although the front and rear gun turrets were not fitted, the general arrangement would be instantly recognisable by anyone familiar with the later four-engined Lancaster. The two Vulture engines were set in rather bulbous cowlings in the 80 ft 2 in wings. The 28 ft span tailplane had neat twin endplate fins.

The test pilot for the initial flight trials was Avro's Captain H. A. Brown. The test flights were to be conducted under extreme secrecy – the Second World War was only weeks away – and, in view of the unprecedented power of the new Vulture engines, red flags were stuck into the ground behind the aircraft to keep people from straying into what was thought to be the dangerous slipstream (propwash).

The first flight on 24 July 1939 was of 17 minutes duration and it was immediately apparent that, for all the impressive sound and fury from the Vulture's 48 cylinders, the new engines were not developing their design power. This, added to the already high wing loading, plus a marked instability, must have made that 17 minute circuit of Ringway seem a good deal longer to Captain Brown. The general impression was that the new wonder bomber was not, to say the very least, an easy proposition to fly.

In the course of these early flights the Royal Aircraft Establishment was consulted about the marked instability from which the prototype suffered. To alleviate this, a third central fin was added on the fuselage centre line. This may have helped to correct the directional instability but it did nothing for the aircraft aesthetically.

A total of eight short test flights was made from Ringway, though because of the strict secrecy being observed, no release of the existence of the new bomber was made to the press.

All in all, the test team at Avro's must have had a very worrying time during those early flights; the aircraft, still known as Type 679, was far from satisfactory. The war had broken out; 200 production aircraft were on order; several sub-contractors in the new 'shadow factories' were actively preparing to build the bombers. To assist in the now urgent development, it was decided to fly the aircraft to the A&AEE; L7246 landed at Boscombe Down on 10 December 1939. The weather, that first winter of the war, was very bad, it being one of the coldest within living memory; the wide open downland of Salisbury Plain was arctic and, to add to the difficulties, A&AEE was only just settling in to its new wartime base. However, no time was lost in the task of investigating the performance of the prototype Manchester, as it had now been named.

A summary[1] of the preliminary flight trials of L7246 at Boscombe was to reveal several shortcomings that rendered even this unarmed prototype quite unsuitable for squadron service. The surviving files at A&AEE[2] show that the prototype was test flown at all-up weights of 34,050 and 40,000 lb. The aircraft, at this stage, had 80 ft span wings and a 28 ft span tailplane, with the triple fins fitted as a result of the RAE's recommendations. Even with the triple fins it was found that, on take-off, a marked swing to port needed full rudder and brakes to contain. The elevators were very heavy, a large force being required to raise the tail to get the aircraft to unstick; even with the reluctant tail up, the take-off performance was found to be very poor. With full take-off power and 15° of flap, the first Manchester (at 40,000 lb) required 1,076 yards (!) to clear 20 ft. This poor performance was considered to be due, in part, to the early Vulture engines being some 100 hp down on the design take-off power.

Once airborne, the Manchester was found to be directionally and laterally stable, but with the centre of gravity (C of G) at the normal aft limit, the aircraft was unstable on the climb and at all speeds in level flight.

The aileron control was praised by the test pilots as 'light and effective at all speeds and is regarded as excellent. . . .' The elevators, already noted as heavy on take-off, were not altogether satisfactory: 'at speeds below 100 mph and over 260 mph IAS [the elevators] became excessively heavy [and are] considered to be somewhat ineffective'.

The shortcomings of the elevators were most marked when high speed dives were undertaken: 'The aircraft was dived to 315 mph. The elevator is satisfactory over small angles [but] dives were not taken over 315 mph because of nose heaviness and [high] control forces'.

The most serious aspect of the marginal lateral control of the prototype Manchester was revealed when landing, the A&AEE test pilots reporting, under the heading 'Approach and Landing', that:

The approach, with full flap and a little engine is straightforward and easy until the aircraft is checked prior to touchdown. The elevator then becomes very heavy indeed and requires considerable force to pull it back. Because of this it is considered difficult to make a . . . controlled landing.

During those tests in that bitter first winter of the war, further shortcomings in L7246 were apparent:

Single engine flying: . . . the rudder bias trim on this aircraft is sufficient to allow the aircraft to be flown feet off with either engine cut. At 32,400 lbs the aircraft will maintain height at 3,000 ft. It was found that at 40,000 lbs the aircraft would not maintain height after take-off [on one engine].

This last observation was obtained empirically when L7246 lost the port engine on take-off from Boscombe Down, ignominiously ending up in a cabbage patch. The aircraft was salvaged and returned to the manufacturer, Avro.

At the enforced early conclusion of the test programme, a letter[3] was sent by E. T. Jones, Chief Technical Officer at A&AEE, to the Air Ministry, which read (in part):

In order to speed development of the type [the Manchester], preliminary tests have been made at A&AEE at an early stage in the contractor's flight trials of L7246. . . . The tests were terminated by the failure of the port engine during take-off which result in the force landing of the aeroplane and cessation of tests temporarily.

It is said that coming events cast their shadow before them and the early engine failure of the prototype may have been the first but it was to prove far from the last. However, test pilots at A&AEE in general liked the cockpit layout but considered that the throttles were too close to the pilot and the control column too high; the elevator trim was too highly geared and had too great a range. The undercarriage control safety lock was found to be difficult to operate on take-off; the flap control was criticised as not being positive and, when in the 'down' position, tended to butt up against the pilot's knee. Possibly in view of the single engine performance, the report also noted that the emergency escape hatch in the cockpit roof could not be opened quickly.

The report added that a larger tailplane should be fitted to improve stability; although the ailerons were thought to be generally excellent, however, the test pilots suggested adding a bias (trim) control. The elevators were not satisfactory and it was felt at A&AEE that Avro's would have to make them both more effective and with lighter control forces. As already noted, the production Vultures fitted to L7246 were each some 100 hp down from their nominal 1,760 hp; even so, the lamentable take-off performance would have to be improved.

The skill of the A&AEE test pilot in force-landing the valuable first prototype resulted in little damage. Avro's repaired the aircraft and it returned to Boscombe Down in May 1940, substantially in the same form as when previously tested; that is with no armament or turrets, 80 ft wings, 28 ft span tailplane with triple fins, with the same unsatisfactory unbalanced elevators. The engines, however, had been replaced and now offered 3,200 rpm and +6 lb/sq inch boost for take-off. Nevertheless, the subsequent take-off tests showed no real improvement and the results obtained were not considered adequate for the type. The A&AEE recommendation was to fit wings with an increased span to reduce the excessively high wing loading. The longitudinal stability was not regarded as being up to the required RAF standards; to improve this, a larger, 32 ft span tailplane was decided upon. (Due to Manchester production by now being well under way, the increased span tailplane was to be fitted to the twenty-first and subsequent aircraft.)

L7246 returned for the third time to Boscombe Down in July 1940, now with an increased wing span of 90 ft. The original 28 ft span triple fin tail was retained, although the elevators had been modified. On 17 July 1940, a performance figure was recorded with the prototype at a weight of 45,000 lb (without turrets fitted). At maximum power (3,000 rpm +6 lb/sq inch boost), L7246 reached a true airspeed of 275 mph at 16,250 ft. Take-offs were made at +6 and +9 lb/sq inch boost.[4] The actual take-off performance figures are not to be found in the surviving A&AEE files but they must have been fairly satisfactory since, on 8 August 1940, L7246 was returned to the makers for the fitting of turrets and armament.

The prototype later made an appearance at the RAE, Farnborough, where it performed a spectacular test take-off from the 'Frictionless Take-off' catapult; a Handley Page Heyford had previously been successfully tested, though of course it was a much lighter aircraft. In the event, L7246 left the device in a seemingly effortless manner. The project, having at least justified the claims of its creators, was, perhaps wisely, quietly abandoned. From now on Manchesters would have to get themselves into the air.

Having been catapulted from the RAE, the subsequent career of L7246 is obscure; it is known, however, to have ended its days as Instructional Airframe 9422M.

The second prototype Manchester, L7247, arrived at Boscombe Down during July 1940 for armament trials. L7247 was flying with the 80 ft wing and 28 ft tailplane but, unlike its predecessor, it was armed with a total of six .303-in Brownings: two guns each in the nose, ventral and rear turrets. The major aerodynamic modification, probably as a result of the A&AEE test flights with L7246, was an auxiliary aerofoil balance beneath the elevators to act as a servo and thus reduce the heavy control loads. Tests soon proved the modification to be unsatisfactory and later new elevators, with horn balances and geared inset trim tabs, were fitted. These elevators resulted in a big improvement in control at all speeds, including high speed dives.

The front and ventral turrets – the latter eventually to be moved to a dorsal position – seem to have been satisfactory; only the rear turret proved troublesome. It was found to be jerky in rotation and caused violent buffeting when turned beam on. Deflectors fitted to the fuselage ahead of the rear turret cured the buffeting.

The second prototype, during the tests at Boscombe Down, achieved 266 mph at 14,300 ft at an all-up weight of 45,000 lb, observed rpm 2,970 + 5½ boost. When flown later in August, fitted with the long span 'production' wing of 90 ft 1 in and 32 ft tailplane, the maximum true air speed was 262 mph at 14,250 ft. The modifications to the elevators and the new larger span tailplane were reported as showing a marked improvement in longitudinal stability. L7247 disappears from the A&AEE programme after these tests: like the first prototype, the second became an Instructional Airframe (2738M).

Both aircraft had served their purpose; the tests on the two prototypes at Boscombe Down had enabled the design staff at Avro's to concentrate on getting the early production Manchester Is off the line in a condition which would enable them to enter RAF service with the minimum of delay.

When the first production Manchester I, L7276, landed at Boscombe Down on 5 August 1940 for performance testing, France had fallen, the miracle (or disaster) of Dunkirk had occurred and the Battle of Britain was nearing its climax, though at that stage it was far from clear that it would end as a victory for the RAF. The prospect of a German invasion of the British Isles was still a daily possibility.

Against this background of defeat and struggle, the men and women at Avro's factory, near Manchester, and those of the principal sub-contractor, Metropolitan-Vickers, fervently hoped that the modifications to the aircraft now in production would be few, as a result of the performance testing of the first Manchester off the lines. However, the testing of that first production Manchester, L7276, was to be brief for, as the A&AEE report[5] tersely put it:

Manchester L7276 (1st Production) arrived at Boscombe Down in August 1940. It was fitted with 90 ft span wings, 28 ft tailplane, modified elevators, gun turrets. . . . It was intended to continue performance trials on this aeroplane but it force landed immediately after taking off on 12 September 1940.

The cause of the forced landing was the failure of one of the Vulture engines – so far two out of the first three Manchesters had suffered that nightmare of all pilots (especially those flying fully loaded bombers): E.F.T.O. – Engine Failure on Take-Off.

A replacement Manchester (the second production aircraft, L7277) arrived at Boscombe Down but L7276 seems to have been repaired after its forced landing in August, for brief performance and operating data of this aircraft were published in a report[6] which was issued 3 December 1940. The summary reads:

The Manchester was designed as a medium bomber capable of either long range or heavy bomb load. At a weight of 45,000 lbs, the maximum at which tests have so far been made, the alternative ranges are:

Result No.	Date	Aeroplane	Weight (lb)	Span (ft)	Tail-plane	Turrets	RPM observed	Observed Boost (lb/sq in)	Standard height (ft)	True air speed (mph)
1	14/7/40	L.7247	38,000	80	small	On	2970	+5¾	14,600	274
2	26/7/40	L.7247	45,000	80	small	On	2970	+5½	14,500	266
3	19/5/40	L.7246	44,000	80	small	Off	3000	+5¾	15,000	263
4	17/7/40	L.7246	45,000	90	small	Off	3000	+6	16,250*	275
5	1/8/40	L.7246	45,000	90	small	Off	3000	+6	16,250*	270
6	4/9/40	L.7276	45,000	90	small	On	3000	+6	17,000*	261
7	21/9/40	L.7247	45,000	90	large	On	3000	+6	14,250	262

*Full throttle heights

1,760 [statute] air miles with 3,500 lbs bomb load
1,500 [statute] air miles with 4,500 lbs bomb load
1,220 [statute] air miles with 6,000 lbs bomb load
  760 [statute] air miles with 8,000 lbs bomb load.

(This last figure is a good deal less than the original specification which called for a maximum of 12,000 lb, later reduced to 10,350 lb; that load was unattainable on L7276 since, with full fuel, a load in excess of 8,000 lb would have taken the aircraft over its maximum all-up weight of 50,000 lb.)

Performance at 45,000 lbs is as follows:

Take-off run:	700 yds at +5¾ lbs boost
	660 yds at +9 lbs boost
Max. speed:	261 mph TAS at 17,000 ft
Service ceiling:	22,100 ft
Time to 20,000 ft:	30 minutes.

The handling qualities are good and the controls are reasonably light and effective. . . . The night flying characteristics are very good but the navigational facilities are poor for an aeroplane of [this] large size.

  No take-off tests have been made at weight higher than 45,000 lbs and it may be that the take-off at say, 50,000 lbs could be unsatisfactory from an operational point of view. Nevertheless the horsepower of the engines is being increased by 75 hp per engine and it is of interest to forecast the range which could be obtained if the all-up weight could be increased to 50,000 lbs.
a) with 8,000 lbs of bombs the tanks could be filled and the [still air] range is
    1,700 miles.
b) with 11,000 lbs (4 × 2,000 +6 × 500) fuel load must be reduced and the range is
    1,000 miles.

The 1940 A&AEE writer of the above was not far out; one authoritative source[7] gives the following figures for a late service Manchester I:

  8,100 lbs of bombs, range 1,630 miles
  10,300 lbs of bombs, range 1,200 miles

It is interesting to compare the actual full throttle performance figures of the first three Manchesters; the first and second pre-production prototypes (L7246 and L7247) and the first production aircraft (L7276). The results of test flights are tabulated in Appendix I of A&AEE Report 751 Part 2 and are here reproduced.

As the report notes:

  An examination of the table brings to light certain discrepancies. Thus comparison of results 5 and 6 indicates that L7276 fitted with turrets is of the order of 10 mph slower than L7246 without turrets, a difference in speed which would seem much too high. . . .

The writer also commented on results 6 and 7 which showed that L7276 was slower (by 7 mph) than L7247 at the same weight, even though that latter aircraft had by then a 32 ft tailplane. Results 2 and 3 also were commented on since they purported to show 'a higher speed for L7247 than L7246 in spite of operating at a higher weight, lesser height, lower engine conditions and the addition of gun turrets. . .'.

The conclusion was that, pending further tests 'the evidence . . . goes to show that the speed of 261 mph quoted for L7276 [the production Manchester] at 45,000 lbs is rather on the low side'.

In fact squadron Manchester Is are usually credited with a maximum of 265 mph at 17,000 ft. That being so, the A&AEE results were not far off the mark.

L7276 was to have a fairly long life for a wartime prototype. After its tests at Boscombe Down (including the forced landing), it was issued to No. 5 Group's 61 Squadron based at Syerston, then, in common with most surviving Manchesters, to No. 28 Operational Training Unit (OTU). Later, in December 1942, L7276 served with a Torpedo Development Unit, being finally written off as the result of a crash on 31 October 1943.[8]

Soon after the preliminary A&AEE tests were concluded, the Manchester entered RAF service with No. 207 Squadron which had re-formed at Waddington to operate the new, untried and still secret bomber.

The first Manchester on RAF charge was L7278 which flew to No. 207 Squadron from No. 27 MU at Shawbury on 1 November 1940, to be joined shortly after by L7279. These two early production Manchesters were to be the subject of intensive flying to accumulate 500 hours. It is significant that a number of Rolls-Royce specialists were stationed at Waddington to supervise maintenance of the still far from proven Vulture engines. No. 207, the first squadron to be equipped with the new bomber, was supposed to receive aircraft as they left the factory lines, but the first 21 production Manchesters did not incorporate all the modifications recommended by the A&AEE (for example, they all had the unsatisfactory 'small' 28 ft tailplane with the triple fins). It was agreed by the Ministry of Aircraft Production (MAP) that the squadron would be equipped for operational flying with Manchesters subsequent to the first 21; in the event, delay in production resulted in No. 207 initially having to operate with just six machines from the early, unmodified batch. Intensive training began, constantly interrupted by aircraft having to be grounded for modifications, the engines in particular causing a good deal of trouble, though the airframes also needed attention. However, 207's C.O. (Wing Commander W. C. Hyde) managed to keep a minimum of four Manchesters serviceable and available for operations.

Prior to that, in early January 1941, the bombers were inspected by HM King George VI and Queen Elizabeth. On 9 January 1941, the Manchester was revealed to the RAF though, as far as the general public was concerned, the aircraft still remained on the secret list; it was Air Ministry policy never to release to the press details of any new operational types until they had, so to speak, been revealed to the Germans by flying operationally over enemy territory.

The detailed operational history of the Manchester is beyond the scope of this book and is recorded elsewhere[9]; suffice it to say that its service debut was an attack upon the heavy cruiser *Hipper* at Brest by the six Manchesters of No. 207 Squadron, together with 25 Handley Page Hampdens. The Manchesters were: L7279, '84, '86, '88, '94 and L7300. All six returned from the raid, though L7284 ('EM-D') crashed on landing at Waddington through hydraulic failure and the C.O. of 207 made an informal appearance at Boscombe Down with L7300, his windscreen obscured with oil.

The de-briefing of the crews, following the first Manchester operation, revealed that the bomb-aimers had difficulties in observing the impact point of the bombs they had dropped: an additional perspex panel was recommended. In point of fact, the A&AEE had found the bomb-aimer's position unsatisfactory on the second prototype and had made recommendations to improve the bomb-aimer's view; the A&AEE armament section, however, considered the Manchester a steady bombing platform, the mean error at 1,000 ft being only 26 yards (with practice bombs).[10]

Other problems were soon evident, the most serious being hydraulic fluid leaks in the undercarriage retraction system. The handling of the bombers was not exactly praised by the pilots and crews, who always had the nagging fear that, if they lost an engine, they had little, if any, real hope of getting back; furthermore, even with both engines operational, the Manchester was seriously underpowered.

There was, however, no hint of these little local difficulties in the official release made to the press on 5 March 1941, which simply stated: Manchester; bomber. Engines; two. Manufacturer A. V. Roe.

The Minister of Aircraft Production, Lord Beaverbrook, was a little more forthcoming when, on 23 April, in the House of Lords, he enlarged – slightly – on speculation about the new bomber which had appeared in the American press: 'The Manchester has a 90 foot wing span, speed of 325 mph and two engines. . . .'

The 90 foot wing span and two engines were correct, but 325 mph! The only way a Manchester could exceed 300 mph was in a dive and, as already noted, the speed of a Manchester I is quoted as a maximum of 265 mph at 17,000 ft.

The sad fact, as far as the aircrews who had to fly them were concerned, was that the Manchester was being built in quantity and issued to the squadrons and, whatever its shortcomings, would have to be flown operationally. No. 207 was soon to be joined by six other Manchester squadrons: Nos. 49, 50, 61, 83, 97 and 106.

Manchesters took part in the, now famous, 1,000 bomber attack on Cologne, to be followed by other attacks on German targets, including Berlin; but their loss rate was becoming unacceptably high, many aircraft undoubtedly being lost, not through enemy action, but by engine failure over Germany. There was, too, a high incidence of Manchesters crashing on landing back at their home base; the pilots, only too well aware of the underpowered and unreliable engines, were overshooting the runways, preferring to land fast rather than risk stalling trying to go round again. The general feeling among the Manchester crews was that the basic airframe was fine but the engines were 'U/S'.[11]

Due to the losses, frequent temporary grounding of the type for modifications, 'hangar queens' and aircraft withdrawn from operations and sent to OTUs, it is doubtful if more than 30 Manchesters were ever available for operations at any one time. The record turnout goes to No. 106 Squadron who, on 3 May 1942, put up the maximum number of Manchesters ever from a single squadron – eight (they lost two). No. 106 was at the time commanded by Guy Gibson, who was later famed for leading the 'Dambusting' raid with Lancasters.

The main concern of the A&AEE at Boscombe Down was to try to improve the handling of the type; it was, after all, being flown by wartime trained pilots, some with as little as 200 hours total time. One report[12] warned, *inter alia*, that although the general flying was satisfactory, the Manchester taking off at 45,000 lb – which the operational aircraft would be – could not maintain height if either engine failed. There was, in short, no Manchester 'safety speed':[13] the speed at which a multi-engined aircraft could sustain an engine failure on take-off and either climb away or at least maintain level flight. The Boscombe test pilots found that L7277 had: 'unpleasant longitudinal stability under all flight conditions accompanied by difficulties in trimming the aeroplane'.

The same report[14] discussed the handling of L7373 a Manchester IA (later to be reported missing as 'EM.T.' of 207 Squadron), when trials of the mid-upper turret were conducted. The turret fitted was a Frazer-Nash FN7A with a 'Lerwick' cupola. This turret was found not to affect adversely the general handling until it was rotated – which, of course, it would have to be when in service – when:

Rotation produces rudder vibration found to be caused by violent vibration of the central fin originating from 'panting' of the fabric covering in the lower part of the fin due to upsetting of the airflow by the asymmetry of the rotated turret. On one occasion most of the fabric on the central fin stripped off during a dive. . . .

Possibly in the light of the above test, it was decided to try the effect of removing (intentionally) the entire central fin. The directional stability was, with and without the mid-upper turret, 'considered [to be] bad in both cases'.

It was decided to continue the test with a modified fin and a circular cupola on the turret.

The problem of baulked landings, about which Manchesters were acquiring an evil reputation, was also looked into at Boscombe. L7247, the second prototype, now with the 32 ft tailplane, was found to be satisfactory at light loads and with the C of G forward of the aft limit for landing. On the other hand, L7281 (the sixth production machine), with the same C of G position, showed excessive and dangerous tail heaviness when the engines were opened up to overshoot, the report adding that:

In view of the dangerous qualities associated with baulked landings on Manchesters with small [i.e. 28 ft] tailplanes, it is suggested that in addition to the 35° of flap restriction the position of the C of G should be restricted for landing.

The restrictions that were, one by one, imposed on the Manchesters must have made the pilot's check list long and complicated, putting one in mind of the memorable advice given to Bob Hope in the film 'Son of Paleface', as he is about to have a shoot-out with a notorious gunman: 'there's a wind from the east, so aim to the west. He draws from the left, so shoot from the right, etc.'

The role of the A&AEE test pilots – most were 'above average' RAF or Fleet Air Arm pilots posted to Boscombe – and that of the civilian observers and scientists was, of course, vital to the many investigations and evaluations done at the A&AEE during the war years; that they almost daily took their lives in their hands was accepted as part of their work. But, behind the laconic wording of the reports, there lies many a desperate struggle with unstable and faulty aircraft. These test crews would abandon an aircraft only when it was obviously impossible for it to continue flying; even then, many pilots, having ordered their crews to bale out, tried to get their aircraft – some on fire – down in as large a piece as possible. The courage of these dedicated and, alas, now largely unknown men was truly amazing; it is one thing to experience say, severe airborne vibration; it is another calmly to continue to increase the airspeed (and the vibration) to try to ascertain at what point the aircraft begins to disintegrate.

One such test flight is the subject of an A&AEE report[15] dated 1 November 1941 and is here summarized.

The many troubles the Manchester encountered in service included severe vibration of the tail unit, amounting to flutter. This was not the same vibration which had earlier been investigated at Boscombe Down and found to be caused by the turret rotation; that had only affected the central fin and had been cured by the A&AEE by the addition of a 'dish plate' to smooth the turbulent air behind the turret. (Later Manchester IAs had been built with the large span tail with taller end plate fins, the central fin being deleted, but the solution was applicable to other aircraft.) RAF Manchester pilots had been reporting severe tail structure vibration when climbing with a full bomb load.

The RAF Manchester Pilot's Notes recommended a climb-out at gross weight of between 125–140 mph and 2,700 rpm, +4 boost. Under these conditions, severe tail unit vibration was occurring. Avro test pilots undertook an investigation, the result of which was a recommendation to climb out at 2,850 rpm, +6 boost; this seemed to eliminate the vibration. In the opinion of the factory testers, the vibration was caused by pre-stall buffeting!

L7320, a Manchester IA, that is one fitted with the twin fin tail and normal turrets, and one of the aircraft on long term test at A&AEE, was used to investigate the source of the vibration. At an AUW of 47,500 lb – corresponding to a fully loaded operational bomber – the Boscombe Down test pilots confirmed that, when climbing at 2,700 rpm, +4 at 6,000 ft, below 145 mph IAS, the vibration of the tail unit was such that the mass balances on the twin rudder tops were observed to be in continuous and violent oscillation.

The test pilot then slowed the climb to 135 mph; the tail structure continued to vibrate, the 32 ft tailplane 'see-sawing'. To ascertain that this severe movement was in fact, as the Avro pilots maintained, a pre-stall buffeting, the nose of the aircraft was raised to slow the bomber to 130 mph; at this speed the Manchester became difficult to control due to powerful rudder snatching which the pilot could not contain, but there was still no stall. The climbing speed was increased to 138 mph, which reduced the oscillation, but at 10,000 ft it occurred again, as severely as before. The speed was increased to 150 mph; this stopped the buffeting but the aircraft would climb no higher.

L7320 was then tested at the speeds then being recommended by Avro's. Climbing at 2,850 rpm, +5 boost, 'very severe' vibration set in at 130 mph. The report of the civilian observer, who probably watched from the mid-upper turret, continues:

The vibration set in with equal violence even when the engines were throttled right back. In order to obtain further information the aeroplane was flown down to the lowest possible speeds. . . . When the speed had dropped 20 mph or so below the critical speed the disturbance reached dangerous proportions. It was estimated that the tips of the tailplane were oscillating with violence over an amplitude greater than 1 foot. The fins were vibrating relative to the tailplane and the whole aeroplane was shuddering. The right wing tended to drop but could be raised by application of aileron.

That the aeroplane was not stalling at 130 mph IAS [as Avro had maintained] when the vibration became serious was shown by the fact that the stall had still not taken place, stick hard back, engines off at 102 mph.

25

When L7320 landed back at Boscombe Down after that test flight, it was found that the rudder mass balance weights had been partly torn from the rudder and both were loose. When these had been secured, another flight was made and the test pilot deliberately induced the vibration again and it was discovered that: 'These unpleasant characteristics can be largely cured at once by the application of slight flap. . .'

With 10° of flap, a vibration free climb at maximum gross could be made at the normal, i.e. 135–140 mph, speed. This of course was only a palliative, not a cure; even with 10° flap, if the speed of climb dropped: 'vibration sets in at 120 mph and becomes violent at 110 mph'.

Having proved that the vibration was not a pre-stall buffet, the A&AEE now turned its attention to tracking down the source of this severe vibration, which occurred only at high wing incidence and low air speeds. It was suspected that turbulent air was affecting the rudders. During the flight trials, the effect of closing the radiator flaps (normally fully open on the climb) was tried and found to make no difference to the vibration.

It was noted that the test aircraft had engines with the latest modifications, including front fairing flanges which had been designed to improve the air-flow of the oil cooler extractor louvres. The A&AEE report was critical:

This front fairing flange has been mounted in what is probably the worst position that any excrescence could be mounted – on the top surface of the mainplane, just behind the leading edge, just outboard of the engine nacelle, in the airscrew slipstream and *in direct alignment with the junction of the fin and tailplane*'.*

When the offending flanges were removed, no vibration was apparent at as low a speed as 104 mph IAS with 10° flaps, and only slight vibration at 102 mph with flaps up. The A&AEE pilots considered that:

removal of the flanges has improved the handling and the 'feel' of the aeroplane at take-off. With flanges fitted pilots were of the opinion that 47,000 lbs was the limiting weight for take-off; once the flanges were removed however they were prepared to take the aeroplane off at higher weight.

The removal of the flanges did, of course, lead to slightly higher oil and coolant temperatures at low altitudes but had little effect at normal operating altitudes. The final recommendations to the squadrons was to use 10° of flap when flying at low speeds and heavy weight, pending the removal of the oil cooler extractor fairing flanges.

The improvement in the maximum take-off weight was confirmed by tests on L7320[16] when take-offs (without the flanges) were made at 49,500 lb and +9 boost (3,200 rpm). With 25° flap, the Manchester unstuck at 830 yards and cleared 50 feet in 1,200 yards.

A sad footnote: soon after these tests, L7320 was lost on a subsequent A&AEE test flight.

By the end of 1941, when the above report was written, it was obvious that the days of the Manchester, or at least the Vulture engined Manchester, were

* Authors' italics

numbered; it was to be withdrawn from Bomber Command's order of battle in June 1942, the last raid mounted with the type being an attack on Bremen on the night of 25/26 June, 1942. The basic problem had been the engines; the failure of the master connecting rod's big end bearing is usually cited as the main cause of the Vulture's unreliability, though there was also coolant trouble. But even when the engines were operating to their rated output, the Manchester was always seriously under-powered; though in fairness to Rolls-Royce, as Sir Stanley Hooker has pointed out,[17] the production Manchester was a heavier aircraft than the original proposal for which the Vultures were selected in 1936. By 1940 Rolls-Royce had neither the time nor facilities to develop their complex V-24 engine under the pressures of wartime; they were fully stretched in producing the Merlin. Avro's chief designer, Roy Chadwick, had foreseen this, for by late 1940 alternative power plants for Manchesters were being considered – one airframe was allocated to Napier's for the installation of two Napier Sabres which offered 2,110 hp each for take-off. (The engines were installed but the aircraft never flew, being used only as a ground test rig.) A second proposal was the use of two 2,300 hp Bristol Centaurus air-cooled radials. A third possibility was to redesign the Manchester's wing centre section and install four 1,280 hp Rolls-Royce Merlin X engines. This last proposal was the one implemented and the Manchester III, as it was at first known (BT308), first flew on 9 January 1941; it exceeded all expectations and became the prototype of a new aircraft, soon to be renamed Lancaster – but that is another story.

The Manchester was, after the war, admitted to be 'a disappointment'; the RAF's Official History[18] dismissed the bomber as having 'a brief and disastrous' operational career, adding that 'Bomber Command would have been ultimately stronger if the Manchester had never been produced'. However, if the Manchester had not been produced, would the Lancaster – the most successful night bomber of the Second World War – have evolved?

Although Manchesters were withdrawn from operations, they were not withdrawn from the RAF. The surviving aircraft of the 159 (including the two prototypes) built by A. V. Roe and the 43 constructed by Metropolitan-Vickers (their first 13 aircraft had been lost on the production line in an air raid on 23 December 1940), went to training units: they were not, one imagines, welcome. Most had disappeared from the RAF's inventory by October 1943. Probably the last in existence was L7420, which was used for ditching training by the RAF and USAAF up to 1945; its remains were unceremoniously dumped in a Lincolnshire sandpit in 1956.

With the end of Manchester production and the cancellation of the Hawker Tornado, the only other aircraft designed to use the Vulture and which ironically was also to be produced by A. V. Roe, Rolls-Royce ceased production of their ill-fated Vulture: one of the very few unsatisfactory engines produced by that illustrious company.

As a footnote to the history of Rolls-Royce, a Vulture engine was used by their supercharger expert, Stanley Hooker, to drive the experimental compressors of the Whittle jet engine that was to take Rolls-Royce into the jet age.

CHAPTER THREE

A&AEE Report No. 766

The Avro Lancaster

The failure of the Avro Manchester, due almost entirely to the shortcomings of the Rolls-Royce Vulture engine, has already been recounted. The basic difficulty was, of course, the immense pressure to which that illustrious company found itself subjected once the war had started. The demand for Rolls-Royce Merlins and the continuous development of that engine, which was powering many of Bomber Command's aircraft and all the Hurricanes and Spitfires, was absorbing their production and research resources. It is probable that, in informal talks between Avro and Rolls, the latter may have conceded that a dramatic improvement in the Vulture was unlikely; in any event, the Avro design staff, led by Roy Chadwick, had early been aware that a reappraisal of the Manchester's Vulture power plant was likely to become a probability in the event that Rolls-Royce could not improve on the reliability of that complex 24 cylinder 'X' engine. Chadwick and his staff had therefore prudently considered alternative engines before the prototype Manchester had flown. At first two Napier Sabres, then two Bristol Centaurus were considered to power the Manchester II – as the derivative was tentatively named; a third, and more radical, possibility was to reconstruct the airframe to accept four proven Rolls-Royce Merlin Xs – this variant was to be known as the Manchester III. The third option, more or less unofficial, was the one decided upon to the extent, initially, of a flying prototype.

Considering the size of the aircraft, the conversion – for that is exactly what it was to be – went remarkably smoothly. An early standard Manchester airframe was taken from the production line; the centre section of the wing was revised and enlarged to accept four Rolls-Royce Merlin Xs, each of 1,280 hp. Apart from the new centre section, which increased the wingspan to 100 ft and the additional engines with their instrumentation, fuel, coolant and control runs, the rest of the aircraft was pure Manchester down to the early 22 ft triple tail unit; hence the name Manchester III, soon to be changed to Lancaster I (partly, one supposes, because of the unfavourable reputation of the Manchester in the squadrons of Bomber Command).

The prototype, BT308, first flew on 9 January 1941 from Avro's factory airfield at Ringway, Manchester. Test pilots from the A&AEE travelled to Manchester and made the preliminary handling trials from Ringway. The prototype, however, arrived at Boscombe Down on 28 January 1941. The results of the initial trials are contained in the 1st Part of A&AEE Report No. 766[1].

BT308, when it arrived at Boscombe Down, was powered by four Rolls-Royce Merlin XXs of 1,460 hp at +14 lb boost. The prototype was unarmed and had neither mid-upper nor ventral turrets. The all-up weight for the trials was 38,000 lb; for comparison, the tare weight of an operational Lancaster III is usually quoted at 41,000 lb. (Maximum overload 68,000 lb). The C of G was near the aft limit.

A&AEE was immediately critical of the layout of the aircraft's cockpit: the inboard throttles were too short and the throttles generally were too close to the dual control bar which linked the pilot and co-pilot's columns. (It might be mentioned, in passing, that this dual control was a 'bolt on' used only at the training and conversion units. Lancasters flying operationally – unlike the early Halifax – did not have dual control: no co-pilot was carried as part of a normal crew). The throttle friction damper (usually applied for take-off to prevent throttles working back) was considered too harsh. The A&AEE pilots complained that the centre boss of the control wheel masked the blind flying instruments. These criticisms apart, the cockpit layout, the instrumentation and controls, were considered good and in general to be an improvement on the twin-engined Manchester.

The take-off was marred by a pronounced swing to port; this was found to be not containable by full starboard rudder and application of opposite brake. To correct the swing it was necessary to apply corrective rudder and throttle back the starboard outer. Avro's had already decided to increase the rudder area to improve directional control on take-off and in asymmetric flight. (One might here observe that the Lancaster take-off swing, though much reduced, was never entirely eradicated; it was usual for operational pilots to use differential throttle on take-off.)

The directional stability of BT308 was assessed: normal flight, i.e. all four engines: stability satisfactory. Asymmetric flight at 6,000 ft, 2,650 rpm +4 lb, starboard outer throttled back and the propeller to full coarse: in this condition the rudders could be trimmed for 'feet off' flight down to 140 mph IAS. At 120 mph, even the application of full rudder was inadequate to prevent a pronounced turn. No airborne tests were made of propeller feathering. The general handling of the prototype was considered to be satisfactory. The speed check was made at 2,650 rpm +4 lb boost, which gave 242 mph TAS at 4,600 ft.

The A&AEE report concluded that:

The Lancaster possesses very good flying qualitities and promises to give a good performance. The rudder control [however] . . . likely to be quite inadequate with two engines on one side throttled. Increased rudder area should effect an improvement.

Modifications were recommended to ease throttle operation, shorten the control column, improve the Blind Flying Panel and improve pilot comfort. The aircraft was considered excessively noisy. The rudder trim gearing was too low and improvement was stated to be essential.

Considering the magnitude of the conversion from two to four engines, it would seem that the faults found by the A&AEE were remarkably few; indeed, the Lancaster files at Boscombe Down contain little drama. The basic Manchester airframe, as designed by Roy Chadwick and his staff, was excellent; given the reliable power plants that the Merlins undoubtedly were, the Manchester was at once transformed from a 'disappointment' to what was to become one of the great war planes of the Second World War. The 90 or so A&AEE reports on the Lancaster, issued between March 1941 and October 1945, are therefore in the main concerned with operational modifications and armament trials, not the eradication of basic faults. A representative selection follows.

The next A&AEE report[2] was simply concerned to assess the maximum level speed at the slightly greater AUW of 38,000 lb at 3,000 rpm +8½. The speed was 310 mph TAS at 21,100 ft; at the lower power setting of 2,650 rpm + 4, 288 mph TAS at 22,800 ft. It is interesting to compare these early test figures with the Manchester prototypes; for example, Manchester L7247, which had an identical fuselage to BT308 down to the small tailplane, was at 38,000 lb able to achieve only 274 mph TAS at 14,600 ft: 36 mph TAS slower than the Lancaster prototype.

During April 1941 the trials with BT308 were continued but with the aircraft now fitted with the definitive Lancaster tail and rudders; that is the 90 ft twin fin unit as recommended, and fitted to the production Manchester 1A, the ugly early 'Manchester' central fin being deleted.

The tail modification was to effect a considerable improvement, as reflected in the subsequent A&AEE Report[3]:

Take-off. The swing is now slight and can be corrected with rudder.

Control effectiveness. The aircraft was dived to 315 mph. The ailerons were light and effective at low speeds but heavy above 260 mph. The rudder trim gearing was improved, but the [rudder] tab not adequate for flight on two engines. [i.e. two dead on the same side].

Longitudinal Stability. At aft C of G the aircraft is stable in level flight at low speeds and on the glide but unstable in the climb and at high speed.

Asymmetric. At 8,000 ft with maximum continuous power (2,650 rpm +7) on the live engines, the aircraft could be flown hands and feet off down to 170 mph with both [engines] feathered on one side. The foot load became heavy at 120 mph. By applying 5° bank minimum 'feet off' the speed could be reduced to 150 mph.

The A&AEE test pilots reported the handling qualities of this heavy bomber, with one or two engines feathered, as being 'excellent'; it was found possible to make turns against the live engines at speeds above 140 mph IAS, the only caveat being: 'An increase in trim tab size is desirable to achieve [straight and level] flight on two engines without foot load'.

The only clue to the, of necessity, hasty splicing in of the enlarged wing centre section was a tendency for certain panels in the airframe to flex and distort, both when taxiing and in flight, with the aircraft at the maximum trial AUW of 42,500 lb. It was recommended that: '[It is] desirable for the plating to be stiffened in order that the Lancaster should be sufficiently strong for operation at high loads'.

By the time the Lancaster prototype had completed its handling trials at Boscombe Down, it was clear that the improvement conferred by the change to four Merlins was such that the Air Staff had no hesitation – or indeed alternative – but to abandon the Vulture-engined Manchester and to produce the succeeding aircraft as Lancasters. The excellent aerodynamic qualities of the original design meant that, engines and centre section aside, the disruption to the production lines would be minimal. BT308 had been a 'one-off' but it was soon followed by the pre-production prototype, still 80 per cent Manchester, DG595, which first flew on 13 May 1941. By then the paperwork had caught up with the project and all existing contracts for Manchesters were redrawn to cover the production as the Type 683 Lancaster. The first true production Lancaster I, L7527, followed the last Manchester IA, L7526, on the lines and it first flew on 31 October 1941. In all, the first 243 Lancasters built by Avro at Woodford and the 57 built by their main subcontractor, Metropolitan Vickers, had been intended originally to be constructed as Manchesters. As the tempo of production increased, the aircraft gradually departed from its Manchester ancestry until eventually it was a distinct type.

After the A&AEE trials the first prototype, BT308, left Boscombe to lead a long and varied career, first, during January 1942, with several squadrons of Bomber Command: Nos. 44, 97 and 207, presumably to introduce the aircrews to the new bomber. After that tour it went to Rolls-Royce at Hucknall for flame-damping tests in April 1942. It was then returned to Avro's and was, remarkably, to end its days as a flying testbed with a Metrovick F2/1 Beryl axial jet engine fitted in the tail.

The second Lancaster to appear at Boscombe Down was the pre-production prototype, DG595. During tests conducted by the A&AEE in December 1941, general handling was investigated.[4]

Among the tests was an assessment of the speed penalty which resulted from the fitting of flame-dampers for the engine exhausts of the Lancaster. These dampers were, of course, essential for a night bomber; the difficulty lay in providing adequate masking of the exhaust flames without either overheating the manifold or causing sufficient backpressure significantly to reduce the engine's power output, although some power loss was inevitable. DG595, powered by four Merlin XXs, was flown with A&AEE designed 'cascade box' dampers. The test, made in December 1941, showed that at full throttle: 3,000 rpm +8½, the maximum level speed was reduced by the dampers by approximately 5 per cent or 14 mph TAS at an AUW of 45,000 lb. At the same time, the fitting of a dorsal (mid-upper) turret cam track had no discernible effect and, in another test, larger bomb doors caused a three mph TAS loss of speed at the same throttle settings used for the flame-damper tests.

The actual flame-damping of the A&AEE cascade box left something to be desired; indeed, the Mk II box was in this respect inferior to an earlier Mk I design which was louvred and was adopted as a provisional standard.

For the flame-damping trials, flights were made at various mixture settings, since the carburettor mixture had a profound effect on the visibility of the exhaust flames. A moonless night with 5/10ths cloud was used for the tests. DG595 was successively flown at 300 ft over ground observers at maximum continuous lean mixture, maximum continuous rich mixture and finally full combat emergency throttle (3,000 rpm +12), the settings corresponding to cruise and fighter evasion. The distances at which exhaust flames were visible as the Lancaster receded were:

A&AEE Mk II cascade box:	130 yards weak and rich mixture
	320 yards full throttle
A&AEE Mk I cascade box:	100 yards weak and rich mixture
	230 yards full throttle

The standard flame-dampers fitted by Rolls-Royce were inferior to either of the A&AEE dampers, typical figures being: 400 yards at cruising mixtures and 700 yards at full throttle.

The time lag between a wartime prototype being tested at Boscombe Down and the production aircraft entering RAF service was usually very short. As a background to the pressure of work of the A&AEE connected with the Lancaster, it is pertinent to note that the type went into service with No. 44 Squadron based on Woodhall Spa and this unit dropped the first of a Lancaster total of 608,612 tons of high explosive bombs from two Lancaster Is on the night of 10/11 March 1942: just three months after the above flame-damper tests. The target was Essen. As the operational use of the type increased, as more squadrons became equipped with Lancasters, there were inevitably shortcomings reported, though the design as a whole gave astonishingly little trouble throughout its long service life.

One result of intensive flying trials at the A&AEE and the mounting operational experience of the RAF squadrons indicated that the wingtips of the initial batches of Lancaster Is needed to be strengthened. These outer wing sections had been designed for the AUW of 45,000 lb: Lancaster Is were flying operationally at 60,000 lb gross.

A Lancaster I, R5539, from a production batch of 200 (R5482–R5763) delivered by A. V. Roe in February/July 1942, arrived at Boscombe Down for diving trials with the strengthened tips. The pilot for these hazardous tests was Flt. Lt. S. Reiss (The Polish test pilot who was to lose his life in the Halifax trials).

R5539 was put through a programme of high speed dives, to which operational pilots would be likely to resort to in order to escape searchlights or night fighters. The A&AEE[5] tests concluded that the Mk I Lancaster had a tendency to accelerate in a high speed dive and that the control forces needed to recover were very high and the 'G' loading on the airframe excessive. A second Lancaster I from the same production run, R5546, was then tested, with similar results. The aircraft's behaviour in these high speed dives was not considered unduly dangerous in itself, providing that elevator trim had not been used to assist entry, but only to trim out the control force in the later stages of the dive. Elevator trim was found to be essential to effect a recovery from dives above 360 mph IAS. This reliance on the elevator trim was considered to be dangerous for the obvious reason that it could ice up or be shot away, in which case recovery from a high speed dive could prove impossible.

The undesirable Lancaster I diving characteristics were thought to be the result of a critical airflow over the tail or a twisting of the elevators or tailplane.

As an illustration of the nature of an A&AEE test flight, it is interesting to read in the reports that the maximum speed attained by the Lancaster Is under test was 400 mph in a dive from 13,000 ft to 4,500 ft. This must have been distinctly unpleasant, for the pullout took 28 seconds and required a control column force of no less than 250 lb to achieve 2G with 1½ turns of 'up' elevator trim.

In dives at the lower speeds of between 320–350 mph IAS, the stick load was 160 lb for recovery at 1½G. In one of the dives at 350 mph, perhaps not surprisingly, a gap appeared in the plating of the centre section of the wing. In a dive at 380 mph, the wing flaps suddenly opened in recovery and petrol streamed from the port wing tank. During the recovery from a 355 mph dive, the aircraft swung to port and 'considerable force was needed to keep it straight'.

If anyone should doubt the very dangerous nature of such test flying under the considerable pressures of wartime, let it be noted that on 18 April 1942, R5539 crashed with the loss of its A&AEE crew during further diving tests. R5546 survived its tour with the A&AEE but was subsequently lost on operations with No. 50 Squadron on 31 March 1944.

During a later series of test dives 'to a high Mach number', a Lancaster VI, ND558, was dived from 30,000 ft to Mach 0.72. (IAS 350 mph.) At 25,000 ft an escape hatch blew away and the dive was discontinued.

The rugged Lancaster airframe was, like any willing horse, loaded to its limit; then the limit was increased, as the Lancaster became, with the Halifax, the main 'heavy' of Bomber Command. In the autumn of 1943 it was decided to increase the maximum permissible overload of the Lancaster I to 63,000 lb, an increase of 3,000 lb over current operational Lancasters.

A Lancaster I, W4963, of a Metropolitan Vickers built batch of 200 aircraft (W4761–W5012) delivered between September 1942 and May 1943, was selected for the trials at Boscombe Down. It was probably the first Metropolitan Vickers Lancaster to be flown by the A&AEE. It was powered by four Merlin XXs with multiple ejector exhaust stacks without flame dampers and had standard nose, tail and mid-upper turrets and flush fitting bomb doors that could accommodate a 4,000 lb 'cookie'. The brief for the A&AEE was to ascertain take-off, climb and level speed performance and general handling at an AUW of 63,000 lb.[6]

The limitations imposed on the engines were:

Take-off:	3,000 rpm +14 lb boost
Climb:	2,850 rpm + 9 lb boost
Combat emergency	
5 min. max:	3,000 rpm +16 lb boost in FS supercharger gear
	3,000 rpm|+14 lb boost in MS supercharger gear
Continuous cruise:	2,650 rpm + 4 lb boost

The take-off run at maximum AUW (63,000 lb) for Standard Day[7] sea level conditions in zero wind was 750 yards for a take-off speed of 90 mph IAS and the distance to clear a 50 ft screen was 1,230 yards. IAS at lift off was 90 mph.

The performance figures, other than those for the take-off, were quoted in accordance with current A&AEE practice at that time at 95 per cent maximum take-off weight (i.e. 60,000 lb):

Maximum rate of climb (MS gear)	720 ft/min
Maximum rate of climb (FS gear)	460 ft/min
Service ceiling:	21,400 ft
Time to 21,000 ft:	44.2 mins
Max. speed:	269 mph TAS at 6,000 ft MS gear
Max. speed:	282 mph TAS at 13,000 ft FS gear
Max. cruise speed:	242 mph TAS at 13,800 ft MS gear
Max. cruise speed:	237 mph TAS at 18,000 ft FS gear

The AUW of 63,000 lb was soon to become the Lancaster standard and would be progressively increased to 68,000 lb. Modified Lancasters were to lift even greater weights when armed with the Barnes Wallis designed 22,000 lb Grand Slam 'earthquake' bombs; such aircraft would tip the scales at 70,000 lb, or nearly double their empty weight.

Apart from specialised testing of new or 'factory fresh' aircraft, the A&AEE began, in 1943, to make handling and performance trials of standard squadron aircraft selected more or less at random. These tests were usually made from the RAF airfields which were the aircraft's normal base; they were thus, in every way, representative of the machines the operational crews were taking to war, reflecting not only the manufacturing standards but also the maintenance of combat stressed aircraft.

A Mk I Lancaster (DV297) of 106 Squadron, based at the Lincolnshire airfield of Syerston, was the first to be tested under the scheme. It was powered by four Merlin 22s (the limits for take-off and climb were the same as for the XXs). The aircraft was tested at 63,000 lb.

DV297, a Metropolitan Vickers built Mk I, incorporated 'Mod 780' which provided a longer transparent nose to accommodate the Stabilised Bombsight Mk II (SABS Mk II). The cockpit had a clear vision 'blister' only on the starboard side (for the navigator). Normal HF and VHF aerials were carried, in addition to aerials on the tail for the early fighter warning radar 'Monica'. The turrets carried the usual .303-inch armament.

The general finish of DV297 was reported as normal and there appeared to be no evidence of poor workmanship (not unknown on wartime aircraft). The performance figures obtained by the A&AEE test[8] were:

Maximum rate of climb:	(60,000 lb) MS gear 2,650 +7: 550 ft/min
	FS gear 2,850 +9: 480 ft/min
Service ceiling:	21,600 ft
Time to 20,000 ft:	49.3 mins
Continuous cruise speed:	2,650 +4, 230 mph TAS at 14,000 ft (MS)
	228 mph TAS at 19,700 ft (FS)

It is interesting to compare these figures of a standard combat aircraft with those obtained by the brand new W4963; DV297, actually had a slightly better ceiling and rate of climb (in FS gear).

The test included general handling and, in this respect, DV297 was found to be normal for the type. The clean 'power off' stall at 59,700 lb was at 110 mph IAS; with landing gear down and full flap, at 90 mph IAS.

Lancasters at that time (October 1943) had a maximum permitted airspeed of 360 mph. The A&AEE test pilot, however, dived DV297 to 390 mph. On the way to that illegal figure the pilot's starboard windscreen cracked but the dive continued to the speed quoted and was successfully recovered.

The aircraft's asymmetric flying capabilities were also assessed; with the port outer stopped and feathered and with the port inner windmilling, the starboard engines were opened to 2,850 +9 lb boost and full corrective rudder trim applied. The aircraft flew straight and level at 180 mph IAS with zero foot load on the rudder bar.

After the A&AEE test, DV297 returned to operations and was ,soon after, lost over Berlin on the night of 26/27 November 1943, having flown a total of only 86 hours.

The total Lancaster production of 7,366 aircraft (including 430 built in Canada) was mainly of only two basic types, the Mk I and Mk III. In point of fact there was little difference even between these: Mk IIIs were powered by American Packard Merlins; these engines, designated Merlin 38s, though based on the Rolls-Royce Merlin 22, used USA threads, magnetos and carburettors and were thus not directly interchangeable with the British engines, therefore a separate Mk number was issued, though even an expert would find it impossible to differentiate between Mk I and III at a distance. There was, however, a third variant which anyone could spot – the Mk II. This was a batch of 300 Lancasters produced by Sir W. G. Armstrong Whitworth Aircraft at Baginton, powered by Bristol Hercules, air-cooled radials. The Mk II had been planned at an early stage of the Lancaster production programme as a precaution against a shortage of Rolls-Royce Merlins. However, from 1942, the Americans were producing licence built Merlin 38s in ever increasing numbers (not only for Lancasters, but also for the Merlin powered P-51 Mustang, used both by the USAAF and the RAF) and a shortage of Merlins never in fact occurred but, at the time the Mk II was mooted, this was not of course known. Two prototype Lancaster IIs were proposed; in the event, only one, DT810, was completed and first flew on 21 December 1941, powered by four Bristol Hercules VIs, 14 cylinder air-cooled radials, each of 1,734 hp. DT810 was extensively tested by the makers and did not come to Boscombe Down until the spring of 1942.

Two Boscombe Down scientists, J. J. Unwin and W. J. D. Annand, conducted a comprehensive investigation of the Mk II's performance under the title 'Fuel consumption range and operation of a Lancaster I'.[9]

The tests were made during June and July 1942, the brief being to ascertain the entire operational performance and capability of the Lancaster II at light and maximum overload weight. After some very careful fuel flow observations the A&AEE scientists were able to show that the fuel flow for a given height and engine setting (i.e. throttles and boost pressure) increased by about ½ per cent per 1,000 ft of height when the superchargers were in the MS (low altitude) gear and 1 per cent in the FS gear. This finding was precise enough to be expressed by a simple formula.[10]

The fuel flow figures might seem somewhat trivial but it enabled Bomber Command (mostly Canadian) crews to operate their Mk II at maximum efficiency.

A second discovery as a result of the A&AEE work was that if, when flying with a rich mixture on the climb – a normal procedure – the throttle settings were reduced to the point at which the boost pressure just began to fall a substantial fuel saving was feasible. Further savings in fuel when climbing were shown to be possible with as lean a mixture as was prudent, the cylinder head temperatures being a limiting factor.

It was further demonstrated that, by using weak mixture in a climb to 18,000 ft, 89 gallons of fuel could be saved, which increased the still air range of the Mk II Lancaster by 90 statute miles. The effect of the fuel savings on the operational capability were shown to be as below:

At 62,300 lb the aeroplane takes off in 620 yards and [clears] a 50 ft screen in 970 yards. A height of 15,000 ft is attained in 20 minutes, 20,000 ft in 36 minutes. [Service ceiling of Mk II 21,000 ft.]

The report continues:

In the near future it is possible that the fully equipped weight (without bombs or fuel) will be about 42,000 lb. A typical loading for a take-off weight of 63,000 lb will be 2,154 gallons of fuel and a bomb load of 5,500 lb.

Assuming 60% of the fuel to be used on the outward flight the aeroplane reaches the target at 53,700 lb, leaves at 48,200 lb after the disposal of the bomb load. On reaching the target the aeroplane could bomb from a service ceiling around 24,000 ft.

Maximum still air range with full fuel [2,154 Imp. gallons]:
 2370 st. miles at 15,000 ft
 2240 st. miles at 20,000 ft
 2340 st. miles at 1,000 ft
These ranges could be extended by using weak mixture for the climb.

The above figures are, of course, for maximum range in still air, an unlikely eventuality over Northern Europe. The practical ranges for the same fuel/bomb load were:

 1780 st. miles at 15,000 ft
 1680 st. miles at 20,000 ft
 1750 st. miles at 1,000 ft

which correspond to durations of 12, 10½ and 14½ hours.

By sacrificing fuel for the offensive load, it was possible, at an AUW of 63,000 lb, to carry 12,750 lb of bombs and 1,200 gallons of fuel, which gave a range of 900 miles at 15,000 ft and 870 at 20,000 ft, the duration being 6½ and 5½ hours. If the pilot was prepared to fly at 1,000 ft, then he could obtain a range of 1,010 miles and 8½ hours duration.

The level speeds attained by DT810 were assessed by the A&AEE.[11] The tests were made at 2,900 rpm +8 boost. (This power level could only be maintained for a maximum of five minutes.) At this engine setting the maximum speed at 95 per cent take-off weight, 5,900 lb, trued out to 270 mph at 7,000 ft, full throttle, in MS gear and 273 mph at 14,000 ft in FS gear.

From early in 1943 the aircraft of RAF Bomber Command were being fitted with the navigation aid H_2S. This radar, operating on 10 cm, required a rotating aerial under the aircraft's fuselage, which, in turn, necessitated a 'blister' to protect the radar scanner. After H_2S had entered general service, A. V. Roe Ltd complained that the 'blister' was causing a substantial loss of performance; A&AEE were therefore asked to assess the penalty the use of this important aid was imposing on operational Lancasters. One of the Boscombe Down test aircraft, a Mk I, W4963, was fitted with a 'blister' and the performance measured. The results[12] did not uphold the pessimistic assertions made by the makers: the Boscombe Down test showed that the H_2S had no significant effect on either the initial climb or the level speed:

The absence of any measurable change [with or without the radar] suggests that the drag of the blister is not more than 6 lb at 100 ft/sec. This is not inconsistent with drag measured on streamline underfuselage drop tanks when favourably positioned.

 It should be noted that the drag increment due to blisters of this type appears to depend on the position of the blister along the fuselage and on the shape of the fuselage concerned. It should not be assumed that a similar blister in a different position or on a different aircraft [i.e. Halifax] will have the same effect. It is also possible that the tailwheel on the present aircraft [W4963] has affected the results; if the tailwheel were retractable the effect of the blister might be greater.

As the air war progressed, it became obvious that radar fits such as H_2S were to be a permanent feature of most RAF bombers. The tests reported above were made in the summer of 1944; a year later, in May 1945, the A&AEE were investigating the effect of an enlarged H_2S ventral blister on another Lancaster I, W9408.

The blister on this production aircraft was to accommodate a six foot diameter scanner and the A&AEE tests[13] were:

To determine whether the strength of the blister and its attachments was adequate to withstand the aerodynamic forces in dives to the limiting diving speed of 360 mph and to assess the effect of the blister on handling.

The trials proved that the radar blister had no apparent effect on handling. Tests were made at the stall, in dives, asymmetric flight and at take-off and landing at various weights; not only was the handling in each case unaltered with the blister fitted, but the strength of the fitting appeared to be capable of withstanding the aerodynamic forces. Although the actual flying characteristics of the Lancaster were unimpaired, the H_2S blister appeared to have a noticeable effect, up to 20 mph, on the indicated airspeed at the stall (the static vent for the air speed indicator was on the port side of the fuselage above the blister). It was decided to test W4963, which was still at Boscombe Down, to find a position for the vent that was unaffected by the enlarged H_2S blister. (It is not known if this was, in fact, done; W4963 went to 10 MU in July 1945, where it apparently remained until scrapped in November 1946.)

As related at the beginning of this chapter, most of the work required of the A&AEE on the type was to ascertain the effect of purely operational requirements, the H_2S blister being a typical example. At about the same time as those trials, June 1944, another series of tests was made with 'paddle' blade propellers.

The airframe of the Lancaster, irrespective of the Mk, was so clean that little could be done to improve the aircraft's performance. For example, the tailwheel of Lancasters was never made retractable: the weight and complication of the required hydraulics was not considered to be worth it (unlike the contemporary Halifax, which was fitted with a retractable tailwheel as part of the A&AEE recommendations to 'clean up' that bomber). The Lancaster did, eventually, have more powerful engines: Rolls-Royce 24s offering 1,610 hp at +18 lb boost for take-off. To utilise the increased performance of these power plants it was proposed to fit broad blade propellers, the so called 'paddle blades'. The A&AEE was asked to undertake tests to evaluate the effects of the new propellers when fitted to Rolls-Royce Merlin 24s.

A Lancaster I, JB127, arrived at Boscombe Down in April 1944 for the tests. It was the first Lancaster to be tested by the A&AEE powered by Merlin 24s and, for comparative purposes, JB127 was first flown with 'standard' Lancaster propellers: de Havilland Hydromatic AS/138s, on all four engines (Hamilton propellers were also fitted to many Lancaster Is). The aircraft was a standard Mk I, apart from the then new Merlin 24s which were rated for 3,000 rpm +18 boost for take-off and combat emergency (five minutes limit). Take-off weight for the tests was 63,000 lb. The climb and level speed of JB127 was measured as follows:[14]

Maximum speed at 60,000 lb (95% of take-off weight):
281 mph TAS at 9,900 ft MS gear
271 mph TAS at 21,000 ft FS gear   Max. boost obtainable +17 lb

Maximum cruise at 60,000 lbs:
249 mph TAS at 9,900 ft MS gear
247 mph TAS at 16,000 ft FS gear

Service ceiling 22,000 ft: time to ceiling 48 minutes.

The report noted that JB127 did not climb noticeably differently from the A&AEE 'Hack' Lancaster I, W4963, powered by Merlin 22s. The maximum speed of the later aircraft was six mph slower in FS supercharger gear but one mph faster in MS.

Having ascertained the basic performance of JB127 on standard de Havilland propellers, the next series of tests before the fitting of the paddle blades was fuel consumption trials.

Fuel tankage of the aircraft was standard at 2,154 Imperial gallons. The tests were corrected to the 'Standard Day' and to an AUW of 51,000 lb; that is, half fuel, half bombs, from take-off at 63,000 lb. The results of the tests, expressed as specific range (i.e. air miles per gallon) were:[15]

10,000 ft, Carb. air cold MS Gear 1.25 ampg at 165 mph IAS (1,950/+1)ϕ
10,000 ft, Carb. air hot MS Gear 1.06 ampg at 160 mph IAS (2,000/+0.4)
15,000 ft, Carb. air cold FS Gear 1.25 ampg at 160 mph IAS (2,000/+1.2)
15,000 ft, Carb. air hot   FS Gear 1.03 a mpg at 155 mph IAS (2,100/+0.2)
ϕ rpm and boost

The calculation of the still air range to be expected from the above was based on a law determined empirically by the A&AEE from some earlier trials with yet another Lancaster I (R5546). This law stated that 'the optimum still air range is inversely proportional to the square root of the weight'. Using the law and assuming the bomb load to have been dropped, the maximum ranges in still air, with no reserve but allowing for distance on the climb, were:

2,540 miles at 10,000 ft in MS
2,500 miles at 15,000 ft in FS

assuming 63,000 lb at take-off; i.e. maximum fuel, 2,154 Imp. gallons, 8,500 lb bomb load.

At the conclusion of these tests, JB127 was fitted with four Nash Kelvinator paddle blade propellers with de Havilland governor units. The test flights were the subject of an A&AEE report[17] dated 28 June 1944.

JB127 as tested was, propellers apart, in identical condition as for the 'standard' propeller trials. The results with the paddle blade propellers were as follows:

Rate of climb in MS gear: 800 ft/min at 9,500 ft
Rate of climb in FS gear: 610 ft/min at 16,200 ft
Service ceiling 23,000 ft
Time to 23,000 ft, 44 mins

At 60,000 lb AUW the maximum level speed was:

(MS gear) 268 mph TAS at 2,500 ft

(FS gear) 280 mph TAS at 10,000 ft
Maximum cruise (MS) 249 mph TAS at 10,000 ft
Maximum cruise (FS) 258 mph TAS at 16,200 ft

The conclusion from these initial trials was that the paddle blade propellers gave an increase of six to ten mph TAS above 16,000 ft and an increase of 1,500 ft to the service ceiling when compared with the same engines fitted with standard airscrews. The results at lower levels, however, were slightly inferior.

The report concluded with the observation that further tests were to be made.

The same aircraft (JB217) underwent fuel consumption tests to ascertain if the paddle blade propellers conferred any advantage in range. The findings were reported on 10 August 1944. At 60,000 lb the results were:

10,000 ft cold air intake,	MS gear,	paddle blades:	1.32 ampg
10,000 ft cold air intake,	MS gear,	standard blades:	1.25 ampg
10,000 ft hot air intake,	MS gear,	paddle blades:	1.13 ampg
10,000 ft hot air intake,	MS gear,	standard blades:	1.06 ampg
15,000 ft cold air intake,	FS gear,	paddle blades:	1.27 ampg
15,000 ft cold air intake	FS gear,	standard blades:	1.25 ampg
15,000 ft hot air intake,	FS gear,	paddle blades:	1.04 ampg
15,000 ft hot air intake,	FS gear,	standard blades:	1.03 ampg

The engine power settings for maximum still air range were lower with the new propellers than the standard ones fitted to the same aircraft, which: 'indicates that the efficiency of the [paddle blade] propellers at low forward . . . speeds has been improved', which, in simple terms meant that for a given range a heavier bomb load could be carried for the same distance, or a standard load for a greater distance.

'Paddle steamers', as the Lancasters fitted with the Merlin 24s and Nash Kelvinator propellers were called, became, during 1944, the standard as all new production Lancaster Is and many re-engined earlier aircraft were issued to the squadrons.

Any major modification to service aircraft usually caused problems which only came to light under the stress of operational flying: the 'paddle steamers' were no exception.

Take, for example, the case of the Lancaster I, LL773 'SR.U', of No. 101 Squadron, based at Ludford Magna; this paddle-bladed aircraft was flying on an operational sortie at 23,000 ft under continuous cruise conditions: 2,650 rpm/+1 boost. The bomber had been flying straight and level and was put into a 'gradual dive', the pilot not touching the throttles. Before long, the port and starboard outer propellers began to overspeed; the airspeed went up to 290 mph IAS, the pilot pulling out of the dive at 19,000 ft with both the other engines on fire. The ignition was cut and the propellers feathered; the Graviner engine fire extinguishers were activated and the fires put out: the aircraft landed safely. (Later, LL773's luck ran out when, following a crash in June 1944, it was struck off charge.)

At the time of the LL773 incident, two other Lancaster Is at Ludford Magna, both fitted with the new Nash Kelvinator propellers and DG governor units, were tested but found to be satisfactory. The defective governor units salvaged from LL773 were sent to Boscombe Down and were rig tested and strip examined, but no conclusive evidence as to the cause of the overspeeding could be found, although a certain amount of foreign matter was discovered in the oil of the units. Since the overspeeding of the propellers was undoubtedly due to the governors putting the blades into fully fine pitch, the units were clearly under suspicion.

Modifications[18] were therefore made to the governor units fitted to the A&AEE's JB127 and the aircraft was test flown from Boscombe Down on 15 May 1944. During the flight, the conditions which had caused the serious overspeeding to the propellers of LL773 were reproduced; the aircraft was dived at 2,650 rpm +1 lb boost from 25,000 ft until 360 mph was reached. The rpm of the port outer engine momentarily went up to 2,725 rpm; between 280 and 300 mph all four engines fluctuated between 2,650 and 2,750 rpm. As the speed rose, however, the rpm settled down to 2,600, at which figure they all remained up to the Lancaster's maximum permitted speed of 360 mph. JB127 was pulled out of the dive without further incident at 13,000 ft. The conclusion reached after the trial was that the 'paddle' blade propellers with their associated governor units were acceptable, provided the A&AEE recommended modifications were incorporated and that the governor units were regularly cleaned and serviced.

Any further investigations that may have been planned with JB127 were unfortunately curtailed, for the aircraft crashed at Boscombe Down soon after the above test flight. The accident occurred on 26 September 1944, after a three hour test flight including a performance climb; the pilot, on landing, misjudged his height above the Boscombe Down runway, due to poor visibility caused by mist and a setting sun. The aircraft stalled from about 20 ft and the port undercarriage was driven through the wing, the Lancaster slewing round 90°, damaging both port engines. Neither the pilot nor the four-man crew, including two A&AEE civilian observers, were injured. JB127 received 'Category B' damage (repairable at base).

When the three wartime 'heavies', the Stirling, Halifax and Manchester, had originally been designed, the thinking of the Air Staff envisaged bombing of enemy targets in terms of a 'saturation' attack by a large concentration of 1,000 and 500 lb bombs. The bomb bays of the aircraft were therefore not required to accommodate any single bomb greater than 1,000 lb. The Manchester had a completely unobstructed bomb bay which was retained when the Lancaster inherited its fuselage. (The Lancaster mainspar, as any ex-crewman will tell you, was across the fuselage above the bomb bay and constituted a formidable obstacle just aft of the wireless operator's position, which had to be climbed over en route to and from all the crew stations, with the exception of the tail and mid-upper gunners.)

Largely due to the unobstructed bomb bay, but also because of the ability of the Lancaster to lift near incredible loads, it was decided to modify a small number of Lancasters to carry the Barnes Wallis designed 22,000 lb 'Grand Slam' 'earthquake' bombs.

The 'Grand Slam' bomb was a truly formidable weapon: the ultimate in conventional chemical explosives. Only 41 were dropped and all against special daylight targets. The philosophy behind these ten ton bombs was the ability to create a local 'earthquake', or mining effect, which simply shook down the target structure rather than blowing it down by direct explosive blast. To achieve this, the bombs had to be dropped from maximum height (20,000 ft) to accelerate to the high speed needed for the bomb, which had a very strong casing, to penetrate the earth deeply before its seven tons of high explosive detonated, producing the devastating tremors which few structures could withstand – even a substantial 'miss' would still be effective.

Lancasters had already been modified to carry the 12,000 lb 'Tallboy' bomb which had sunk the *Tirpitz* but, before the invasion of the continent, no worthwhile targets were within the necessarily limited range of a bomber carrying an offensive load of 22,000 lb. It should be noted that there was only one Allied aircraft which could conceivably lift such a bomb: the Avro Lancaster.

When, in late 1944, the RAF and USAAF Eighth Air Force were briefed to destroy the vital Bielefeld Viaduct, which was carrying the main railway line from Hamm to Hanover, photographic reconnaissance proved that, although it had been directly hit many times by 1,000 and 500 lb bombs, only the spans were destroyed; the stone piers remained and German army engineers replaced the spans with temporary steel girders carrying the railway tracks between the piers. To destroy these piers with relatively small general purpose demolition bombs was a virtual impossibility and many aircraft would be lost in the daylight sorties in trying. It was decided that the viaduct would be attacked by the 22,000 lb 'Grand Slam' bomb.

Once the target had been decided on, two Lancasters, PB592/G and PB995 (both late production B1s (Special), powered by Merlin 38 engines), were prepared for trials with 22,000 lb bombs. The modifications were not extensive; the bomb doors were removed and the massive bomb suspended beneath the aircraft, more or less in the open. No H_2S was carried.

PB592/G, the first Lancaster to be modified, arrived at Boscombe Down early in October 1944. The first trials were to ascertain the handling without the bomb. The unarmed take-off weight was 42,170 lb and, despite the absence of bomb doors: 'The aircraft was easy to fly and no undue concentration in longitudinal control was necessary'.

At all speeds and heights the aircraft returned to straight and level flight, following deliberate disturbance in roll and yaw. A slight tendency for aileron overbalance was noted above 220 mph IAS. Behaviour in dive to 360 mph was found to be normal for a Lancaster. Stalls were gentle and recovery straightforward.

Take-off weight with the 22,000 lb bomb was 63,370 lb. The aircraft was flown up to 20,000 ft and the handling tests began. Only gentle manoeuvres were contemplated – no stalls – and dives were to be limited to a maximum speed of 320 mph. With the bomb, longitudinal stability appeared neutral at low speeds but improved as the airspeed increased. The test pilots found that the aircraft was comfortable to fly straight and level. When deliberate lateral or directional disturbances were made, the Lancaster returned to straight and level flight but with a heading error of between 15° to 20° from the original course, in the direction of the disturbance. The aircraft was found to be exceptionally stable laterally: 'which can be attributed to the increased wing flex and hence [an increased] dihedral due to the abnormal concentration of load. . .'.

Surprisingly, the controls remained light and effective at low speeds in level flight. With an increase of speed, the controls became heavier but 'still pleasant'. Above 230 mph IAS, heaviness increased rapidly, particularly the ailerons, to the extent that it was possible to execute 'only very gentle turns owing to the pilot's inability to apply [aileron] control'. The A&AEE report [19] commented that:

It is thought that the heaviness of the aileron controls may be largely frictional due to distortion of the wings resulting from the unusual load distribution.

41

Throughout the tests with the bomb 'there was vibration of the rear fuselage and tailplane which was manifest by a continuous shaking of the entire aircraft'.

It says a great deal for the reputation of the Lancaster's structural strength that the A&AEE test crews, despite the wings' continuous flexing and the vibration, which became 'excessive' above 240 mph, dived the aircraft up to 320 mph from level flight at 240 mph. The dive was discontinued at 320 mph IAS due to the vibration becoming 'serious' at that speed.

The report concluded that, on the flight to the target, a maximum permitted speed of 260 mph IAS was recommended. On return, with the bomb dropped, the modified Lancaster behaved and could be handled as a standard aircraft.

The A&AEE continued to test the 'Grand Slam' Lancasters into 1945, when trials were conducted to ascertain the still air range (SAR) of a modified Lancaster with the 22,000 lb bomb fitted.[20]

The aircraft, PB592/G, took off at 63,700 lb AUW. The maximum rate of climb was 720 ft/min at 9,900 in MS gear and 470 ft/min at 16,700 ft: time to 20,000 ft, 38 minutes: service ceiling 21,000 ft: remarkable figures for an aircraft carrying its own weight in armaments.

The still air range was determined at 60,000 lb. Optimum range was at 15,000 ft, superchargers in FS gear and engine settings 2,250 rpm +3 lb boost. Cruising at 165 mph IAS, the specific air range was 1.11 ampg.

The sheer efficiency of Roy Chadwick's design is apparent when one considers that PB592/G, with four V-12, 1,610 hp engines, carrying a ten ton bomb suspended largely as an external store, returned an average fuel consumption at 165 mph of 1.11 air mpg: a modern (1982) turbo F.I. Grand Prix car, weighing less than one of the Lancaster's main wheels, returns a figure of less than three mpg at a lower average speed.

A&AEE's trials culminated with a drop of a live 'Grand Slam' on the Ashley Walk bombing range in the New Forest on the morning of 13 March 1945. The following day came the first operational use of 'Grand Slam': the destruction of the Bielefeld Viaduct by a single 22,000 lb bomb, dropped from a modified Lancaster (PD112) of No. 617 Squadron, flown by Sqn. Ldr. C. C. Calder.

Under the pressure of operational requirements, the Grand Slam bombs were used by the RAF against a number of targets that could only be attacked effectively by this unique weapon, the crews of No. 617 Squadron accepting the shortcomings of the modified Lancasters which carried them, and the problem of excessive vibration which limited the maximum speed. Once the basic object of using the bomb in action had been successfully realised, the A&AEE turned to the question of alleviating the vibration which both the smaller 12,000 lb 'Tallboy' and the 22,000 lb bomb caused.

It was thought that the vibration of the aircraft was arising from turbulence from the 22,000 lb bomb's fins affecting the Lancaster's tail unit. The rear fairing of the bomb bay was therefore modified to allow fins to be rotated through 45°.

The A&AEE tests were, in one sense, disappointing in that the vibration was still apparent:[21]

A vibration of the rear fuselage which can be felt throughout the aircraft and in the rudder and elevator controls is present at all speeds and increases with speed. It does not appear to differ from that experienced previously and could undoubtedly prove disconcerting to the tail gunner. Inspection of the rear bomb bay baffle plate showed it to be in a state of vibration and this is probably the main source. . .'.

The report recommended that the previous maximum permitted speed of 250 mph IAS should remain.

When either the 12,000 lb or the 22,000 lb bomb was carried by PB592/G, it was noted that:

The handling characteristics . . . are satisfactory up to 250 mph IAS. With the 22,000 lb bomb fitted the aircraft wallows slightly at all heights and speeds. Pilots should not attempt to prevent this motion as experience shows this may aggravate the condition.

PB592/G was subjected to performance tests with the modified bomb bay, with and without the 22,000 lb bomb.[22]

With the bomb fitted and at an AUW of 72,000 lb, the Lancaster climbed at 500 ft/min at 10,000 ft and 240 ft/min at 16,700 ft; the service ceiling, however, was now 18,600 ft and it took 50 minutes to 18,000 ft.

Maximum cruise:	245 mph TAS at 16,200 ft, at 68,500 lb
	15,000 ft, 68,500 lb
Still air range:	0.99 ampg at 175 mph IAS
Without bomb at 47,000 lb:	1.31 ampg at 145 mph IAS

72,000 lb was the maximum overload for the aircraft which, it should be borne in mind, was a modification of a standard production Lancaster, not a special 'one-off'. In point of fact, after the tests, it was discovered that, due to a loading error, several flights had been made at an AUW of 73,880 lb!

The other Boscombe Down Lancaster modified to carry the 22,000 lb bomb, PB995, seems to have figured little in the trials. An A&AEE report[23] dated 30 July 1945 notes that this aircraft was used in a 'still air range' trial with a 22,000 lb bomb. PB995 differed from PB592 in several minor ways but a major difference was that the former Lancaster still carried its nose and mid-upper turrets; due to these, the range was reduced by 3 per cent.

PB592 was disposed of (to 46 MU) on 8 April 1945, having donated its 22,000 lb bomb crutches to PB995, but with the end of the European war in sight, PB995 soon followed (28 April 1945) the other A&AEE 'Grand Slam' Lancaster to an MU, both aircraft being ignominiously scrapped: '592 in January 1947; '995 in March 1948.

Apart from the A&AEE tests of the 12,000 and 22,000 lb bombs, which were essentially tactical weapons to be used in support of ground forces in Europe, the question of operating Lancasters against the Japanese in the Far East was also the concern of Boscombe Down as the European war ended. The fundamental problem in that distant theatre was primarily one of range.

The maximum practical range of standard service Lancasters taking off at 68,000 lb (14,000 lb of bombs) was 1,660 statute miles. This was considered inadequate for operations against the Japanese in the Pacific; the American B-29 Superfortress, used by the USAAF against targets on the Japanese Home Islands, could carry a 10,000 lb bomb load for 3,250 miles. To be able to operate over similar distances, Lancasters would have to be revised considerably, an interim proposal being the installation of an additional 1,000 Imperial gallon fuel tank to bring the total fuel capacity up to 3,154 Imperial gallons.

Two Lancaster Is, SW244 and HK541, were modified by A. V. Roe. Both had the 1,000 gallon 'saddle' tanks fitted: these tanks were faired into the top of the fuselage from just aft of the cockpit to the position of the mid-upper turret, the turret being deleted. These two special Lancasters, designated Lancaster I (F.E.) – 'F.E.' signifying 'Far East' – were sent to the A&AEE for 'Overload trials . . . to determine the operational capabilities of the Lancaster under high temperature conditions'.[24]

SW244 was the second aircraft of one of the last production batches of Lancasters and came new from the makers, A. V. Roe. HK541, on the other hand, was a Vickers built veteran, having served firstly as 'KO.P' of 115 Squadron, then with Training Units, No. 3 LFS (Lancaster Finishing School) at Feltwell and, prior to coming to the A&AEE, No. 1651 HCU (Heavy Conversion Unit) at Woolfax Lodge.

For the high temperature trials, HK541 was tested by the A&AEE at Manipur in India between May and June 1945. The saddle tank fitted was a mock-up, ballast representing the fuel load. The aircraft was tested at the maximum overload of 72,000 lb.

The A&AEE brief was to assess overload operations at high temperatures and to determine an operating technique to enable RAF crews in the Far East to obtain the extreme ranges required for ferrying and operations in semi-tropical conditions – conditions, incidentally, for which the Lancaster had never been designed.[25]

HK541 was powered by Merlin 24s which clearly would be hard pressed to lift 72,000 lb off a high temperature airfield. The A&AEE test crew first tried a tail-down 'pull off' technique at between 85–90 knots*; the unstick distance at 72,000 lb was 1,050 yards. Using the RAF standard 'tail up' technique the aircraft became airborne at 105 knots, after a take-off run of 1,450 yards. The climb out was at 2,850 rpm +9 lb boost (the 'one hour' rating of the Merlin 24). Maximum rate of climb was only 340 ft/min: time to 10,000 ft, 31.1 minutes in MS gear. At 63,000 lb a service ceiling of 20,000 ft was obtained, though it took HK541 65 minutes to reach it.

After the high temperature trials, the A&AEE recommended that, for operational sorties with a 6,000 lb bomb load, the technique was a climb to 5,000 ft, level off at that altitude, reducing rpm to maintain 150 knots IAS. After 3½ hours, reduce IAS to 145 knots for a further 3 hours, then climb to 18,000 ft at 2,650 +7 lb to 11,000 ft, then 2,850 +9 lb at 18,000 ft. Cruising at 18,000 ft at 135 knots IAS, bomb at 18,000, then descend to 10,000 ft and cruise home at 130–135 knots. The still air range, with these rather involved parameters, was calculated at 3,540 statute miles or, since the RAF had by now gone nautical, 3,070 nautical miles.

Long range test flights were actually made and empirically confirmed the tentative figures. In the event, the USAAF soon dropped the atomic bombs (from B-29s) and the Pacific War ended. The long range Lancasters never went into action. Perhaps it was just as well: the Lancaster was unbeatable as a heavy bomber over Europe; the Pacific was out of its league, as would have been the European theatre for the B-29. (After the long range trials SW244 and HK541 took the sad route to 10 MU and the scrap heap.)

---

* Knots had replaced mph in the RAF by this time (early 1945).

One of the last A&AEE reports concerning Lancasters was of some unusual trials made at Boscombe Down just post-war (August 1945). The aircraft was a Lancaster I, LL813, which had been operated as a flying testbed by de Havilland's propeller division and had been fitted with experimental reversible pitch airscrews. These airscrews anticipated the reverse pitch of modern jets, universally used now as a means of shortening the landing run, but in 1945 still experimental. They were designed by de Havillands as a landing brake and the A&AEE was asked to assess the suitability of the systems for release to the RAF for Service evaluation. The A&AEE report[26] summarizes the trials as follows:

Reverse pitch was selected for release in most cases just after touchdown, but some selections during the float prior to touchdown were also made. The braking effect when the throttles were opened was satisfactory, but great difficulty was encountered in attempting to correct an inadvertant swing because the controls were 'unsensed'. It is recommended that Service trials should not be undertaken with the present 'unsensed' controls.

30 landings were made by five A&AEE test pilots, following several hundred by Avro pilots. The A&AEE report anticipated that:

the system as arranged might prove unsatisfactory for general Service use owing to the unorthodox manner in which asymmetric braking was effected.

The procedure adopted by the A&AEE test pilots was to close the throttles and then select a reverse pitch of $-17°$ by two buttons on the console just ahead of the throttle levers; one button controlled the inner, the other the outer propellers. When the blades had moved to $-17°$, the throttles were opened. The landings were not without incident, including several impressive ground loops caused by one engine (usually the port inner) stalling as the throttles were opened in reverse pitch. No damage was caused, however.

The report commented that:

... The firm's 'Pilot's Notes' recommended that the throttles be advanced evenly and the aircraft be kept straight by use of wheel brakes. It is customary, however, for pilots of multi-engined aircraft to correct a bad swing by opening the throttles of the engines on the inside of the swing. This instinctive action on the present aircraft [LL813] made the swing worse. The recommendation that wheel brakes only be used would avert the danger of using the wrong throttle but could result in more tyre wear and the chance of a tyre burst.

Conclusions: The Lancaster with de Havilland braking propellers is not suitable, in the opinion of this Establishment, for release for Service trials.

It did not really matter for, by the time that was written (October 1945), the Lancaster was rapidly disappearing from the inventory of the RAF.

From an aircraft which, as the Manchester, had begun its service career as a 'disappointment', the Lancaster became one of the truly great military aircraft of the Second World War: Lancasters flew 156,000 sorties and dropped 608,612 tons of bombs and countless incendiaries. The cost was high: over four thousand Lancasters lost to enemy action. The last of the 7,366 Lancasters built was

TW910, a Mk I (F.E.), delivered from Armstrong Whitworth on 2 February 1946. Though Lancasters continued post war with Coastal Command as maritime reconnaissance aircraft (to replace Lease Lend Liberators), the type was soon supplanted in Bomber Command by the Lincoln – a development of the Lancaster. The last RAF Lancaster, RF325, was struck off charge at the School of Maritime Reconnaissance at St Mawgan on 15 October 1956.[27] Between that date and 28 January 1941, when the prototype arrived at Boscombe Down, the AA&AEE had been responsible for numerous trials on Lancasters of every Mk, including several prototype aircraft and specialised armament, for example the 'Dam Busting' bouncing bomb.

Lancasters gave the test flight crews at Boscombe Down a fairly easy time: few aircraft have proved more adaptable; furthermore, the Lancaster, unlike some of its wartime contemporaries, needed remarkably few modifications other than those to meet Service requirements.

Most Lancasters came to Boscombe Down for normal A&AEE evaluation trials. There were, however, two exceptions: Lancasters which arrived at the A&AEE accused of being 'rogues'.

Wartime aircraft production in Britain was, of necessity, hurried and invariably done under conditions of great hardship by a hastily trained workforce, 44 per cent of whom were women. The *average* working week was over 66 hours and the workers had to suffer the blackout and wartime rationing, in addition to the universal dangers and bereavements of war. The standard of workmanship in the circumstances was extraordinarily high; however, complex military aircraft were built, not to absolute limits but to given tolerances, the philosophy being that these small variations of measurement and fit tended to cancel out, the resulting aircraft being able to meet the required Service specification. Nevertheless, no two aircraft of a given type, even successive production serials, were *exactly* the same. Any minute differences in rigging could nearly always be trimmed out though an aircraft which, following its Service acceptance trials, just met the required standard might, say, following an engine change or repaired battle damage, handle badly and defy all subsequent efforts by the squadron's engineering officers to get it to conform to standard. Such aircraft were called 'rogues'. The A&AEE usually got these malfunctioning machines for testing, which leads us to PB731 and DS670.

PB731 was one of a very large production batch of 800 Lancasters (PA964–PD196) ordered from A. V. Roe in April 1943. It was powered by four Rolls-Royce Merlin 22s and was issued new, in the autumn of 1944, to No. 227 Squadron of No. 5 Group, then based at Balderton. On 22 March 1945, it was reported by HQ Bomber Command to the A&AEE as a 'rogue' aircraft; No. 227 Squadon pilots had complained that when flown fully loaded PB731 exhibited excessive yawing and rolling when the tail turret was rotated. The 'rogue' arrived at Boscombe Down and handling trials were undertaken and a report issued.

The engineering report from No. 227 Squadron had complained that the rolling and yawing condition described had become more marked after PB731 had completed 150 hours. A complete rigging check had then been made but the condition persisted, particularly at full load, making it difficult and tiring to fly over enemy territory when, obviously the tail turret had continuously to be rotated as the rear gunner quartered the sky. Three squadron pilots flew the aircraft and each confirmed the original report. Yet another rigging check was made by the squadron but no discernible fault could be found.

The subsequent A&AEE investigation was thorough in the extreme and illustrates well the day to day work of the Establishment.

The A&AEE report[28], after a summary describing No. 227 Squadron's complaint, continued:

2. *Condition of aircraft relevant to tests.*

2.1 *General.* The aircraft was fully equipped for operational use and had no unusual features which would affect the handling. The following points were noted:–

> The tail turret was on FN.120 with 'Gransdon Lodge' clear view opening. Kilfrost paste was applied on the leading edge of all control surfaces. A Mk. II H_2S blister was fitted.

2.2 *Airspeed system.* All speeds quoted refer to the pilot's ASI, the pitot side of which was connected to the MK. VIII head on the side of the fuselage (Mod. 803 position) and the static side to the port static vent (Mod. 1157 position).

2.3 *Loading.* The aircraft was flown at an all-up weight of approximately 64,000 lb with the centre of gravity approximately 59 in aft of datum (undercarriage down). This loading is similar to that used by the three pilots who made the check handling flights.

The design limits of the centre of gravity range are 60.6 in and 41 in aft of the datum (undercarriage down).

3. *Tests made.*

The aircraft was first inspected on the ground. Flight tests to assess the effect of rotating the tail turret were then made. Subsequently the history of the aircraft was investigated and Squadron personnel questioned.

4. *Results of tests.*

4.1 *Inspection of aircraft.* A careful examination of the airframe and control surfaces revealed no fault of sufficient magnitude to account for the complaints made.

4.2 *Flight tests.*

4.21 *Handling with tail turret central.* The take-off was normal and easy with no tendency to swing. The aircraft was then trimmed to climb at 155 mph ASI at maximum climbing power and the controls tested for heaviness and effectiveness. The rudder and aileron controls were light and effective without any tendency to snatch or overbalance and each could be applied fully without undue exertion by the pilot.

Sudden displacement of the rudder or aileron controls in either direction, the control then being released, resulted in the disturbed control returning to neutral and the aircraft returning to straight and level flight after rapidly damped oscillation. Phugoid tests resulted in a slowly damped oscillation.

Similar characteristics were observed in level flight and dives, and the pilot considered that the aircraft was very pleasant to fly, considering the aft centre of gravity position.

4.22 *Handling with tail turret rotating.* The handling characteristics with the tail turret rotating were normal for the loading and only light footloads were necessary to keep the aircraft straight. The pilot estimated the footloads to be 10–12 lb for climb and level flight and 15–20 lb for speeds above about 250 mph ASI.

When trimmed for climb with hands and feet off at 155 mph ASI, the turret was rotated fully to port and left there with all controls free. The aircraft started to bank and turn to port, the stick moved forward about 1½ inches and the aircraft entered a diving turn to port. At a speed of 200 mph ASI the aircraft had taken on 30° of bank and a rate

47

1 ½ turn had been reached. The control column then moved back and a phugoid oscillation commenced with the aircraft in a steady rate 1 ½ turn.

Under the same condition as the previous paragraph, the turret was rotated fully to starboard and left there. The rolling and diving tendencies were more pronounced and since the stick did not move back with increase of speed, the aircraft assumed an increasingly nose-down attitude with a consequent increase of speed. The following results were observed and will give some indication of the motion:–

Time	Bank	Rate of turn	ASI	Degrees off course
0 seconds	0°	0	155 mph	0°
18 seconds	10°	½	170 mph	20°
40 seconds	30°	1	200 mph	45°
60 seconds	45°	1 ½	240 mph	85°
70 seconds	60°	2	280 mph	Not observed

The motion was then stopped by the pilot.

From the above, it can be seen that the motion was not unduly violent in the early stages and the pilot would have plenty of time to correct the aircraft's attitude.

The aircraft was flown for about 15 minutes with the turret traversing in the gunner's own time and the pilot endeavoured to fly without concentrating unduly on holding course and speed, as might be the case on operations. An observer watched for changes of course, lateral level and speed; the maximum variations were 3° of bank, 2° in course, and 5 mph in speed.

When the pilot concentrated on flying straight and level, no difficulty was found in eliminating these variations.

On one occasion a steady rate 1 turn was made through about 400° and the pilot was unable to detect any effect due to the rotation of the turret, although it was continuously rotated throughout.

4.23 *General.* The handling characteristics with the turret central were considered normal and the effect of rotating the turret was consistent with the condition of loading over the whole speed range. It is, of course, normal for the adverse effects of turret rotation to become more pronounced as the centre of gravity moves aft, but even with the aft centre of gravity position tested, the aircraft was not considered to be unduly tiring to fly when the turret was rotated.

4.3 *Subsequent investigation.* Inspection of the normal operational loadings on other aircraft at the Station showed that the centre of gravity was usually near the middle of the centre of gravity range. An examination of the Squadron loading records for PB.731, at the time when it was first reported as unsatisfactory, revealed that on the night in question, the aircraft was loaded to a greater weight and the centre of gravity was 3 to 4 inches further aft than it had been on previous operations. The centre of gravity remained in this position for the subsequent three trips, after which the aircraft was withdrawn from operation.

When the aircraft was loaded for the check test flights by squadron pilots, the centre of gravity was moved even further aft to approximately 59 ins aft of the datum.

Conversation with the Squadron personnel showed that while they were conversant with all-up weights, bomb loads, petrol loads, etc., they had little or no idea of the centre of gravity positions occasioned by various distributions of bomb and petrol loads. Furthermore, the pilots did not seem to be very conversant with the effect on the handling characteristics of an aircraft, when the centre of gravity position was moved. Conversation with the Squadron test pilot showed that when he tested the aircraft, he was unaware of the fact that the centre of gravity was nearly at the aft limit.

Thus the cause of the complaint appears to be that Service pilots did not appreciate the fact that aftward movement of the centre of gravity caused the adverse behaviour of the aircraft on rotating the tail turret, to be more pronounced, and attributed this to the development of 'rogue' characteristics in the aircraft.

5. *Conclusions and recommendations.*

As tested, the handling characteristics of the aircraft with the tail turret rotating are consistent with the condition of loading over the whole speed range and the aircraft cannot be considered a rogue. It was not considered unduly tiring to fly in this condition while the turret was rotated.

Investigation into the loading of the aircraft suggested that the complaint was due to the pilots failing to appreciate the fact that the centre of gravity was more aft than they were accustomed to and that this caused some deterioration in behaviour when the tail turret was rotated.

Since this aircraft will probably still be regarded with suspicion at R.A.F. Balderton, it is suggested that it should be transferred to another Squadron where its history is not known.

In spite of that sound psychological advice from the A&AEE, PB731 was not issued to another squadron but returned to No. 227 to survive the war, being scrapped in March 1947.

DS670, the second alleged 'rogue' Lancaster, was a Mk II, powered by four Bristol Hercules XVIs, on charge to No. 115 Squadron of No. 3 Group, based at East Wretham. (No. 115 was the first squadron to be completely equipped with the Mk II Lancaster.) Squadron pilots had complained of severe vibration and 'shake' when cruising at full load at 20,000 ft. The aircraft had been used in a fighter affiliation exercise just prior to the operational flight on which the vibration had first been reported and, since the Lancaster had been handled violently during evasive manoeuvres with the fighters, it had been given a thorough inspection by the Station Engineering Officer. The only fault found was minor, being loose inspection plates for the inboard fuel tanks; these were tightened.

DS670 was tested by the A&AEE at Boscombe Down on 24 July 1943, the subsequent report[29] stating in part:

2. *Condition of aircraft relative to tests made.*

The aircraft was in the 'fully operational' condition and had no unusual features which would affect handling.

The general finish of the skin of the aircraft was good and no signs of strain having taken place could be observed on fuselage, wings or tail unit. The aircraft had been inspected by the Station Engineer Officer, and apart from the previously mentioned tank inspection plates being loose, no faults were found except that the incidence of the tailplane was not quite correct, being some 1° out on each side, measured at No. 3 and No. 11 ribs.

2.1 *Loading.* The aircraft was flown at an all-up weight of approximately 61,000 lb, this load consisting of full fuel (2,154 galls) and 5,000 lb of bombs (10 × 500 lb).

3. *Tests made.*

The aircraft was climbed at the high load to 20,000 ft and flown under various conditions, including evasive action of the 'corkscrew' type; the stalling speeds were also measured. All the bombs were then dropped and the tests repeated at the lighter load.

4. In general the aircraft flew smoothly and pleasantly with no sign of excessive vibration or shake apparent at any of the crew positions or at any position in the fuselage. No excessive wing flexure or tail flutter could be seen during the manoeuvres.

5. *Conclusions.*

As tested the characteristics of this aircraft are normal for the type.

The slight aileron snatch could no doubt be removed by a careful rigging check.

Unless the vibration reported by the Squadron was caused by the loose tank inspection plates the cause for their complaint is not known.

DS670 was returned to its squadron, but they seem to have been unconvinced for they passed it on almost as soon as it arrived back from Boscombe Down to 1678 Heavy Conversion Unit, also based at East Wretham. It was wrecked on 7 September 1943, after flying a total of only 55 hours.

The fact that, of the 7,366 Lancasters produced, only two came to Boscombe Down accused of being 'rogues' is a fitting finale to the Lancaster chapter.

CHAPTER FOUR

'One-Offs' at Boscombe

The major concern of the A&AEE during the war years was mainly with acceptance trials of the aircraft which were to be the mainstay of the RAF and Fleet Air Arm. These warplanes, produced in thousands, have names familiar even now, forty years on.

Boscombe Down also tested and evaluated other interesting and little known aircraft which are now mere footnotes to the history of military aviation. They were usually built to fill a need, real or imaginary, of some particular moment of war: for the most part they were unsuccessful; either the moment passed or never arrived and the prototype was dropped into obscurity. (It is pertinent to point out, in passing, that the de Havilland Mosquito was originally such a 'one-off' private venture.)

Because of the extreme rarity of these types, for which one would search in vain in most of the popular literature, no apology is offered for their inclusion.

A&AEE Report No. 768

The Phillips and Powis M.20.

During the desperate days following the rout of the Allied forces in France, which was to lead to the Dunkirk evacuation, and with the prospect of a German invasion of Britain a very real possibility, it was evident that the supply of fighter aircraft for the RAF could become a crucial factor in the air battles that would clearly have to be fought during that long hot summer of 1940.

The Spitfire, in particular, was not an easy aircraft to manufacture; each Spitfire I, for example, required 330,000 man hours to produce. The Hurricane, though simpler structurally, nevertheless would still need a similar effort.

Phillips and Powis (the firm is usually better known under its later name: Miles Aircraft) had, during the thirties, been foremost in producing neat, high performance, wooden light aircraft for the civil market. In early 1940 the company, based at Woodley airfield, near Reading, was turning out trainers: the Miles Magister – known to the tens of thousands of wartime pilots who received their basic training on the type as the 'Maggie' – and the advanced trainer, the Master.

The Master I was powered by a single 715 hp Rolls-Royce V-12 Kestrel and, although a two-seater, had the respectable top speed of 226 mph at 15,200 ft, with a service ceiling of 28,000 ft.

It occurred to F. G. Miles and his design staff that, by utilising a maximum number of standard Master components and fitting a 1,460 hp Rolls-Royce Merlin XX engine, a simple wooden, single-seater, high altitude fighter of adequate performance could very quickly be produced in substantial numbers. The proposal was put to the energetic Minister of Aircraft Production, Lord Beaverbrook. 'The Beaver' immediately sanctioned a prototype and on 14 September 1940, one day before what is now commemorated as Battle of Britain Day, and just nine weeks after the original go ahead, AX834, the prototype M.20, was first flown.

F. G. Miles had designed a neat low-wing monoplane in which ease of production and performance were the keynote. It was a 'no frills' concept: no hydraulics were used, the undercarriage was fixed and all the controls were manual. The engine was a standard Rolls-Royce 'power egg', as fitted to the Beaufighter and later to the Lancaster. This Merlin XX came complete with all its ancillaries and was simply bolted as a unit to the firewall. The airframe was wooden, with a two-spar wing covered with plywood and fabric. The fuselage was semi-monocoque, also with plywood as the primary structure, terminating in a plywood, fabric covered tail unit.

Eight .303-inch Browning Mk II guns were mounted, grouped closely in fours, as on the Hurricane, midway in each wing; hinged panels on the upper surface of the wings gave access for ammunition. The clean lines of the aircraft were enhanced by a frameless 'blown' bubble canopy, only the second to be fitted to a service aircraft (the first being the Westland Whirlwind), the canopy offering exceptional all-round visibility for the pilot.

Following the first flight of the M.20 on 14 September 1940, an Air Ministry specification, F.19/40, was written round the project. Though details of the performance of the M.20 were not released officially until after the war, a contemporary report credits it as being 'faster than the Hurricane and a little slower than the 1940 Spitfire, which means . . . a top speed about 340'. The same report also stated that the M.20 had a greater range than either and carried more ammunition (625 rounds per gun). Post-war references credit the prototype with 345 mph at 20,400 ft, with a range of 1,200 miles at 210 mph.

The length of the M.20 was 30 ft 8 inches and the wingspan 34 ft 7 inches, giving a wing area of 235 sq ft, compared with 242 sq ft of a 36 ft 10 inch wingspan Spitfire. The shorter span of the M.20 must have conferred a very good rate of roll. Though the test flights were satisfactory, the shortage of existing fighters envisaged by F. G. Miles did not, in fact, occur – the problem during the Battle of Britain was lack of pilots, not aircraft – and the M.20 project was not put into production. The critical phase of the Battle of Britain had been encountered while the M.20 was being built and it is of interest that the Miles Company, as an interim emergency measure, built 25 M.24 single-seater fighter versions of the Master which, so far as is known, were never used operationally.

The first prototype M.20, AX834, was not tested at the A&AEE, but the company, by now renamed Miles Aircraft Ltd, offered as a private venture a second prototype, to a naval specification, N1/41, which had called for a simple single-seater fighter for shipboard operation, stressed for catapult take-off and arrested landing. This aircraft, the M.20 Mk II, carried the Class 'B' marking U-0228 and was first flown in April 1941; unlike its near identical predecessor, it was performance tested at Boscombe Down in the summer of 1941.

The original reference to Boscombe Down's testing of the second M.20 prototype (U-0228) is contained in the 1st Part of A&AEE Report 768 dated 23 May 1941, which was concerned primarily with the construction and maintenance of the aircraft. The 'bubble' canopy came in for criticism, particularly in the vital question of jettisoning – a matter of life or death to the pilot of a crippled aircraft. The A&AEE findings were:

Hood jettison neat but unsatisfactory. Both hands had to be used – almost impossible due to lack of elbow room. Gloved finger cannot be inserted in hole of either operating lever. . . . Jettison [of] the hood is only possible by wangling.
No provision for opening the closed hood from outside.

Less seriously, the testers complained about the lack of a handgrip for climbing on to the wing, which was not easy when encumbered by heavy flying clothing and parachute. The wings also lacked a suitable seal between the fuel fillers and the wing surface, allowing spilt fuel to run into the space between the fuel tanks: 'a few drain holes have been provided in the undersurface [of the wings] but these are quite inadequate and action of fuel could cause damage' and constitute a fire hazard. There was further criticism of the lack of a seal between the oil filler neck and the wooden fuselage, allowing oil to flow over the glued joints and electrical connections.

Oil and fuel apart, the A&AEE considered that normal rain drainage in general was 'totally inadequate' for a wooden airframe. The fact that all the inspection panels were secured by ordinary wood screws, rather than the usual 'half turn' patent 'Dzus' fastening, occasioned adverse comment, as did the tail oleo pneumatic inflation valve, which apparently was 'set so deep in the wheel fork that a special adaptor was needed'.

The 2nd Part of the A&AEE Report was on the preliminary handling trials. It seems the test pilots at Boscombe Down were 'not very impressed with the seating position which consists of sitting on the floor with the legs straight out, [and] the floorboards are too close to the rudder bar'. On the other hand: 'The hood gives an exceptional view, particularly to the rear, but for operational work a bullet proof screen would be essential'.

The test pilots warned that a tendency to swing to port on take-off had to be countered early with an immediate application of full rudder, for: 'If [the swing] is allowed to develop it cannot be checked'.

If a ground loop was avoided, once airborne the M.20 was found to be stable about all axes at all speeds, though the controls were heavy and ailerons a touch overbalanced. The stall was at 90 mph IAS with flaps up and at 73 mph with full flap. The M.20 was dived at 450 mph, the pilots remarking that:

Acceleration is remarkable and the absence of wind noise round the hood makes this high speed feel quite pleasant . . . the aeroplane behaves normally in the dive, and recovery is straightforward.

Having handed out that bouquet:

Approach and landing. Approach speed considered high at 100 mph, with touchdown at 80 mph. The fact that the undercarriage is fixed . . . introduces a real source of danger in the event of a forced landing. There is no strong point fitted to protect the pilot in the event of the aeroplane overturning on the ground, and unless a sufficiently large and smooth field is available should engine failure occur the pilot would have to choose between abandonment and a crash with risk to his life.

Considering that the M.20 had only mechanical brakes, this was a very real possibility.

(Though the A&AEE reports do not comment on the subject, the lack of a jettisonable undercarriage is surprising on an aircraft competing for a contract calling for shipboard operation: the M.20, N.1/41, would almost certainly have somersaulted when 'ditched'. The German J87T, the maritime version of the Stuka, intended for embarkation on the never to be completed carrier *Graf Zeppelin* had explosive bolts to jettison its fixed undercarriage, in the event of a forced landing on water.)

The third part of A&AEE Report 768, issued on 18 September 1941, deals with the more detailed performance trials of the M.20, now known as the N.1/41, naval prototype. The Class 'B' marks were no longer used; the second prototype had been placed on Ministry charge and now carried the Service Serial DR616.

The performance figures of this, the second M.20, seem to be a little down on the (post-war) figures attributed to the first aircraft, AX834. The tests were conducted at an AUW of 7,650 lb.

Engine:	Rolls-Royce Merlin XX offering 1,460 hp for take-off
Maximum rate of climb:	2,300 ft/min
Time to 20,000 feet:	9.6 mins
Service ceiling (estimated):	32,800 feet
Maximum speed:	333 mph TAS at 20,400 feet
Take-off run:	270 yards
Distance to clear 50 ft screen:	450 yards

Coolant system satisfactory for temperate climates.
Oil cooler satisfactory for temperate and tropical operations.

The figures reveal a respectable performance. The contemporary Hurricane I was only 6 mph faster at 22,000 ft and was slower (9.1 minutes) to 20,000 ft. The Hurricane ceiling was better, however, by some 2,000 ft. The Spitfire had, of course, a better performance than either aircraft.

The armament specialists at Boscombe issued a short report on the Browning guns fitted to the aircraft, following air firing trials: the tests were made at 30,000 ft at 170 mph ASI with an outside air temperature of $-43°C$. The gun heating system – essential for high altitude fighters – was found to maintain the required gun temperature $(-10°C)$ even in the theoretical worst case of an OAT of $-60°C$. However, when the guns were fired, there was a number of 'cook offs' – that is spontaneous detonation of the ammunition in the breech; also it was found that barrel wear was excessive. The reason was heated air passing down the guns' blast tubes en route for the gun bay, preventing the barrels from cooling. The A&AEE recommended that the heated air be routed directly over the breech blocks and away from the blast tubes.

In spite of the A&AEE criticism – that was, after all, their function – this small wooden fighter, designed and built in only nine weeks at a time of great national stress, by a small company which up to that time had produced only light aircraft and trainers, was a commendable attempt to provide an emergency fighter and, whatever its shortcomings, the M.20 possessed a performance which, if less than the fully developed Hurricanes and Spitfires, was at that time ahead of any contemporary American single-seater fighter and could, had it been necessary, have been produced in any furniture or cabinet maker's factory in considerable numbers (as indeed was the Mosquito). The M.20 could lay claim to be the first 'throw away' fighter. The two prototypes were, however, the only examples of the type completed: the Royal Navy did not proceed with N.1/41 specification. The role was to be filled by the Grumman Martlet, the Fleet Air Arm's equivalent of the F4F Wildcat which, together with its later development, the F6F Hellcat, was to contribute very materially to victory over the Japanese in the Pacific War.

A&AEE Report No. 694

The Tandem Winged Lysander

In 1934 the Air Ministry issued a Specification (A.39/34) for an army co-operation aircraft to replace the elegant Napier Dagger powered Hawker Hector biplane. The Westland Company tendered a design which was accepted and, within a year, the west country firm – one of the few pre-war aircraft companies which still exists under its original identity – had constructed a high-wing monoplane which was to become legendary: the Lysander.

The Lysander, though originally designed for army co-operation, principally artillery spotting, later gained fame flying 'cloak and dagger' night sorties, transporting agents in and out of French fields. The 'Lizzie' was possibly one of the first true 'STOL' aircraft and could fly to and from landing grounds that other aircraft could not reach; indeed, the ability of the Lysander to achieve near impossible feats of flying was early demonstrated. The second prototype, K6128, when under test at the A&AEE pre-war base of Martlesham Heath, lost most of the fabric covering the wing in a terminal velocity dive. The test pilot, Flt. Lt. Collins not only discovered that the full span Handley Page slots were capable of sustaining flight, but he was able to land the virtually wingless machine safely.

The first prototype Lysander, K6127, was flown in June 1936 and was to have a much photographed, long and colourful career, being sent pre-war to the north-west frontier of India for operational tests under active service conditions. That particular aircraft was to be the subject of A&AEE Report No. 694g and to become unique among the 1,368 Lysanders built.

Known as the Tandem Wing development, the prototype, K6127, was modified to take a wide span tailplane – virtually a second wing designed to the French Delanne formula – with twin end-plate fins. That was not the extent of the modification, for as Report 694 states:

The fuselage was terminated by a mock-up of a Frazer-Nash 4 gun (.303-inch) turret. The principle was merely an experiment to determine whether it was possible to provide really adequate rear defence on small aircraft without destroying the general flying characteristics.

The second wing, which is what in reality the tailplane became, provided no less than 43 per cent of the net wing area. The size, and therefore lift, of this 'tailplane' was required because of the weight of the rear turret; its guns and gunner were at the maximum moment removed from the C of G datum. The C of G limits of this unique aircraft, from forward to aft, expressed as a percentage of the forward wings chord, were from 45.5 per cent to 58.2 per cent – a considerable range.

It is not clear from the extant reports if the Tandem Wing Lysander flew to Boscombe Down or arrived by road; in either event, the brief performance tests began sometime in late January or early February 1942 (the report is dated 17 February), the first tentative ground taxiing trials being conducted below 40 mph. Handling was easy but, above that speed, it was discovered that neither brakes nor full rudder could cope to keep the Lysander on course. Hardly surprisingly, in view of the weight aft, it was found that a full application of the wheel brakes produced no tendency for the aircraft to nose over, even with the C of G fully forward.

In spite of the marginal directional control, the take-off seems to have been normal and the aircraft was reported as neutrally stable on the climb with the C of G aft, otherwise stable. The twin rudders were light and effective, though the test pilot found them moderately heavy at 285 mph in a dive.

The ability of the standard Lysander to fly slowly was always considered its main asset. The stalling speed is usually given as 65 mph but in fact the 'Lizzie', in the hands of a skilled pilot, could be trimmed into a stable, nose high, steep controlled stall, with the rate of descent determined by the throttle. It was possible, when in this condition, to continue to a perfectly satisfactory three point landing, though pilots were warned that they might thus land safely in a field so small that to fly out of it could prove impossible.

The Tandem Wing rear turret modification does not seem materially to have compromised the ability of the Lysander to emulate, if not a helicopter, certainly an autogyro: the A&AEE test pilots found that, even with the C of G at the maximum forward limit, the aircraft remained in level flight under full control with the stick right back, at the very low speed of 58 mph – this at an all-up weight around 6,000 lb. With the C of G aft, the testers noted a slight tendency of the wing to drop when the stick was brought right back at 60 mph. Interestingly, the famed Lysander stalled stable glide could still be made (with the slats fully open) at 58 mph. Conventional dives were reported as 'smooth and remarkably steady'. With the C of G forward, the Lysander would, if trimmed for full throttle level flight, recover itself from a dive, hands off. At normal or aft C of G, however, the pilot had to initiate the recovery, though the stick force required was not excessive and recovery was positive and immediate.

Unfortunately the brief A&AEE handling report on this unusual aircraft does not contain sufficient data to permit an analysis of the performance penalty of the extensive modification, neither is there any information as to the subsequent career of the Tandem Wing experiment, though the aircraft is known to have gone on to the RAE at Farnborough where it remained until struck off charge in June 1944. If K6127 continued flying with the RAE in the Tandem Wing configuration, it must have perplexed the many aircraft spotters of those war years, for it was often said that aircraft recognition could be divided into two categories: aircraft and Lysanders – standard ones, that is.

The Half Size Bomber

The Short Stirling, the first RAF four-engined heavy bomber, is the subject of a separate A&AEE Report. When the specification for the Stirling was first issued in 1936, it was then such a radical venture it was deemed prudent to assess the flying quality that the bomber, then known as the S.29, was expected to possess by building a roughly half scale flying model. This aircraft, the Short S.31, was constructed during 1937 and was first flown in 1938, originally powered by four 90 hp, seven cylinder Pobjoy Niagara III engines. Its handling was assessed by the A&AEE, though to be strictly accurate, at the pre-war base at Martlesham Heath. However, the aircraft is known to have subsequently flown from Boscombe Down.

The two-seater S.31, was a faithful scale model of the eventual Stirling, even down to the fully operational bomb doors. As the pilot on the first flight, Lankester Parker, remarked, he was the only item not to scale; everything else was: engines, airscrews, turrets, undercarriage, all were almost exactly half full size. The wings were Short S.16 Scion components, modified to take four Niagaras instead of the S.16's original two. The span of 42 ft was near enough half the 99 ft 1 inch of the full size bomber and they were of similar plan.

Before the S.31 appeared at the A&AEE, the engines had been replaced by 114 hp Niagara IVs. Unfortunately the surviving report does not include any details of the performance but, that apart, it nevertheless makes interesting reading:

Note on Handling the Short
'Half Scale Model' B.12/36
(Stirling).

The aeroplane was flown by three test pilots on the 21st and 22nd October 1938. The trials were very brief and were mainly addressed to overall questions of stability, trim and the stall. The aeroplane was flown as delivered and at one centre of gravity position only.

Details of loading.

The following details were supplied by the firm.
Weight 5,370 lb
Power 114 per engine. Total 456 H.P. Max.
Area 330 sq.ft.
Loading – 16.3 lb per sq.ft.
11.8 lb per H.P.
Centre of gravity 28% mean aerodynamic chord.

Handling – Controls.

The general view for take-off and landing is good. The aeroplane tends to swing to the right at take-off, but it takes itself off without change of trim. Control effectiveness engine 'on' is good generally; the rudder loses some effectiveness on the glide, but the control remains adequate. Response to aileron movement is slow but sufficiently effective on the glide. At cruising speed it was possible to move the control column fairly quickly over an appreciable range, with no effect whatever on the flight path. Controls are light and well harmonised; the aileron is exceptionally light.

Trim.

There is little change of trim due to the use of flaps or throttle and there is no change of directional trim with change of speed; there appears to be a slight change in lateral trim with change of speed. The rudder bias control is ineffective at all speeds. Feet off, at cruising speed, no yawing effect was noted for full range of rudder bias control. The full longitudinal trimming range is required, between gliding flight and cruising level flight; there is not sufficient trim for full throttle level flight with control column free. As rigged, the aeroplane was left wing low at cruising speed with control column free and right wing low at full throttle level flight.

Stability.

The longitudinal stability appears to be neutral on the climb, in cruising and in level flight at full throttle.

Note. An experimental device is fitted to the elevator, consisting of a hinged tab controlled by the aerodynamic load on a hemispherical cup, facing forwards, coupled to a light spring. As rigged the device has a stabilising effect. Thus it is not possible to assess what the longitudinal stability would be without the device, and it is probable that the device would give rise to oscillations in the dive.

Laterally the stability is neutral but the ailerons are barely self-centring. Directionally the stability is such that, with the two port engines throttled back, only a slow swing develops rudder free; slight foot load is sufficient to maintain direction in this condition.

Stall.

With flaps up the stall is fairly gentle and there is lateral control right down to the stall. There is no warning of the stall; the rudder control becomes ineffective as the stall is approached. With flaps and undercarriage down a wing drops suddenly at the stall and there is no warning, but the lateral control is effective right down to the stall; at the loading of the tests there was little margin of elevator control beyond that required to stall the aeroplane flaps down.

Landing.

There is very little change of trim as the flaps come down; the flaps appear to be barely sufficiently effective in steepening the approach glide. There is sufficient elevator control for landing, and the landing is easy at the above load and centre of gravity.

General conclusions.

(i)   Controls are very satisfactory for harmony and effectiveness, except for the loss of elevator effectiveness over a small range of movement. Possibly the elevator is being masked by the tail plane over this range.

(ii)   Bearing the full scale operational duty in mind, it is considered that slight increases in longitudinal and lateral stability are desirable.

(iii)   The directional trim control should be made more effective and the range of the longitudinal trim control should be more fully investigated.

(iv)   It is considered that a lateral trimming device is desirable.

The S.31 seems to have fulfilled its role; its flight characteristics undoubtedly gave the Short designers and their test pilots a clearer indication of what the full size prototype's handling would be like. The first flight of that prototype Stirling (L7600) followed in May 1939. Unfortunately the S.31 trials did not include a landing with the wheel brakes binding; if they had, then the flight crew could have anticipated that the undercarriage would be likely to collapse and the first prototype be a total write-off which, sad to relate, is exactly what was to happen.

A&AEE Report No. 812

The Wolverhampton Dreadnought

The S.31 half size Stirling was not the only such model tested at Boscombe Down; there was at least one other which was unique in that the full size aircraft it was intended to simulate never materialised. In 1937, when the panic re-arming of the RAF was at its height, a Ministry Specification F.11/37 was issued which called for a twin-engined fighter, improbably armed with a 37-mm cannon mounted in a shallow cupola above the wing centre section; the cupola was required to rotate through 360°.

Perhaps wisely, in view of the rather unusual armament, Messrs. Boulton & Paul, of Wolverhampton, decided that their proposal to Spec. F.11/37 would be tested, in the first instance, by a half scale model. The result was the Boulton & Paul P.92/2 – the /2 presumably indicating half size. The aircraft bore the service serial V3142 and was tested by the A&AEE during July 1943. The subsequent brief report reveals certain design shortcomings that must have made the P.92/2 one of the least sought after aircraft on the flight line at Boscombe Down.

The machine, a single-seater, was powered by two 145 hp de Havilland Gipsy Major IIs. The aircraft could only be entered or left with both engines stationary; to effect an entry – or exit – the entire canopy had to be removed and could only be replaced, once the pilot was inboard, by outside help. Once inside, the cockpit was found to be 'long, narrow and cramped'. The view was considered good ahead: bad everywhere else.

In spite of the shortcomings of the cockpit, one imagines that it was infinitely preferable to abandoning ship – to contemplate that would require a dire emergency indeed: to bale out of the P.92/2 the pilot had to jettison an emergency panel to port and aft of the seat, then having undone his harness, collapse the seat backwards to the cockpit floor and dive through the exit hatch. Unfortunately, due to a trifling design oversight, it proved impossible for a full size pilot to reach the vital release lever when seated in the cockpit.

While the aircraft was at Boscombe Down the technical staff made a local modification consisting of a piece of stout string attached to the jettison handle and tied off in the cockpit where the pilot could reach it. Not surprisingly, all things considered, it was recommended by the A&AEE that if the pilot had to bale out it would be better to jettison the hood, dive over the side, and take a chance with the propellers.

The aircraft was of plywood construction throughout. Split trailing edge flaps extended from wing root to ailerons. Permanent slots were built into the wing leading edge near the tips. As tested at Boscombe Down, the AUW was 2,800 lb. Generally the aircraft was deemed pleasant to handle; longitudinal stability was satisfactory, though the lateral characteristics 'needed to be improved'.

No figures as to performance were included in the report, which was concerned solely with handling. The stall with both engines at idle and windmilling was at 59 mph IAS without flaps, and 50 mph with full flap, these figures reducing with ⅓ to ½ throttle to 50 and 42 respectively. The stall with the slots sealed proved to be two to three mph *lower* but the ability of the aileron to pick up a wing was then reduced; however, the sealed slots eliminated a pre-stall roll which was apparent with them operational. For landing it was recommended that the maximum flap area be increased to steepen the angle of descent when on finals.

As to whether the A&AEE recommendations were ever implemented and other details of V3142's subsequent career, the records do not reveal, but it remains the least known *rara avis* to have been tested at Boscombe Down. Had the full sized aircraft been built by Boulton & Paul, one wonders what the effect of the firing of that 37-mm cannon broadside would have been.

A&AEE Report No. 838

The M.B.1 and M.B.5

The Fighters That Never Were

'*If a man can . . . make a better mousetrap . . . than his neighbour, though he build his house in the woods, the world will make a beaten path to his door.*'

That quotation, attributed to the American writer Ralph Waldo Emerson, must have seemed equivocal to Sir James Martin, CBE, the founder of the Martin-Baker Company; the statement was to prove absolutely correct with regard to the ejection seats made by the British concern – over 7,000 lives saved bear testimony to that – but in another context Sir James could reflect that an earlier venture, his series of most excellent fighter aircraft, left the path to his small factory virtually untrodden for more than a decade.

James Martin was, like Henry Royce, a self taught engineer imbued with an almost Victorian confidence in his own ability: he simply decided, in 1929, to go into aircraft production. Not for him the backing of city merchant bankers and boards of directors; just two employees and hand tools in some near derelict ex-Army huts near the village of Denham in Buckinghamshire, 20 miles to the north-west of London.

The first aircraft was referred to simply as the 'M.1'. Little is now known of this ephemeral machine other than that it was a two-seater, side-by-side, light aircraft; a monoplane, at a time when most of its contemporaries were biplanes, with the two man crew sitting above and in front of a 120 hp Hermes engine which was buried in the fuselage, the propeller being driven, *à la* Bell Airacobra, via a long shaft. The bold and original design was partly completed and ground run but by that time the great 1931 depression had made the market for sports aircraft – always tenuous – virtually altogether disappear.

The infant company, doubtless due to its minimal overheads, just survived and, in 1935, James Martin was joined by a capable ex-RFC pilot, Captain Valentine Baker, and together they formed it into a new company, Martin-Baker Ltd, which to the present day bears their names – still, incidentally, based at Denham, though the Army huts have long since been superseded by rather more extensive buildings. In the mid-thirties, with minimum financing, the company, the staff now increased to 15, led by the irrepressible James Martin as chief engineer and designer, produced the M.B.1, a neat, tandem seat, enclosed cockpit, low-wing civil monoplane. Since the workforce, with the exception of a draughtsman, were all local and semi-skilled, the structure of the M.B.1 was based on prefabricated steel tubing, most of it bolted together. The wings, using an unusual mainspar of three steel tubes, were able to fold. The whole design was extremely well thought out and bristled with innovations.

In March 1935 (or April – the surviving records are unclear), the aircraft, bearing the civil registration G-ADCS, its fabric covering painted in gleaming black, was towed by road to the nearby RAF airfield of Northolt. Captain Baker started the 160 hp Napier Javelin engine (loaned by the company) and took off. The aircraft seem to have been satisfactory but, due to the economic stringency of the time, orders were not forthcoming and 'ADCS', the sole example, was accidentally destroyed in a hangar fire at Denham in 1938. By that time the Martin-Baker Company had set their sights on bigger things than light private aircraft; nothing less than a high performance RAF fighter, built to Spec. F.5/34, which had called for an armament of eight machine guns. The result was the M.B.2, a 300+ mph single-seater monoplane fighter built, like the earlier M.B.1, from steel tubing and, unlike most contemporary service aircraft, with maintenance and accessibility very much in mind.

The M.B.2 first flew, with Capt. Baker at the controls, from RAF Harwell on 3 August 1938. It was powered by an air-cooled, in-line, 24 cylinder, Napier Dagger III engine, offering a nominal 800 hp (Martin had tried to get a Rolls-Royce Merlin but had to be content with the Dagger freely given by Napiers). In theory, this rather complex 'H' engine could be boosted to +13 lb to offer 1,000 hp for take-off, but it is unlikely that in actual practice it did attain that figure, which must have made take-off, with a fixed pitch wooden airscrew, marginal from a short field.

The M.B.2 (a rather confusing number: the aircraft bore on its fuselage 'M.B.1.' and was registered as a civil aircraft, G-AEZD) appeared as a very

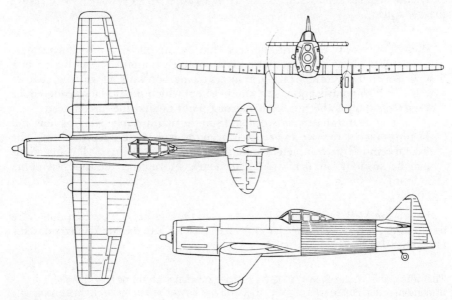

M.B.2 Profiles.

clean, cantilevered, low wing monoplane, with a somewhat square-cut appearance, its air of military purpose emphasised by a low profile cockpit, set well back, and a trousered fixed undercarriage. The fuselage was 34 ft 6 inches long and, unusually for its time, therefore longer than the wingspan of 34 ft, a feature retained in the subsequent Martin-Baker designs. Looking at a contemporary photograph the most striking feature was the exceptionally small fin, virtually all of which comprised the rudder, the designer considering (wrongly as it was to turn out) that the slab-sided fuselage would provide adequate directional stability. The most forward looking feature of this neat prototype was, however, the eight .303-inch Browning guns, set in fours just outboard of the undercarriage. The M.B.2 is believed to be the first aircraft to carry this armament; indeed the guns themselves were from the very first batch to be manufactured in Britain under licence. It certainly must have been the only civil registered machine to be so armed.

After the first flight, Captain Baker suggested that the finless rudder be augmented by a conventional fin as the lack of directional control was disconcerting. The prototype was test flown on a number of occasions, attaining a level speed of 320 mph with the aircraft carrying a full service load of guns and ammunition. *The Aeroplane* reported: 'In spite of its fixed undercarriage, the M.B.2 had a performance as good as that of contemporary fighters. . . .'

The attitude of the Air Ministry to the M.B.2 was muted; it could have been something of an embarrassment: here was a very private venture produced by an obscure firm, employing under 40, that nevertheless was of undoubted promise, so much so that the one and only prototype was sent, on 10 November 1938, to the A&AEE, then at Martlesham Heath, for evaluation. A letter dated 28 November 1938 from the Director of Technical Development at the Air Ministry to the A&AEE said, *inter alia*: 'In view of the interest in this aeroplane at this headquarters will you please submit an interim report as soon as possible.'

The subsequent report, due to bad flying weather, dealt primarily with ease of maintenance:

Many features are excellent and seem hardly capable of improvement. The accessibility of the gun installation is a notable example. The provision of a sorbo covered platform for the armourers to kneel on while at work is a feature well worth standardisation. . . . Another item which should be considered for standardisation is the retractable strong point behind the pilot's head. . . .

The engine installation is excellent from the maintenance point of view and the time taken to remove and replace an engine is the best in recent years. [The time to remove the complete installation, including cowlings, all connections and the airscrew spinner was 3 man hours. To replace, the time was 3 hrs 33 min.].

Although the M.B.2 received full marks from the engineers, the test pilots were less fulsome, as is revealed in a letter from the A&AEE to the Air Ministry dated 7 December 1938:

This aeroplane Martin-Baker (P.V.) M.B.1 has now completed brief handling and armament trials. Full results of these trials will be forwarded in report form as soon as possible.

The letter continued:

2. The aeroplane has many good features of design and construction, but does not handle well. The following points have been mentioned by pilots.

(i)   Controls.

(a)   *Rudder.*   Not sufficiently effective at low speeds either engine on or off. Adjustable bias required to overcome tendency to swing to starboard.
(b)   *Ailerons.*   Rather heavy for a fighter.
(c)   *Elevator.*   Satisfactory.

(ii) Stability.

(a)   *Longitudinally.*
   The aeroplane would be improved if it were slightly more stable. It appears to be just stable engine on at normal and forward C.G. positions, unstable engine on with the C.G. aft and unstable under all conditions engine off. The instability on the glide makes the approach unpleasant rather than dangerous.
(b)   *Laterally.*
   The lateral stability is difficult to assess on account of slight reversibility of ailerons, but appears to be slightly unstable or neutrally stable.
(c)   *Directionally.*
   The aeroplane is stable directionally except at maximum level speed and during the dive. This cannot be assessed at low speeds as the aeroplane cannot be trimmed directionally.

(iii) Stall.

   The aeroplane stalls at 73 m.p.h. A.S.I. flaps up and 68 m.p.h. A.S.I. flaps down. The stall is gentle with flaps up and with flaps down. Warning of the stall is given by a slight snatching of the ailerons and the wing drops gently to the left, but control is quickly regained. No vicious tendencies are experienced.

(iv) Acrobatics.

   Loops, rolls, stalled turns were done. The loop is normal for the type. The lack of rudder control combined with an absence of lateral stability makes it difficult to keep straight in rolls.

(v) Approach and landing.

   Approach and landing are easy and a good view is obtained through the glass windscreen, though a clear view panel would be an advantage. Slight aileron snatch is experienced just before touching down. Sideslipping is difficult. Gliding turns do not inspire confidence. The undercarriage and brakes are satisfactory. The aeroplane will climb with the flaps set for landing, but there is a pronounced sink when the flaps are put up.

(vi) General.

   Owing to the peculiarities of the rudder and ailerons the aeroplane is not pleasant to fly, it requires considerable concentration to fly accurately in turns and in level flight. The view is good in all directions when flying level. It is considered that some alteration to the rudder and aileron control is necessary before the aeroplane is acceptable.   ,
   No speed trials have been made but from isolated speeds observed during the handling trials, the true airspeed seems to be about 290 m.p.h. at 9500 ft, the correction for position error being − 14 m.p.h.

It is understood from the pilot that they contemplate fitting a retractable undercarriage and a more powerful engine, and modifying the rudder, and they are anxious to have the aeroplane back as soon as possible. In view of these proposed alterations it is suggested that the aeroplane should be returned to the makers forthwith and the performance trials left over for the present.

On the same day, 7 December 1938, as that letter went to the Air Ministry, another was written by the then Acting Commanding Officer of the A&AEE, Wing Cmdr. R. St. Hill Clarke, which must be unique and is here reproduced:

AEROPLANE AND ARMAMENT EXPERIMENTAL ESTABLISHMENT

MARTLESHAM HEATH,
Suffolk.

7 December 1938.

Our Ref:– M.H./4487/27 – A.S.62.
Yr. Ref:– 485656/36/R.D.A.1/(b)/CMB.

Martin Barker (P.V. to F.5/34).
M.B.1.

Sir,
    I have the honour to refer to the Martin Barker aircraft P.V. to F.5/34. M.B.1.

2.   This aircraft has some very good design and construction points. It does not, however handle well. . . .

3.   The firm's pilot, Mr. Baker, is handicapped as a test pilot since he has not flown any modern fighter types, his recent flying experience (apart from that gained on the Martin Baker) being limited to light aircraft of the training class.

4.   There is no doubt from Mr. Baker's handling of the Martin Baker that he is a very capable pilot. It would be a great help to him if he were given permission to fly a Hurricane and a Spitfire. Facilities for this could be arranged here subject to Air Ministry approval.

5.   It is understood that the firm are making application direct to Air Ministry asking that Mr. Baker may be granted the privilege of these two flights. Presumably if permission is given details of insurance will be arranged between the Air Ministry and the firm.

I have the honour to be,
Sir,
Your obedient Servant

(signed) R. St. Hill Clarke
Wing Cmdr.
Commanding A. &
A.E.E.,
Royal Air Force.

The Under-Secretary of State,
Air Ministry (R.D.A.1(b).),
Adastral House,
Kingsway, LONDON, W.C.2.

As a consequence of that letter, agreement was reached on 19 April 1939 for Baker to fly both the Hurricane and the Spitfire; an altogether exceptional precedent: Baker was a civil pilot who had never flown a modern service aircraft, furthermore the Hurricane and Spitfire were still very much on the Secret List.

The Martin-Baker Company was required to insure the aircraft and the total loss cover required gives a rare insight to the 1938 cost of those fighters: Hurricane £7,250, Spitfire £8,000. (Compare these figures with the present day cost of, say, an RAF Jaguar or Harrier!) The hourly rate charged to Martin–Baker is also interesting: the Hurricane was £16.7s.6d. (£16.38p.); the Spitfire was slightly dearer, at £20.5s.0d. (£20.25p.) per flying hour.

Following the A&AEE tests of the M.B.1, the Martin-Baker Company undertook to fit a new effective rudder, also the design was to be revised to include (on later aircraft) a fully retractable undercarriage and the elevator gearing altered to reduce the amount of stick movements. These recommendations were quoted in an A&AEE internal memo dated 31 December 1938 from the Chief Technical Officer (E. T. Jones) to the O.C. at Martlesham Heath, following a meeting to discuss the future of the 'Martin-Baker Aeroplane', at which it was understood that the required modifications would take two months, when the aircraft would return to the A&AEE for 'brief handling tests' and then go to an RAF squadron for service evaluation. The Ministry , the meeting agreed, would pay for the modifications and 'also pay a reasonable price for the aeroplane'.

Thus G-AEZD became P9594 and the rather odd green paint scheme was exchanged for olive drab fighter camouflage with 1939 A1 style RAF roundels and black service serial numbers.

It was in this form and with the enlarged fin and rudder that M.B.1 returned to Martlesham Heath on 12 July 1939. It was subjected to further handling trials and a report was issued, dated 17 July 1939:

Swinging tendency on take off can now be corrected with a little left rudder. The aircraft was directionally stable throughout the speed range and can be trimmed satisfactorily. There is no tendency to spin in stalls flaps up or down. [Stall flaps up 76 mph; full flap 60 mph.].

The new enlarged fin and rudder evinced the commendation: 'The rudder control can now be taken as a desirable basis to which the other controls should be matched.'

With that report, the remarkable M.B.1 prototype disappears from the A&AEE files, but there is at Boscombe Down an allotment notice, dated 4 July 1939, stating that P9594 was allotted to the makers, Martin-Baker, for installation and flight trials of 'cannon guns', presumably 20 mm, under Contract 2472/39, the flying to be from RAF Northolt (only four miles from Denham). After these trials the aircraft went into storage at Denham to be dismantled there during the war years.

Many writers have wondered why the M.B.1 did not get into production for the RAF; it has been hinted darkly that there was some sort of conspiracy: the 'old boy network' in operation to prevent this interloper into the ranks of established constructors. The rather more prosaic answer is to be found in the 2nd and 3rd paragraphs of the hitherto unpublished A&AEE memo of 31 December 1939, from the A&AEE Chief Technical Officer, E. T. Jones.

2. ... The Chairman did not hold out much hope to the firm of repeat orders. ... The reason ... was that it is built to a specification [F5/34] which is already five years old, and although it was agreed that the aeroplane had good constructional points, by the time a number had been manufactured it would be out of date.

The memo concluded, however, on an optimistic note:

3. The Chairman said that the A.M. [Air Ministry] were keen to encourage the firm and it was probable that the firm would be asked to make a limited number of aeroplanes to a new specification.

The new specification was F.18/39, which called – rather vaguely – for a Hurricane/Spitfire replacement; since, so far as is known, no other aircraft company was invited to tender, it is probable that 'F.18/39' was drawn up to cover Martin-Baker's future proposal. In any event, the performance required by the Air Ministry included a maximum level speed of not less than 400 mph at 15,000 ft and a service ceiling of 35,000 ft. The F.18/39's all up weight was not to exceed 12,000 lb. The armament specification was no fewer than six 20-mm cannon: a far greater fire power than any RAF fighter then in service.

Clearly the existing M.B.1, even with an uprated engine and retractable undercarriage, could not hope to meet the above requirements; Martin-Baker therefore decided on an entirely new design, utilising the lessons learned from the earlier machine. RAF serials were allocated for three F.18/39 prototypes: R2492, R2496 and R2500, the project to be known as the Type M.B.3. It is not certain when the contract was signed, but if the serials were allocated in chronological sequence it must have been in the summer of 1939, since other RAF aircraft within that 'R' range were ordered about that time.

By the time the 'M.B.3' was actually under construction at the Denham works the war had, of course, begun and the company was busy with other contracts, including barrage balloon cable cutters fitted to RAF bombers (over 80,000 Martin-Baker cable cutters were to be supplied during the war years), a patent belt feed for 20-mm Hispano cannon and – a harbinger of things to come – an explosive hood jettison system for fighters. The company had earlier provided a manual jettisonable hood for Spitfires which saved many pilots' lives during the Battle of Britain. With the amount of work at the small factory, it is not surprising that the construction of a complex modern fighter took some time.

The prototype M.B.3 (R2492) was not completed and ready to fly until August 1942. It proved to be a purposeful looking, low-wing monoplane bearing a superficial likeness to the original Typhoon, though smaller and lighter than the Hawker design. It was powered by a 24 cylinder Napier Sabre II of 2,000 hp. Martin had wanted to install a Rolls-Royce Griffon but was pressed to accept the Napier. As one would now expect, the fighter was very carefully thought out and was meticulously built, with a flush riveted stressed skin on a steel tube skeleton. The keynote of the entire structure was simplicity, strength and accessibility.

After the M.B.3's maiden flight on 31 August 1943 from RAF Wing, in Buckinghamshire, Capt. Baker reported the aircraft to be highly manoeuvrable and easy to fly. R2492 was never to be evaluated at the A&AEE, or anywhere else, for on a subsequent flight on 12 September 1942, a crank driving one of the sleeve valves of the complex Sabre broke, causing total engine failure on take-off from Wing. The pilot attempted to force-land the valuable prototype in a field bordering the small airfield, but the aircraft struck a tree stump and was destroyed. Tragically, Capt. Baker received fatal injuries. At one cruel stroke, James Martin had lost his partner, test pilot and friend, together with the aircraft on which so much hope had rested.

With the loss of the M.B.3 prototype, the question as to whether to drop the whole idea of aircraft manufacture altogether must have arisen. What preserved the continuity, apart from the sheer obstinacy of James Martin, was possibly the existence of the partly built second M.B.3 prototype, R2496, and the excellent flight characteristics of the first prototype reported by Capt. Baker during the limited flying before the fatal crash. In the event, the design changed to the extent that the second aircraft to F.18/39 received a new type number, 'M.B.5'. This machine, hardly surprisingly in the circumstances, was not to be powered by a Napier Sabre; three alternative engines were considered: the Rolls-Royce V-12 Griffon, Bristol Centaurus radial and Rolls-Royce Vulture.

Fortunately the engine selected was not the Vulture but the Griffon 83, that magnificent and ultimate development of the V-12 Merlin. It was to represent the apogee of Rolls-Royce piston aero engines and able to offer 2,340 hp for take-off on 130 octane fuel, with a boost pressure of 25 lb/sq in. To cope with the torque, contra-rotating propellers were specified for the M.B.5. (The later Griffon engined Spitfires did not have contra-props and their take-off swing became legendary.)

The M.B.5 was completed at the company's Denham works by the spring of 1944. With its long mid-fuselage air intakes for oil, coolant radiators and intercooler, the M.B.5 bore a superficial likeness to the P-51D Mustang. The massive contra-props, however, were at that time unusual, if not the then fashionable 'blown' bubble canopy, giving the pilot an excellent all-round vision, which James Martin had fitted to his first military design and which hard won experience had shown was an absolute necessity for a day fighter. The undercarriage, in sharp contrast to all marks of Spitfire, was very wide, the oleo legs being set at mid-span of the wings. The angular fin and rudder showed an unmistakable affinity with the earlier Martin designs. The prototype did not, at this stage, carry any armament, the four 20-mm cannon positions being blanked off with neat stub fairings. (The six cannon required by the original F.18/39 specification were never fitted.)

The completed M.B.5 prototype was finished in standard 1944 temperate day camouflage with 'CI' roundels and a large ringed yellow 'P', denoting prototype, on the fuselage sides. The Service serial R2496 does not appear in all extant photographs. (The aircraft certainly carried that number by the time it arrived at Boscombe Down.)

The date for the first flight of the M.B.5 was to be 23 May 1944, the pilot being the Rotol Propeller Company's chief test pilot, Bryan Greensted (then working on behalf of the Ministry of Aircraft Production). Following the disaster which befell the M.B.3 when taking off from the small airfield at Wing, the M.B.5 was to be test flown from the much larger and open airfield at RAF Harwell.

The prototype was to be taken to Harwell by road and, uniquely, it was possible to dismantle the aircraft at Denham and load it onto an RAF transport in about an hour during the morning, drive the 'Queen Mary' – as these admirable vehicles were named – to Harwell, unload around lunch time, re-erect and inspect in a little over an hour and hand the airworthy M.B.5 to the test pilot for him to sign the Form 700* by early afternoon. Few, if any, contemporary aircraft, including simple trainers, could have come within hours (or days in some cases) of that time scale; the reason was, of course, James Martin's obsession with ease of maintenance and serviceability.

During the afternoon of 23 May 1944, the first flight of the M.B.5 took place. Capt. Greensted took to the aircraft as soon as he strapped in; the only criticism, following the uneventful first flight, was a deficiency in directional stability: a design 'blind spot', it would seem, of James Martin, requiring, as had his preceding aircraft, a hasty redesign of the fin and rudder. After that modification, the handling was reported as superb, with the 2,340 hp bestowed by the Griffon conferring a top speed of 460 mph at 20,000 ft: possibly the fastest single-engined piston aircraft at that time; only the Vickers Supermarine Spiteful – a later design – would exceed it.

The flight testing proceeded slowly and, by October, James Martin was told by the Ministry that, excellent though the M.B.5 undoubtedly was, it would not be going into production. The reason was that future fighters would be jet propelled and, in any event, the massive air superiority achieved over the Luftwaffe by the end of 1944 indicated that existing designs would carry the burden of air fighting until the end of the European war, which was now clearly only a matter of time.

When the war finally ended, the M.B.5 was shown publicly at Farnborough, where the RAE put on a massive air display of the latest British aircraft and some captured German machines. It was a three-day event and the M.B.5 was impressively demonstrated before a huge crowd. Later, also at Farnborough, when Capt. Greensted flew the aircraft before the Prime Minister, Winston Churchill, and senior Air Marshals, including the CAS (Chief of Air Staff), its Griffon engine failed on take-off, but on this occasion the pilot pulled off a perfect dead-stick landing on the long Farnborough runway.

There is no doubt that James Martin had the cruelest luck with his engines; out of his three military aircraft, two had suffered total engine failure, one fatally.

The M.B.5 was undamaged by its forced landing; its engine was soon replaced and the aircraft went to the A&AEE for assessment. Not that there had been second thoughts about its being produced: it would have taken at least three years to get it into RAF service and even the most enthusiastic proponent of the design would admit that, by that time, it would have been out of date. The reason for its going to Boscombe Down was, in a way, a greater compliment to its designer; the many original features which made it such an outstanding aircraft could, it was considered, well be incorporated into other, later designs.

The subsequent A&AEE report was, without doubt, one of the most fulsome ever written by that coldly professional establishment, considering it was on an aircraft which it was known would never see RAF service. It is here reproduced in full:

---

* To be strictly accurate, he may have been required to sign Form 1090, as the aircraft was on the firm's charge.

1st Part of Report No. A.&.A.E.E./838

AEROPLANE AND ARMAMENT EXPERIMENTAL ESTABLISHMENT
BOSCOMBE DOWN

Martin Baker M.B.5 R.2496
(Griffon Mk.83)

Engineering and Maintenance Appraisal.

A.&.A.E.E. ref: AAEE/6056/A/1/WERT
M.A.P.   ref: SB.61931/01
Date of Tests 1st March, 1946.

Summary

This aircraft was examined in order to assess its characteristics from the point of view of servicing, maintenance, repair, and general accessibility.

Particular attention was paid to the manner in which installations were laid out and to the question of whether the aircraft could be considered up to the general standard of those at present in service.

It is considered that the general design and layout of the Martin Baker 5 is excellent and is infinitely better – from the engineering and maintenance aspect – than any other similar type of aircraft.

1. *Introduction.*

An examination was made of the aircraft to assess its characteristics from the view-point of servicing and maintenance.

Only a short time was available for the examination but in view of the excellent layout of the aircraft, services, and equipment, it is possible to render a reasonably full report.

The aircraft is known as the 'Martin Baker MB.5'. It is a low wing monoplane, single seater fighter powered by a Rolls-Royce 'Griffon 83' engine driving de Havilland constant speed contra rotating propellers. The relevant specification is F.18/39.

At the time this inspection was made, the contractors stated that their pilot had flown the aircraft for approximately 80 hours. During this time no component had required changing, other than for design alterations, with the exception of an engine which failed in flight.

2. *Power Plant.*

2.1 *Engine.*   The engine installation may be regarded as either an 'Engine' or as a 'Power Plant'. This is due to the manner in which the cowls, bearers, pipes, and fire proof bulkhead have been arranged. A special engine mounting makes removal of the engine still more simple. All engine cowls are quickly removable. The carburettor, fitted at the lower rear of the engine, is easily reached for routine maintenance and can be changed completely in a very short time. The Coffman starter system is fitted to the upper rear of the engine and access is gained through a small, easily accessible, panel. Spare cartridges are carried in a stowage immediately above the pilot's head at the rear of his seat. Worth oil dilution system is used.

2.2 *Propeller.*   This is a 'double three' de Havilland contra rotating propeller controlled by a lever under the pilot's throttle lever. The installation is clean and easily accessible for maintenance.

2.3 *Auxiliaries.*   All auxiliaries are operated simply and attached in many cases to the bulkhead or airframe by brackets supported on anti-vibration mountings. The main auxiliary gear box is at the rear top of the engine, easily accessible or removable, and carries the conventional services, compressor, generator, engine tachometer drive connections, etc.

2.4 *Cowlings.*   The design and layout of these is excellent. The engine may be laid completely bare within a few minutes, with the exception of one ring bolted to the forward face of the engine. All the fuselage panels are quickly detachable and immediate and easy access is available to all parts of the aircraft structure, all accessories, attachment points of all components and all filters. All cowlings and panels are secured by easily operated 'Dzus' fasteners and are snugged down on to very heavy rubber beading. One small criticism is that this rubber, in the vicinity of the exhaust manifold (below the filler neck of the main fuel tank) appears to be susceptible to attack by heat and/or petrol. It is suggested that at this point the rubber be replaced by a petrol and heat resistant material.

2.5 *Exhaust System.*   All exhaust stubs lie in troughs formed by detachable fairings on the upper sides of the engine. They are quickly detachable either singly or as sets.

2.6 *Power Plant Controls.*   These are tubular shafts operating a conventional system of levers. All parts are easily accessible for lubrication or maintenance and are adequately supported in well disposed bearings.

2.7 *Fuel System.*   This comprises two tanks, one containing 70 gallons, forward of the pilot, and the other containing 130 gallons, aft of the pilot. Filler necks are almost flush with the decking and could not be overfilled unless the operation was most carelessly handled. It is suggested that, as a minor refinement, the filler neck be held by a flexible petrol resistant ring in a well draining outboard. This would prevent any petrol, in the event of overflowing, being spilt inboard.
The system is easily drained by replacing the drain cock plug by a hose and moving the cock to the 'on' position.
Tank capacities and details of fuel used are clearly marked on the decking in the immediate vicinity of the filler necks.

2.8 *Air Intake System.*   This is very neatly laid out and is in the form of a broad, shallow, trunk extending from just aft of the propeller spinner to the carburettor. It is easily detachable as a complete unit. Neither air filters nor ice guards are fitted.

2.9 *Oil System.*   Only one tank is carried with a total capacity of 18 gallons, made up by 14 gallons oil and 4 gallons air space. The tank is easily removable. Similar remarks regarding overflowing apply to this system as to the fuel system.
The tank cap is scalloped for easy handling and includes a short dip stick screwed into the centre of the filler cap. The tank is full when the oil is level with the lip of the filler neck.
Tank capacities and details of oil to be used are legibly marked on the coaming.

2.10 *Coolant System.*   The coolant is carried in an easily detachable and accessible horse-shoe shaped tank, mounted immediately above the front of the engine. The coolant passes, via large diameter tungum piping, down the side of the fuselage through the main radiator and returns on the other side of the fuselage to the engine. All pipes are in easily replaceable sections. Thermo pockets are provided at the radiator inlet and outlet. Bleed valves are situated adjacent to the tank and engines. The radiator, if damaged, or defective, may be removed quite simply by disconnecting four bolts. There are three positions for the radiator flap control, all shown by indicators, i.e., 'Fixed open', 'Automatic', and 'Fixed closed'.

2.11 *Ignition System.*   All component parts of this system are easily serviced. Adequate doors are provided to gain access to the magnetos. The ignition harness, plugs and suppressors, are easily removable, either as individual parts or in toto.

2.12 *Miscellaneous.*
Intercooler System. This is laid out in a similar manner to the main coolant system. Everything is easily accessible.

3. *Airframe.*

3.1 *Fuselage.* This is of tubular construction. All joints are made by tapered bolts turned to fine limits. Every strut or member in the fuselage is easily accessible, due to the splendid cowling, and panelling arrangements. In the event of damage to any members, it would be simple to have them replaced.

3.2 *Cockpit and Cabin.* The layout of the cockpit is excellent. The pilot's control assembly (a Martin-Baker patent), may be removed en bloc by the withdrawal of a few easily accessible bolts. The control settings are not altered if this is done. The seat is easily removable. There are no excrescences of any kind to catch the clothes of the pilot or ground crew. The cockpit is fully floored and could be cleaned out completely in a few minutes.

The one-piece transparent cabin roof is beautifully fitted. It is operated by the pilot by a small wheel control. The mechanism is perfectly balanced. The hood can be opened externally by pressing a plunger, sunk flush in the decking, which disengages the pilot's control. No handle or projection is provided as the hood is so well balanced that one is unnecessary. The hood may easily be jettisoned from the aircraft by operation of an emergency control.

It is considered that de-icing should be provided for the pilot's windscreen.

3.3 *Wings.* These are stressed skin structures and are most easily removed by the disconnection of the three main attachment bolts. All service joints are easily reached and may as easily be disconnected.

The undercarriage retracts into apertures on the lower surface of the main planes.

Two cannons are mounted each side in quickly opened bays in the upper surfaces of the main planes. A servicing platform may be quickly attached to assist the armourer.

An adequate number of smaller detachable panels are provided wherever required for ingress to control circuits, etc.

3.4 *Balance and Control Surfaces.* These are of all metal construction, with the exception of the rudder which is fabric covered.

In all cases the components are ingeniously attached in such a manner that the few attachment bolts used are most easily disconnected. All components may be changed without upsetting any control adjustments.

All control surfaces are fitted with spring loaded servo tabs. That fitted to the rudder may be operated from the cockpit. The elevators are also fitted with normal trim tabs.

The flaps are split trailing edge type and are pneumatically operated.

3.5 *Flying Controls.* These are simply arranged conventional type, operated by tubular push-pull rods. The rods pass through generous bearings and are easily lubricated and easily accessible for any changes or adjustments necessary.

The patent Martin-Baker control unit in the cockpit is easily and quickly removed complete, without upsetting any control adjustments.

3.6 *Undercarriage.* This is a novel feature and consists of two retractable main wheel units and a retractable self-centring tail wheel unit. The main wheels retract inwards and upwards into the apertures on the lower side of the main planes.

Operation is achieved by a large pneumatic ram mounted aft of the rear fuel tank. Connection is by cables and lowering by spring operated radius rods. The rate of descent of the undercarriage is controlled by a hydraulic damper built on the ram. All components are easily accessible.

A safety device is incorporated which makes it impossible to retract the undercarriage whilst the aircraft is standing on the ground. Undercarriage warning lights are fitted.

3.7 *Wheels, Tyres and Brakes.*   Dunlop pneumatic brakes are fitted. Differential braking effect is obtained by moving the rudder bar with the handbrake 'on'.

The main wheels are easily removable. A removable extension piece is provided for the stub axles. This fits over a small bottle jack, enabling the wheel to be lifted easily.

The tail wheel is changed by fitting a jacking pad into an insert forward of the tail wheel on the underside of the fuselage and resting this on either a jack or a pedestal. In the latter case, if equipment is lacking, the tail of the aircraft may be raised by passing a bar through a tube athwartships of the tail end and having this raised, by say, six men, when the tail may be lowered on to any convenient support.

All essential details such as brake pressure, tyre pressure, etc., are shown clearly on labels conveniently situated on the oleos.

4. *Services.*

4.1 *Hydraulics.*   With the exception of the damper referred to in 3.6 above, no hydraulic operation is employed.

4.2 *Pneumatics.*   These are extensively employed and are referred to in the relevant sections.

It is noted that services are operated independently and, in the event of damage to any one service, no other is affected.

All filters are grouped together on a panel mounted on the port side of the fuselage, facing outboard. Each filter is clearly marked showing its use and the frequency at which it should be cleaned or serviced.

The supply is through two large bottles which may be charged either from the ground or by the engine via water traps. The bottles are readily removable for replacement.

4.3 *Electrical Installation.*

4.31 Lucas connector bank earth return wiring is used throughout the aircraft. Plugs and sockets for disconnecting all services at the wing roots and at the power plant bulkhead are provided. All fuse banks, terminal blocks and connector banks are numbered and identified. Cables are identified both by number and by letter to indicate the individual cable and the circuit. Standard multicore cables are used.

4.32 Power is supplied by a 24 volt 1500 watt engine driven generator which charges two 125V 15 AH accumulators stowed one on each side of the rear fuselage immediately aft of the electric panel. This panel is in the form of a bulk head across the fuselage behind the pilot's cockpit. The ground starter socket is adjacent to the port accumulator, five feet from the ground just forward of the wing trailing edge. Easy access is obtained through a flap in the cowling. A master switch adjacent to the pilot's left knee is easily operated even with heavy gloves on.

4.33 Pneumatic control solenoids are used for landing gear retraction radiator flap operation and supercharger speed control. All pressure and temperature gauges, fuel pumps, and landing gear and flap indicators are electrically operated.

4.34 TR.1464 and R.3090 radio is installed, the crates and wiring being in the rear fuselage and easily accessible due to the ease with which the fuselage side panels can be removed.

4.35 Standard navigation and identification lighting is fitted. No lighting for pilot's instrument panels is provided, but ample space exists on the forward coaming to fit dimmer switches and lamps if required.

4.36 Without the experience gained by a period of intensive flying, it is difficult to say positively whether any defects are likely to occur. The micro-switches cutting the circuit to the pneumatic control solenoid for the landing gear retraction, are in an exposed position on the undercarriage members, and it is felt that mud would cause faulty operation. Guards could easily be fitted to protect these items. Apart from this, the layout and design of the whole electrical system is most practical, ready accessibility and freedom from congestion being found throughout. Maintenance times for servicing should be considerably less than for any comparable aircraft now in service.

4.4 *Heating and Ventilation.*   None is provided.

4.5 *De-icing Equipment.*   None is provided.

4.6 *Oxygen System.*   The pilot's supply is obtained via a standard regulator, from a standard bottle stowed in the top decking to the rear of the pilot's seat. The bottle is easily accessible for servicing.

5.   *Instruments.*

5.1 *Engine.*   These are situated on the starboard section of the main panel. Fuel, oil, coolant, temperature and pressure instruments are on the starboard side panel.

All instrument panels, centre and two side, hinge fully foward by undoing two quick release handles at the top of each panel. All instruments may be changed with a minimum of effort. The general layout is splendid. Subsidiary gauges, switches, etc., are mounted on two long panels at the pilot's side. These, too, are hinged to permit of easy access.

5.2 *Flying.*   These are grouped on the main centre panel, which is a standard panel except that a remote reading compass replaces the rate of climb indicator. This panel is on anti-vibration mountings.

6.   *Ground Handling, Ancillary Equipment, etc.*

6.1 The arrangements for the ground handling are quite simple. A female threaded socket, recessed into the rear end of the fuselage forward of the tail oleo, takes either a ball ended plug or an eyebolt. The first is used when the tail end is lifted and the second is used as an attachment point for either the picketing shackle or the ground running cable.

A set of three cables is provided. These are secured to an eyebolt in a concrete base. Two are attached, one each, to the undercaraige axles and the third to the tail fitting referred to above. This provides for any ground running or picketing that may be required. The main axle attachment may also be used for ground towing when this is required.

Fittings are provided for engine slinging.

The aircraft may be trestled abaft the engine on the lower side of the fuselage by a special trestle supporting the aircraft by two points normally covered by small fairings.

7.   *Conclusions.*

Accessibility and ease of maintenance have been given careful consideration during the design of this aircraft. No features likely to cause difficulty in servicing or overhaul could be found in the short time available for the examination.

The general design and layout of this aircraft is excellent and is greatly superior from the engineering and maintenance aspect to any other similar type of aircraft.

The layout of the cockpit might very well be made a standard for normal piston-engined fighters; and the engine installation might, with great advantage, be applied to other aircraft.

The time necessary for a quick turn round, i.e., arming, refuelling, replenishing oxygen and accumulators, would appear to be very low when compared with existing types of aircraft.

8.   *Modifications Suggested.*

(a)   The rubber beading supporting the cowling in the vicinity of the exhaust stubs should be replaced by material with better heat-resisting properties (see para. 2.4).

(b)   Guards and/or filters should be fitted at and in the air intake trunk to prevent the ingress of ice etc. (see para. 2.8).

(c)   Although there is no excuse for over-filling, the filler necks for fuel and oil tanks should be held in shallow trays, venting outboard. This would prevent spilt fuel or oil from dripping inboard. (see paras. 2.7 and 2.9).

(d)   De-icing should be provided for the propellers and front of the pilot's canopy. (see para. 3.2).

(e)   A guard should be provided for the micro-switches on the undercarriage to prevent mud causing faulty operation. (see para. 4.36).

Addendum to 1st Part of Report No. A.&.A.E.E./838

1.   This aircraft has now been at A.&.A.E.E. for brief handling tests when the opportunity was taken to examine it further from the engineering and maintenance aspect.

The relevant particulars are:–

Aircraft arrived 15.4.46   Aircraft departed 21.5.46

Airframe hours on arrival	89 hours 45 minutes
Airframe hours on departure	111 hours 50 minutes
Time flown at A.&.A.E.E.	31 hours 05 minutes
Engine hours on arrival	40 hours 35 minutes
Engine hours on departure	71 hours 40 minutes

'30 hour' inspection, 3rd cycle, carried out at 93 hours, airframe time.

2.   The only defects observed on the airframe during these tests were:–

(a)   *Cannon bay doors.*   These large doors on the top surface of each wing are hinged at the forward edge and secured at the rear edge by two pegs. When the aircraft was dived at high speeds the door arched about ½" in the centre.

Additional locking pegs on the sides of the doors should be provided.

(b)   *Tail fillet.*   A large aluminium fillet joins the fin, rear fuselage, and tail plane root ends. The fillet is rigidly secured at all edges and due to flexing of the fin, fuselage and tail plane, cracked at these attachment points. Repairs were carried out but further cracks developed and rivet heads pulled out.

The defect could be overcome by fastening the fillet securely to the fuselage and allowing it freedom to slide on the fin and tail plane.

3.   Only one defect occurred on the engine installation, viz., the oil pressure transmitter which became defective but was easily and quickly replaced.

4.   The 30 hour inspection was quickly carried out, due largely to the ease with which the structure and equipment was uncovered for inspection. Only one man was engaged on the airframe and one on the engine. No special effort was made to decrease the normal time for such an inspection.

5.   The good accessibility and ease of maintenance referred to in this report were fully confirmed during the time this aircraft was at A.&.A.E.E.

Because of the M.B.5's limited future, the A&AEE did not undertake extensive handling trials. For interest, however, the following figures relating to this memorable aircraft are reproduced from another source:

Martin-Baker M.B.5.
Power Plant one Rolls-Royce Griffon 83 engine with two-stage, two speed supercharger; maximum power 2,340 hp at 1,750 ft (M Gear); 2,120 hp at 12,250 ft (S Gear) with 25 lb/sq inch boost.

Dimensions
Span	35 ft (10.67 m)
Length (finial tail unit)	37 ft 9 in (11.51 m)
Height	15 ft (4.57 m)
Wing Area (gross)	262 sq ft (24.3 m²)

Weights
Empty, equipped	9,345 lb (4,230 Kg)
Gross	11,500 lb (5,216 Kg)

Performance
Max level speed	460 mph at 20,000 ft (740 Km/h at 6,096 m)
Stalling speed	95 mph (153 Km/h)
Range at 225 mph (362 Km/h) 1,240 miles (2,000 Km)	

After the trials at Boscombe Down in June 1946, the M.B.5 made a final public appearance at Farnborough in the hands of Sqn. Ldr. Jan Zurakowksi, which one writer, the aviation historian Bill Gunston, has described as: 'the most staggering, breathtaking show I ever saw with a piston-engined fighter. . . .'

At the end of 1947 the M.B.5 was still airworthy at Chalgrove, an airfield leased to Martin-Baker and on which the early ejector seat trials were made. Staff pilots from the aeronautical press were invited to fly the aircraft, though now the engine was derated due to the lack of 130 octane fuel. After that the M.B.5 disappeared, almost certainly scrapped at Chalgrove. James Martin toyed with the idea of a jet fighter but his work on ejector seats was now claiming his full attention and no further aircraft were forthcoming. The account of the M.B.5, the finest fighter that never was, makes, therefore, a fitting end to the 'one-offs' at Boscombe Down.

CHAPTER FIVE

Made in USA

It would be true to state that if the United States had not supplied many thousands of military aircraft to Great Britain during the Second World War, the operational capability of the RAF, and more particularly the Fleet Air Arm, would have been greatly diminished.

Most of the thousands of American aircraft in British service were supplied as a consequence of President Roosevelt's 'Lease-Lend' Act of March 1941 which, in effect, made free gifts of armaments, including aircraft, as the USA, in the President's words, became 'The arsenal of Democracy'.

Prior to the Lease-Lend Act, and before America entered the war in December 1941, military aircraft were supplied on a commercial basis to Britain with the wholehearted assent of the American Government, in spite of loud protests from Germany that such trade was in contravention of US neutrality – which of course it was.

As a matter of historical interest, the first American front line aircraft supplied to the RAF were 200 Lockheed Hudsons ordered in 1938, at which time there was a good deal of criticism in England that 'foreign' aircraft were being bought in preference to those of British manufacture. The only other American aircraft type ordered in any numbers pre-war was the North American Harvard trainer, 1,100 of which were eventually bought outright, though Lease-Lend would bring the total to over 5,000.

Immediately after the outbreak of the war in Europe, a number of American aircraft types was acquired for the RAF and Fleet Air Arm as a consequence of cancelled contracts following the fall of France and the Low Countries.

The Curtiss Hawk

The first of these wartime American aircraft tested at Boscombe Down was a Curtiss H-75A-1 Hawk belonging to the French *Armée de l'Air*. This fighter was briefly flown in France by Sqn. Ldr. J. F. X. McKenna, AFC, arriving at Boscombe Down on 9 November 1939 for A&AEE evaluation.

The Hawk was a single-seater fighter powered by a single Pratt & Whitney R-1830 SG3-G Twin Wasp, fourteen cylinder, air-cooled radial of 1,200 hp. The French armament consisted of twin 7.5 mm FN-Browning machine guns, synchronised to fire through the airscrew, and twin 7.5s in each wing. The low wing monoplane had a retractable undercarriage and was of all-metal construction.

The A&AEE report[1] of the brief handling trials was issued on 13 November 1939; the report noted that:

> The handle [of the sliding hood] provided sufficient purchase to open the hood at the maximum speed reached: 310 mph ASI. There was no provision for cleaning the windscreen [i.e. wipers] and in aerobatics some oil got onto it which made it necessary to land for cleaning.

After that criticism the report commended the variable pitch airscrew, which in 1939 was still far from universal on British fighters:

> A Curtiss electric controllable pitch airscrew is fitted providing constant speed or fixed pitch at will. This is an excellent feature.

On the other hand:

> It was impossible to move the [engine cooling] cowling gills at high speed. A notice in the cockpit stated that they should not be operated at speeds above 140 mph ASI.

The report commented that the six FN-Browning guns could be selected by the pilot to fire the twin fuselage guns, the four wing armament, or all six together. The guns were aimed by a reflector sight of a somewhat complex design, so complex in fact that it had been reported that the French pilots of the *Armée de l'Air* found it impossible to use it as designed and had the guns bore sighted to harmonise at 200 yards, using the reflector as a simple 'Bead and Ring' sight.

As a gun platform – a basic requirement for a fighter which some designers nevertheless overlooked – the Hawk had:

> just the right amount of stability about all axes for a fighter.
> the ailerons are the lightest and most powerful control . . . their great power enables very rapid changes of banks to be made even at high speeds. . . . The light rudder control enables the aircraft to be turned flat [i.e. without banking] if required, at a reasonable rate and it is easy to get the sights on the target.

The Hawk, like most US fighters was, as noted, powered by an air-cooled radial engine. Radials, though less susceptible to machine gun battle damage, due to their lack of vulnerable 'plumbing' associated with the radiators of the liquid-cooled engines favoured by Britain and Germany, presented designers with severe problems, one of which was the difficulty of providing an adequate field of view for the pilot. The Hawk was no exception, the A&AEE report noting that: 'The large radial engine makes the forward and downward view inferior to that with . . . [liquid-cooled] engines.'

The Boscombe Down report does not include level speed evaluation but the test pilots considered that the Hawk 'is more manoeuvrable at high speed than the Hurricane or the Spitfire and is even easier to fly than the Hurricane and is definitely easier than the Spitfire'.

The aircraft had a very docile stall; 74 mph clean and 68 mph with under-carriage down and full flap. The stall onset was indicated by an increasing 'sloppiness' of the controls, the aircraft however remaining stable and under control, a considerable nose up attitude being required to initiate the stall. Recovery was possible with only 'the slightest forward movement of the stick [which] causes the aeroplane to unstall'.

The highest speed attained at Boscombe Down with the Hawk was in a dive when 310 mph ASI was recorded, at which fairly modest speed 'the aeroplane was very steady'.

A total of 1,300 Hawks was exported to several Air Forces, the largest number (291) of which was on charge to the French *Armée de l'Air*. During the German advance in May/June 1940, French Hawks fought with five French fighter groups: GC1/4, GC11/41, GC1/5, GC11/5 and GC111/2. During the fighting, these units claimed a total of 230 enemy aircraft as shot down and a further 81 'probables' – a magnificent record when considered in the light of the conditions under which those engagements were fought; the French pilots being invariably outnumbered and opposed by the cream of the pre-war Luftwaffe, many of whose pilots had seen combat over Spain with the Condor Legion. After the collapse in France, the outstanding French orders from Curtiss were supplied to Britain, the aircraft being re-named Mohawk.

Before considering these later H-75s, it is interesting to note that, after the French Armistice, a number of surviving Hawks continued to serve with the Vichy Air Force based at Dakar and Rabat. The Germans had captured many French Hawks, including some new aircraft still in their delivery crates; 36 of these were overhauled, given German panels and radios and sold to Finland.

Over 100 Mohawks (beginning AR630) were supplied to Britain directly from the USA between July and September 1940. These were the aircraft originally ordered by France; they had French panels and – disconcertingly – the curious French reversed throttle and mixture controls. After arrival in the UK they were assembled, modified and issued to several RAF MUs pending a decision as to their future RAF role. Though the Hawks had fought well with the French, they were not really in the same class as the best European fighters: the Me 109, Spitfire and Hurricane; eventually all the RAF's surviving Hawks were shipped to India. It was not until April 1941 that two Mohawks, AR645 and AR648, arrived at Boscombe Down for performance trials.[2] These aircraft, designated 'Mohawk IV' by the RAF, were the equivalent of the French H-75A-4 and were powered by Wright Cyclone GR-1820-G50As of 1,200 hp.

The A&AEE test flights established the following Mohawk IV performance figures at an AUW of 6,330 lb:

Maximum speed:	302 mph at 14,000 ft
Take-off run:	295 mph
Distance to clear a	
50 ft obstacle:	485 yds
Maximum rate of climb:	2,600 ft per min
Service ceiling	
(estimated):	33,800 ft

For comparison, the 1940 contemporary of the Mohawk IV, the Spitfire II, had a maximum speed of 357 mph at 17,000 ft and a service ceiling of 37,200 ft. By 1941 when the Mohawks were tested at Boscombe Down, the Spitfire IV had a maximum speed of 372 mph, could climb at 4,200 ft per minute (almost double the Mohawk rate) and had a service ceiling of 39,600 ft. In the light of these figures – the Me 109's were similar – it is not surprising that Mohawks were relegated to what was (at that time) considered an operational backwater, the Far East, where in Burma they eventually had the impossible task of fighting the Japanese Zeros.

Whatever its shortcomings, the Curtiss Hawk secured its place in aviation history as the first American built fighter aircraft to be used operationally in the Second World War. The basic H-75 airframe was a very strong structure, able to withstand considerable punishment. When the Curtiss Company decided to re-engine it with an in-line Allison and later a Rolls-Royce Merlin engine, they created an immortal fiighter, the P-40, Kittyhawk family, which fought with great distinction in Russia, the Mediterranean and the Middle and Far East and, last but by no means least, with the famed Flying Tigers of General Chennault in China.

The Douglas A-20

In some respects, the combat career of the Douglas A-20 was much less spectacular than those of many other bombers employed by the combatants. It was associated with no outstanding operations but remained in first-line service throughout the war; it did not distinguish itself on any particular battle-front, but flew with equal distinction over them all. It did as well in Russia as it did in the Pacific or the Western Desert and withal was one of the most pleasant of all combat aircraft to fly.

That appreciation of the A-20, better perhaps known by its RAF name as Boston, was written by William Green in an authoritative book.[3] Although an aircraft of the Second World War, it was, like many of its contemporaries, designed before the conflict; indeed it owed a good deal to the air fighting of the Spanish Civil War. Military observers of that bitter struggle had been alarmed by the performance of the modern medium bombers – the He111s and Do17Fs of the nascent Luftwaffe rehearsing under the guise of the infamous Condor Legion in 1937. The Dornier 17Fs, of which the Legion had only a single *Staffel*, proved virtually immune from interception by Republican fighters. Even before the Spanish Civil War, the unmistakable signs of growing international tension in Europe made a second world war seem a very likely eventuality. In Britain, the rise of Hitler made even the most obdurate realise that modernisation of the RAF was a matter of urgency; in America too, a few far sighted aircraft designers and constructors, aware of the inertia in official government procurement departments, anticipated the future requirements of the United States Army Air Corps for aircraft which could match the best already in service with the Luftwaffe. Jack Northrop and Ed Heinemann, working for the Douglas Company, had designed the Model 7a, a twin-engined attack bomber, a type which up to that time – 1936 – had never been in US service. The detail design was nearing completion when reports of the Spanish Civil War reached America; the Douglas Company then revised their Model 7A into the 7B. The first flight of the prototype was on 26 October 1938 when it became immediately apparent that the 7B was an outstanding aircraft judged by any standards. Powered by two 1,100 hp Pratt & Whitney Twin Wasp R-1830 radial engines, the 7B had a maximum speed of 295 mph at 13,000 ft, a service ceiling of around 26,000 ft, a range of 1,000 miles;

this performance was wedded to excellent manoeuvrability and the design incorporated many, then, novel features, the most obvious of which was a fully retractable tricycle undercarriage: the first to be fitted to a military aircraft.

At about the time of the flight trials of the 7B, a French Purchasing Commission was visiting America, with official US Government approval, to procure modern aircraft for the *Armée de l'Air*. The performance of the Douglas 7B impressed the French to the extent that, in February 1939, they signed an immediate contract for 100 aircraft, the initial order soon being extended to 380. Thus an aircraft designed for the US Army Air Force as a response to developments in Europe was first sold not to the US forces but to a European Air Force – the French. In point of fact, the French demanded extensive modifications to the original design, including a deeper fuselage. The many alterations were such that when the French order went into production at Santa Monica it was virtually a sub-type and received a new designation – the DB-7 (Douglas Bomber – 7) – to become in turn the prototype of the USAAF's A-20.

Despite the modifications and the loss of the prototype, which spun in following an engine failure at low altitude, killing the American pilot and a French captain of the Purchasing Commission, the first 100 DB-7s were completed by the end of 1939; a very remarkable achievement. Although the 100 aircraft were manufactured and handed over to the French, about 64 were assembled (at Casablanca) and only twelve had become operational with the *Armée de l'Air* by the time of the German May 1940 offensive.

One of the original 64 machines was evaluated by the A&AEE, though not at Boscombe Down.[4] Wing Cdr. J. F. X. McKenna, AFC, who had earlier evaluated the Hawk, went to France to fly a DB-7; the flights took place on 2/3 April 1940. From his Hawk experience, McKenna was familiar with the French reversed throttle and mixture controls, though his report begins by drawing attention to this eccentric practice, adding that:

> The flap and undercarriage controls are similar. There is no lock to prevent accidental raising of the wheels in mistake for flaps when on the ground. . . .

This had been done by an unfortunate French pilot. McKenna recommended that:

> It is essential that a lock, as on the Beaufort and Halifax, operated by a weight on the wheels be provided.

The vulnerability of the undercarriage to accidental retraction was only one feature of that essential appendage; the DB-7 was, as stated, the first military aircraft to feature the now universal tricycle chassis, it was therefore McKenna's first experience of one:

> Ground handling is very easy once one has become used to the characteristics of the tricycle. . . . Take-off is very simple and straightforward when one has grasped the fact that the stick should not be eased forward [as is essential with tail-wheel aircraft] but a slight backward pressure should be maintained throughout the take-off. Also it is necessary to line the aeroplane up with some care before take-off as the stability is such that it is not easy to turn the aeroplane once any considerable speed has been reached.

McKenna had some additional difficulty when he consulted French pilots about take-off technique: 'One was told . . . to use no flap for take-off. . .'.

After the trials were over, McKenna was informed by a representative of the Douglas Company that he should have used *full* flap – about 50° – for take-off. This was in turn hotly contested by an American test pilot present; he held that:

> while admitting that full flap gave a shorter run to 'unstick' he insisted that the loss of climb outweighed this and also objected to the risk of loss of control following an engine failure [as may have occurred with the prototype].

The flaps in general were praised by McKenna, who noted that 'the flaps were arranged to come up slowly, taking 18 seconds. This is an excellent feature and avoids sink'. With the flaps safely up the single engine handling of the DB-7 was:

> remarkable, on throttling one engine the swing seems to be less than on comparable British types, e.g. Beaufort and Botha. [This is an understatement; the Botha was virtually impossible to fly on one engine and the Beaufort had a distinctly marginal single engine performance]. Full rudder can be applied without excessive force, enabling the aeroplane to be kept straight while the airscrew is feathered and the rudder foot load trimmed to zero.

The ease of control remains as speed is reduced. With one engine at cruising power speed was reduced to 97 mph which is 3 mph above the stalling speed on the glide. At about 125 mph the aeroplane climbed steadily with the working engine at cruising power. Weight at the time was, however, only 13,000 lb compared with a typical service load of 16,500 lb.

The A&AEE report then summarised the flying characteristics:

> This aeroplane represents a definite advance in the design of flying controls. The designer has achieved controls which, while light enough to obtain full movement at high speed are in no way overbalanced for small movements. Thus the aeroplane is extremely pleasant to fly and manoeuvre. The tricycle undercarriage makes take-off and landing and ground handling very simple, and pilots should be able to fly the type successfully with the minimum of instruction.

There was no opportunity to do performance trials but the A&AEE report[5] includes an appendix which quotes some American figures for the type:

Weight:	14,730 lb
Maximum sea level speed:	278 mph
Maximum at 10,000 ft:	310 mph
Maximum at 15,000 ft:	317 mph
Climb to 12,000 ft:	6.4 mins
Climb to 26,250 ft:	19.7 mins
Service ceiling:	31,650 ft
Single engine ceiling:	22,500 ft
Performance at maximum gross, i.e. full fuel and bombs:	
AUW:	16,730 lb, 271 Imperial gallons of fuel, 2,000 lb of bombs.

| Climb to 26,250 ft: | 33.1 mins |
| Service ceiling: | 27,400 ft |

It is interesting to compare the above with later trials of an RAF Boston II, AE478, one of a number of cancelled Belgian and French contracts following the capitulation. The trials took place at Boscombe Down in early September 1940, the A&AEE report[6] noting that:

> As a bomber its performance is very good and its handling characteristics excellent.
> Maximum speed at 10,000 ft: 307 mph.

(AE758 must have been unarmed, for the report concedes that 'with armament fitted speed will be at least 10 mph slower'.)

> Maximum speed at 15,000 ft: 307 mph
> Service ceiling: 28,000 ft at an AUW of 16,000 lb
>   Operationally, however, its assessment as a bomber is low because:
> 1) rear defence is inadequate.
> 2) the crew of three is completely separated.*
> 3) at overload it can carry a 2,000 lb bomb load 880 miles only.
>   A larger bomb load at the expense of reduced fuel could not be carried externally, and a smaller bomb load could not be carried a greater distance without additional tankage [standard internal tanks had a maximum capacity of 371 Imperial gallons].

Having dismissed the Boston as a medium bomber, the A&AEE report writer then made a perceptive assessment of its other virtues:

> The aeroplane has excellent night flying qualities and this, with the good rate of climb, fair ceiling, fair top speed, good handling and good view, prompts the suggestion that it would make a good night fighter. Conversion to a night fighter (4 × 20 mm guns) would entail some modification but it could, we think, be effected without major structural modification.
>   The general layout of the front cockpit lends itself to conversion to a multi-gun installation and the back cockpit could, it is thought, accommodate a rear gunner and a wireless operator for RDF [radar] work.

Those recommendations made by the A&AEE were accepted and immediately put into effect at the Burtonwood Aircraft Repair Depot in Lancashire where over 100 Boston IIs were converted into night fighters named Havoc I. The major alterations included a 'solid' nose with eight .303 Browning machine guns, additional armour plating and an early 1½ metre A.I. (Airborne Interception) radar with operator. Flame dampers were fitted to the exhaust stacks and a black matt overall night fighter finish applied. The first Havoc I (BJ464) was delivered to the RAF in December 1940, just three months after the A&AEE report.

* Because it was impossible for the crew to change places in flight, the Boston had rudimentary flight controls for the rear gunner to control it in an emergency.

An additional night defence role for the Havoc was the Turbinlight, known originally as the Helmore light after its inventor. This version carried no forward armament but had in its nose a powerful searchlight to illuminate the target for accompanying night fighters. Improved A.I. radar rendered this somewhat vulnerable device unnecessary, though the concept was later developed into the Leigh Light which, when fitted to Wellingtons, was effective in attacking surfaced U-boats.

Martlet I

There can be no doubt that the Fleet Air Arm, without American aircraft, could not have made the contribution it did during the Second World War. The reasons for the inadequacy of the aircraft embarked on RN carriers in 1939 were historical: the Admiralty had fought an internecine struggle with the Air Staff from 1918 to 1938, during which period the Navy had to accept such aircraft as the Air Ministry thought fit. The result was either adaptations of machines primarily designed for land use with the RAF or a very small number of truly naval aircraft of which only one, the Fairey Swordfish, was to acquit itself well during the war. When the Admiralty at last gained total control of the Fleet Air Arm in 1938, the standard fleet fighter was the Gloster Sea Gladiator which, though an excellent biplane (it was the last biplane fighter to serve operationally with British forces), was hardly a match for German Messerschmitts, let alone Japanese Zeros. The only modern monoplane on FAA charge at the outbreak of the war was the Blackburn Skua – a dive bomber, the fighter variant of which, the Roc, carried a power operated turret and was next to useless, being 20 mph *slower* than the Gladiator it was intended to replace.

The American Grumman Company had produced an excellent monoplane carrier fighter, the G-36/F4F. The F4F had first flown in September 1937 but, surprisingly, was not selected for the US Navy which, very mistakenly, opted for the rival Brewster F2A-1 Buffalo.

The Grumman design was not, however, abandoned and in October 1938 the US Navy contracted for a modified version of the F4F with an up-rated two-stage supercharged engine and longer span wing. The revised fighter proved capable of 333 mph at 21,300 ft. Fifty-four F4F-3 Wildcats, as they became known in the USA, were ordered for the US Navy. The type was offered for export and the peripatetic French Purchasing Commission ordered 81 G-36As in 1939 for use aboard the French carriers *Joffre* and *Painlevé* then being constructed; with the fall of France, the entire order was transferred to Britain in June 1940. The first aircraft, named by the Royal Navy Martlet* I, was delivered on 27 July 1940. Martlets entered service with the Fleet Air Arm with No. 804 Squadron, land based at Hatson in the Orkney Islands, in October 1940, superseding Sea Gladiators and becoming the first of the type to enter operational service. The US equivalent, the F4F-3 Wildcats, were not accepted on US Navy charge until December 1940.

Compared with the best European land based fighters, the Martlet was, to some extent, outclassed but as a carrier fighter it was superb, being rugged,

* The name Martlet was used by the British until January 1944, when the American name Wildcat was adopted.

reliable and easy to fly. It had a maximum speed of around 315 mph, a ceiling of 28,000 ft and – vital for a fleet aircraft – a range on standard tanks of 1,150 miles.

Two of 804 Squadron's Martlets had the distinction of being the first American fighters to shoot down an enemy aircraft, which they did on Christmas Day 1940 when they intercepted a Ju88 which was attempting to attack the Fleet at anchor in Scapa Flow. The subsequent long and successful career with the Royal and US Navies is beyond the scope of this book; suffice it to say that the F4F Wildcat and its successor, the F6F Hellcat, bore the brunt of carrier warfare all over the world during the Second World War.

The Martlet I which the A&AEE received for handling trials was AX826, one of the original cancelled French contract. The subsequent report[7] complained about an initial very high level of carbon monoxide contamination in the cockpit which was reduced subsequently, following A&AEE recommendation (principally lengthening the exhaust pipe).

The A&AEE trials pilots also commented on the 'almost unbearable draught' which was sufficient to buffet the pilot's head 'violently except at very low rpm'. The buffeting was such that the report noted that 'most pilots prefer to take off with the hood closed'. It is most unlikely that operational carrier pilots took that view: in the event of 'ditching', should an engine fail on a carrier take-off, a closed hood could mean the difference between death and survival. Carrier pilots, certainly until the jet age and universal ejector seats, invariably took off with the hoods firmly open. The hood fitted to AX826 could not even be jettisoned, though later Martlets had that vital facility. The report went on to state that:

> The hood cannot normally be opened at high speed. It is unlikely it could be opened if the aircraft were inverted on the ground even from the outside. However the hood is relatively fragile and could be broken from outside.

The question of the hood being considered in some detail, the report was then critical of the boost controls and the lack of a CSU (Constant Speed Unit), as fitted to British built aircraft:

> As with other American types there is no automatic boost control and the boost [manifold pressure] must be hand fed to the desired value with the throttle lever . . . this is a very considerable disadvantage on a fighter aircraft.

The propeller pitch control was a push-pull knob at the bottom left hand side of the instrument panel.

The lack of a CSU was a consequence, at that early stage of the war, of American designers' relative inexperience of modern air combat; European designers had soon realised that, in the heat of air fighting, no pilot could be expected to monitor boost and RPM instruments. The result was either over-boosted engines or overspeeding propellers or, if the pilot tried to fly by the book, an Me 109 on his tail. On British fighters the pilot simply selected 'combat boost' and concentrated on flying, the CSU taking care of the RPM.

The undercarriage of the Martlet was fully retractable but, unlike most contemporary fighters, it was raised and lowered manually. The A&AEE report commented that: 'operation is quite easy for a manual system and the wheels can be fully retracted in 25 to 30 seconds'. The response to the flying controls was found to be 'quick and they are light and effective'. The stall with flaps and undercarriage up was at 83 mph; this reduced to 70 mph with flaps and wheels down. The recommended approach with full flap was 90 mph.

The A&AEE test pilots did not entirely approve of the view from the cockpit, describing it as 'not good unless windscreen perfectly clear'. Since the canopy and windscreen remained unchanged through nine Mks and 7,898 Wildcats produced, perhaps the testers at Boscombe Down were a little too critical.

The short A&AEE report does not include performance figures, perhaps because by the date of the trials the Martlet I had been superseded by the Martlet II which incorporated a different engine, folding wings and was, by September 1941, embarked on a British escort carrier, HMS *Audacity*. The A&AEE did measure the performance of a Mk II (AM991) in the summer of 1942:[8]

Power Plant (Mk II):	One 1,200 hp Pratt & Whitney Twin Wasp S3C-G
Performance at 7,800 lb AUW:	
Maximum speed:	293 mph at 13,000 ft
Rate of climb:	1,940 ft/min at 7,000 ft
Service ceiling:	31,000 ft
Armament (Mk II):	Six .50 inch guns in wings

The Brewster Buffalo

'The Brewster fighter turned out to be a perfect dud' wrote the US Marine ace, Major 'Pappy' Boyington.[9] It is an evaluation with which few, if any, American or Commonwealth pilots who had the misfortune to fly the type would disagree; indeed the melancholy fact is that very few of those who flew Buffalos against the Japanese survived their first sortie. It now seems incredible that the original Model 239-F2A-1s were selected by the US Navy in preference to the Grumman F4F Wildcat but such was the case; that decision was soon to be reversed, however, though not in time to prevent the Buffalo's disastrous operational career, the only major engagement of which was Midway, where the US Marine Squadron VMF-221 was virtually wiped out to a man. By the time the Americans were fighting the Battle of Midway, the 154 RAF Buffalos in the Far East had also been lost. That, of course, was in the future when, in 1939, the British Purchasing Commission, desperate for fighters, signed a contract for 180 Brewster Model 339s, equivalent to the US Navy's F2A-2. The RAF named the type Buffalo, possibly influenced by its squat appearance. The RAF's order was augmented by a further 38 aircraft originally ordered by the Belgian Government and directed to Britain after the capitulation of that country in 1940.

The first of the Buffalos arrived in Britain in July 1940 and were tactically evaluated by the RAF's No. 71 Squadron in July/August. Even though Britain was at that time fighting for its very existence – the Battle of Britain was then at its height – the Buffalo was rejected out of hand as a fighter in Europe, the Air Ministry shipping the 154 aircraft out to the Far East to augment the already inadequate defences of Singapore and the Straits Settlements. Although rejecting it as a front line fighter in Europe, the Air Staff considered the Buffalos to be a match for the Japanese whose Air Force was, at that time, treated by the West with amused contempt.

The A&AEE received AS412 (Brewster Model 339B), the third aircraft of the original cancelled Belgian order, on 9 July 1940. Unfortunately its Wright Cyclone engine failed before the performance trials got under way and the aircraft was replaced on 31 July 1940 by AS425 but that machine 'arrived with the undercarriage retracting structure damaged'. In August a third Buffalo, AS430, was available at Boscombe Down for take-off trials which are recorded[10] as '235 yards zero flap, 215 yards take-off flaps'. After that test AS430 went to the RAE Farnborough on 5 September, returning to the A&AEE only to be written off in a crash soon after.

Yet another Brewster 339B was to appear at Boscombe Down, AS426 (on 3 February 1941), to continue performance trials, supplemented by the first aircraft of the ex-Belgian order, AS410, which was used for armament trials.

The first definitive RAF Buffalo, the Brewster Model 339E, the sub-type ordered directly by the British Purchasing Commission, was W8133 which incorporated factory modifications to British standards. These included a Hamilton hydromatic propeller – the 339B used a Curtiss with the pitch electrically operated. The 339E also had a pitot head and instruments which differed from the ex-Belgian aircraft. W8133 provided the following performance data at an AUW of 6,430 lb:

Top speed:	294 mph at 18,200 ft
Maximum rate of climb:	2,240 ft/min from sea level to 8,200 ft
Time to 20,000 ft:	10.5 mins
Service ceiling:	31,800 ft

The maximum speed recorded by the A&AEE test was a good deal less than the 'Brochure' speed of 315 mph claimed by the manufacturers. The A&AEE reported that both the oil and cylinder head temperatures were such that the type was considered unsuitable for tropical conditions (ICAN +25°C, i.e. +40°C at sea level), which makes the RAF decision to ship their unwanted Buffalos to the Far East even more reprehensible.

There was a final A&AEE report[11] concerning the Brewster Buffalo: handling trials with the CG extended aft. (These tests were probably with W8133.) The tests were done with the aircraft loaded to maximum take-off weight, i.e. normal operational load: full fuel and ammunition for its four .50 guns. (Later in the Far East, the RAF, in a desperate attempt to wring a better performance against the Japanese A6M Zero, replaced the .50 guns by .303s, cutting the ammunition and restricting the fuel load to a mere 84 Imperial gallons.)

The Buffalo with its CG 25.6 inches aft of the datum was found to be 'very unstable in all conditions', difficult to trim and liable to go into a steep dive or stall without the control column being disturbed. Reducing the aft CG to 24.9 inches, it was just possible, with care, to trim for 'hands off' level flight but it was found to be impossible to achieve trim to climb without the pilot continuously controlling the aircraft. At 24 inches the Buffalo was stable in all conditions except the climb. 24 inches was recommended by the A&AEE as the normal aft CG for Service pilots of average experience, with 24.9 inches as the absolute maximum in Service use.

Apart from the lack of performance and the difficulties of trimming, the Brewster aircraft had a dangerously high level of carbon monoxide contamina-

L7245, the second prototype Halifax at Boscombe Down. This was the aircraft that was the subject of the original A&AEE Handling Tests during January 1941, when the first indications of rudder overbalance were discovered. The aircraft in the background is a Vickers Wellington IA *(Crown copyright)*.

W7776, the Halifax II (Special Conversion). This aircraft was one of a number which the A&AEE used to 'clean up' the airframes in an endeavour to improve the type's dangerously low performance. When compared with L7245 above, the deletion of the front turret is noticeable, as is the revised bomb aimer's position. This particular Halifax arrived at Boscombe Down in poor condition; the report (20th Part/760) noted that: 'The aeroplane had been treated with a very rough special night finish [repainted when this photograph was taken] . . .. There were evidences of poor workmanship — some of the fuselage plating was warped and the bomb doors were fitting badly. Engine cowlings were also in bad condition' *(Crown copyright)*.

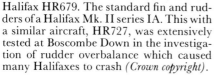
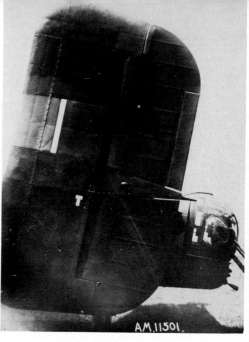

Halifax HR679. The standard fin and rudders of a Halifax Mk. II series IA. This with a similar aircraft, HR727, was extensively tested at Boscombe Down in the investigation of rudder overbalance which caused many Halifaxes to crash *(Crown copyright)*.

The final form of Halifax fin and rudders which, as a consequence of the A&AEE investigations, cured the rudder overbalance completely. (The aircraft is DK145) *(Crown copyright)*.

The elevator of a Halifax VI, TW783, showing damage sustained during A&AEE testing (possibly as a result of a terminal velocity dive). This photograph illustrates the hazardous nature of wartime test flying at Boscombe Down *(Crown copyright)*.

L7276, the first production Manchester, photographed at Boscombe Down in the summer of 1940. The aircraft has a 90 ft wingspan and the original 28 ft tailplane with the ventral fin and short endplate fins. The rather cluttered Vulture engine cowlings are well illustrated. This aircraft was to suffer an engine failure taking off from Boscombe Down on 12 September 1940. After extensive test flying at the A&AEE, it went to 61 Squadron, then followed other surviving Manchesters to an O.T.U. (No. 25). It was wrecked in an accident on 31 October 1943 *(Crown copyright)*.

A Manchester IA illustrates the final form of the type with the long span tail, twin extended fins and the 'Lerwick' upper turret. This aircraft, L7320, the last Manchester tested at Boscombe Down, was used to investigate severe tail vibration; on one A&AEE flight this was to cause the rudder mass balance weights to be torn loose. L7320 was lost on a subsequent test flight from Boscombe Down on 12 December 1941 after flying a total of only 118 hours *(Crown copyright)*.

The second Lancaster I prototype, DG595, photographed at Boscombe Down in August 1941. The Manchester lineage is apparent. DG595 was used by the A&AEE to test the Establishment's 'cascade' flame-dampers which can clearly be seen fitted to the port outer Merlin XX. The ventral barbette is also visible. DG595 was to have a long life, being finally written off following a crash at a Torpedo Development Unit in February 1944 *(Crown copyright)*.

The (gunless) mid-upper turret of DG595, clearly illustrating the detent cam track and follower which prevented the gunner from shooting off the tail fins or hitting the wings and cockpit! *(Crown copyright)*.

The first prototype Lancaster II, DT810, was one of two pre-production Lancaster IIs; although the production of subsequent Lancaster IIs was undertaken by Armstrong Whitworth, the prototypes were constructed by A. V. Roe. DT810, powered by four Bristol Hercules VI engines, was test flown at Boscombe Down in the spring of 1942 to investigate the alleged high fuel consumption of the B.II Lancasters *(Crown copyright)*.

A standard Lancaster B.III of No. 617 'Dam Buster' Squadron which came to Boscombe Down in the autumn of 1943. This bomber unfortunately collided with an Airspeed Oxford trainer over High Post, near Boscombe Down on 10 September 1943 *(Crown copyright)*.

NG408: a late production Lancaster B.I at Boscombe Down in 1945, displaying the final form of H_2S radar blister. The position of the ASI static vent (the small unpainted plate between the roundel and serial number) when H_2S was fitted had been the subject of an A&AEE investigation *(Crown copyright)*.

PB592/G. The first Lancaster to be modified to carry the Barnes Wallis 'Grand Slam', 22,000 lb 'Earthquake' bombs. This Lancaster was test flown at Boscombe Down at an AUW of 72,000 lb. It made the first live 'Grand Slam' bomb drop on the Ashley Walk range just one day before the first operational attack with these huge bombs on the Bielefeld Viaduct on 13 March 1945. It is of interest to note the deletion of power consuming flame-dampers on aircraft used for daylight operations. PB592/G is fitted with the broad chord 'Paddle Blade' propellers *(Crown copyright)*.

HK541, one of two Lancasters modified for service in the Far East. The experimental 1,000 Imperial gallon fuel saddle tank fitted to the top of the fuselage was in fact only a ballasted mock-up to enable test data to be obtained at maximum overload. The A&AEE tropical tests were flown from Manipur in India. Although generally successful in trials, the Pacific war ended before long-range Lancasters could become operational. HK541 was struck off RAF charge in January 1947 *(Crown copyright)*.

The second prototype Miles M.20 fighter. This wooden Merlin powered aircraft was intended as a 'throw away' fighter, designed at the height of the Battle of Britain. U-0228 (later DR616) was the only one of the pair tested at Boscombe Down. The blown hood, possibly the first fitted to a British military aircraft, was praised but the lack of a bullet-proof windscreen was not. This interesting 'one-off' had a performance roughly equivalent to the more complex Hurricane I. Only the two prototypes were ever built *(Crown copyright)*.

The prototype Lysander, K6127, after conversion to carry a Frazer-Nash .303 inch gun turret. The original turretless Lysanders were ordered for Army co-operation squadrons, their only defence against fighter attack being a single observer hand-operated Vickers 'K' .303 inch machine gun. The modification to a power-operated turret required the addition of what amounted to a second wing to balance the turret's weight. Though the Tandem Wing Lysander flew surprisingly well, K6127 remained the one and only turret 'Lizzie' (Crown copyright).

The remarkable half size S.21 Short Stirling. It was said that the only item not to scale was the pilot, as can be seen by the size of the crew ladder in the photograph, taken at Boscombe Down in 1942. The rather unexpected position of the propellers fitted to the Pobjoy Niagara radial engines is due to the reduction gearboxes.
It might be mentioned that the retractable undercarriage seems a good deal more practical than the complex arrangement eventually fitted to the full size Stirlings (Crown copyright).

Although G-ADCS is known as the M.B.1, it was in fact the second Martin-Baker aircraft. It first flew in 1935 and was one of very few early aircraft to have a primary structure of prefabricated steel tubing. It flew well enough but the sole M.B.1 was destroyed in a Denham hangar fire in 1938 *(Martin-Baker, Denham)*.

James Martin's first fighter, the M.B.2 (incorrectly referred to in A&AEE reports as the M.B.1), shown here at Martlesham Heath, with enlarged fin and rudder, as P9594. The A&AEE engineers reported that 'many features are excellent and seem hardly capable of improvement . . .'. The test pilots, however, did not consider that it handled well but it did manage a level speed of 320 mph with service equipment and full armament of eight .303 inch Brownings, which was good going in 1938, especially for a private venture from an engineering firm employing only 40 people. P9594 was dismantled during the war at Denham *(Martin-Baker)*.

R2492, the prototype M.B.3 Martin-Baker, proposed as a Spitfire/Hurricane replacement contracted to an Air Ministry Specification, which called for 400 mph at 15,000 ft and a ceiling of 35,000 ft. Whether or not the M.B.3 would have fulfilled the stringent requirements must remain open to question for the aircraft was written off following a 1942 crash when its Napier Sabre engine failed on take-off from RAF Wing, killing its test pilot, James Martin's partner, Capt. Baker *(Martin-Baker)*.

The second M.B.3, R2496, was revised during construction, to emerge as the M.B.5. Powered by a 2,340 hp Rolls-Royce Griffon engine, driving contra-rotating propellers, it was the final Martin-Baker aircraft and considered by the A&AEE a remarkable aircraft, possibly one of the best piston engined fighters to date. Why it never went into production has been a mystery for some time, the simple explanation being the emergence of jet powered competitors. Ironically it was the pressure of work on Martin-Baker ejector seats for jet aircraft which caused James Martin to abandon plans for a jet powered M.B.6 *(Martin-Baker)*.

A Douglas Boston I at Boscombe Down in the summer of 1940. AE458 was the first of fifteen DB-7 Bostons (AE458 to AE472) delivered to the RAF; the entire order was used for training. They were powered by Pratt & Whitney Twin Wasp engines. The first operational Bostons were the Mk. IIIs, powered by Wright Cyclones. The aircraft ahead of AE458 is a Lockheed Hudson *(Crown copyright)*.

A factory fresh Grumman Martlet I which was probably from the same initial production batch as AX826, the aircraft tested at the A&AEE. The daylight visible through the wheel wells might seem surprising but was a feature of the F4F Wildcat (to give it its American name) throughout its long production life. The narrow chord cowling of the Wright Cyclone engine was confined to Martlet Is. Later aircraft were powered by Pratt & Whitney Twin Wasps *(Grumman)*.

A US Navy Wildcat, equivalent to a British Martlet II, aboard the American carrier USS *Santee*, supporting the invasion of Casablanca in November 1942. The deck handling party have just unfolded the wings — always a manual operation on Wildcats and Martlets. The A&AEE test pilots had complained that the cockpit was very draughty with the hood slid back and recommended that pilots take off with the hood closed, but few, if any, carrier pilots would be likely to take the risk of ditching with a shut canopy *(US Navy)*.

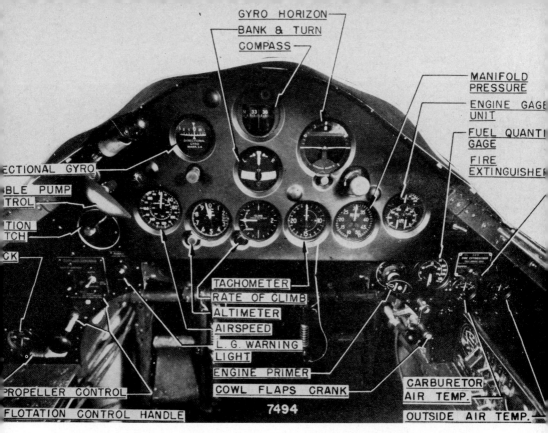

GYRO HORIZON
BANK & TURN
COMPASS

MANIFOLD PRESSURE
ENGINE GAGE UNIT
FUEL QUANTI— GAGE
FIRE EXTINGUISHER

ECTIONAL GYRO
BLE PUMP TROL
TION TCH
CK

TACHOMETER
RATE OF CLIMB
ALTIMETER
AIRSPEED
L. G. WARNING LIGHT
ENGINE PRIMER
COWL FLAPS CRANK

PROPELLER CONTROL
FLOTATION CONTROL HANDLE
7494

CARBURETOR AIR TEMP.
OUTSIDE AIR TEMP. —

The instrument panel of a Wildcat. US aircraft generally had large cockpits with excellent instruments though the layout of the panel was never — unlike British military aircraft — standardised *(Grumman)*.

If the Grumman Wildcat was one of the Second World War's most successful aircraft, its rival, the Brewster F2A-2 Buffalo, was one of the most unsuccessful. AS412, shown here, was soon to suffer engine failure on take-off. AS412 was one of a cancelled Belgian order: the cranked pitot head was unique to these export Buffalos, as was the fitting of an airscrew spinner *(Crown copyright)*.

A US Navy F2A-2 Buffalo flying in the summer of 1942, by which time the type had been withdrawn from operations in America. The aperture for one of the twin .50 inch guns can clearly be seen near the top of the exhaust collector ring, as can the outmoded telescopic sight *(US Navy)*.

The Martin Baltimore, a development of the Maryland. All the Marylands in service with the RAF came from cancelled French contracts; the Baltimores were ordered directly. AG837 was the third aircraft of the initial order and, when photographed at Boscombe Down, carried the yellow 'P' marking, denoting a prototype *(Crown copyright)*.

AL909, a Chesapeake I; one of two such aircraft evaluated at Boscombe Down in late 1941. 'Chesapeake' was the RAF name for the Vought SB2U Vindicator used by the US Navy. The SB2U was designed as a dive bomber; the bomb crutch which kept the bomb clear of the airscrew can be seen, as can the jury struts to hold the folded wings. It had been hoped to use the Chesapeake aboard British escort carriers but the take-off run was too long for the short flight decks. The type was relegated to training duties with the Fleet Air Arm (*Crown copyright*).

For comparison: seen in home waters, a US Navy SB2U-2 Vindicator aboard USS *Saratoga* shortly before the Second World War. It carries the markings of 'Bombing Three' — the famous 'High Hats'. This particular aircraft seems to have been engaged on reconnaissance since the bomb crutch has been removed and a long-range fuel tank carried. US Marine Vindicators fought from Midway in June 1942 (*US Navy via B. Johnson*).

The Bell Airacobra was, in many ways, an unusual aircraft: the engine was behind the pilot and it was one of the first military aircraft to feature a tricycle undercarriage. Unfortunately when it arrived in England its performance was limited by its American Allison engine, to the extent that it was deemed unsuitable as a fighter in Europe. AH573, seen here at Boscombe Down in early 1941, was the third of 675 Airacobras ordered for the RAF but, after its failure with 601 Squadron, the only RAF unit to operate the type, the order was terminated at 80 aircraft, most of which went to Russia where they were employed with success as ground attack fighters. The unusual paint scheme of AH573 is noteworthy *(Crown copyright)*.

AG351, the sixth production Mustang I and the aircraft that was the subject of the original A&AEE Report. This Allison engined fighter showed great promise, limited only by the poor high altitude performance of its American in-line engine; even so, at 15,000 ft it achieved 370 mph and the Mustang would when re-engined with Rolls-Royce Merlins become one of the great fighters of World War Two *(Crown copyright)*.

The final form of the RAF Mustang, the Mk IV. This aircraft, though carrying the USAAF Serial 413332, was in fact on RAF charge as TK 589 and flown at Boscombe Down in July 1944 for level speed trials. The engine was a Packard Merlin V-1650 and the maximum speed of the Mk. IVs was 442 mph at 24,500 ft. As the P51D, USAAF, these late Mustangs were able to escort American bombers to Berlin and back *(Crown copyright)*.

The Consolidated B-24 Liberator was tested at Boscombe Down. It was used by the RAF in a maritime anti-submarine role where its very long range enabled Coastal Command to close the 'Black Gap' in the North Atlantic. The aircraft depicted is a PB4Y-1 the US Navy's version of the B-24, flying with Squadron 106 on maritime reconnaissance in the South Pacific in 1943 *(US Navy)*.

Consolidated B-24D Liberator BZ791. This aircraft was supplied to RAF Coastal Command in mid-1942. The original Sperry ball turret, similar to that fitted to USAAF B-17s, was replaced in RAF service by a retractable radome to house H$_2$S radar for anti-submarine patrols *(Crown copyright)*.

The exhaust driven turbo-supercharger first fitted to the B-24Ds. These superchargers enabled the Pratt & Whitney Twin Wasp S4C4-G to maintain their rated output up to 36,000 ft. 'Turbos' are now, in the 1980s, becoming fashionable for high performance cars but, like so much of today's technology, they had their initial development during the war years *(Crown copyright)*.

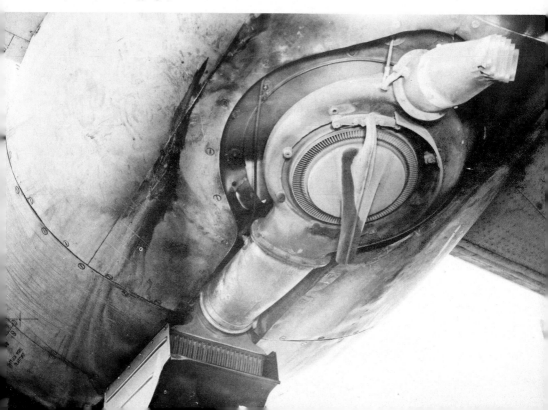

The first prototype B-17, then simply known as 'Model 299', being rolled out of the Boeing plant for the Press on 16 July 1935. A caption to this photograph in the local *Seattle Times* dubbed the aircraft 'Flying Fortress', a name which was to become historic *(Boeing)*.

AN528 (incorrectly marked as AM528), one of 20 B-17Cs ordered for the RAF, on a test flight over Seattle. When the aircraft were delivered to Britain they were finished in standard 1941 camouflage.
AN528 was destroyed by fire at dispersal at RAF Polebrooke when serving with 90 Squadron. With the exception of AN531 tested at Boscombe Down and AN524, damaged on delivery, the remaining 18 B-17Cs were issued to 90 Squadron, though the operational début of the type was to be little short of disastrous *(Boeing)*.

The co-pilot's position in AN528, photographed at Boscombe Down. Though the A&AEE test crews commended the low noise level on the flight deck, the view through the narrow windows was criticised as inadequate for a daylight bomber *(Crown copyright)*.

As a consequence of the unfortunate early operation of the Fortress I, a much improved aircraft, the B-17E was produced, incorporating modifications which hard won RAF experience had proved essential. The aircraft depicted is FK187, a Fortress IIA. The photograph was taken at Boscombe Down in 1942. Nearly all RAF Fortress IIAs went to Coastal Command for maritime reconnaissance *(Crown copyright)*.

The Lockheed P-38 Lightning is famed in the annals of the USAAF, particularly in the Pacific, during the Second World War. Only three Lightnings: AE978, AF105 and the example depicted, AF106, were ever on RAF charge. The aircraft supplied to Britain did not have the essential exhaust turbo-superchargers; they were considered too secret to risk over Germany. (In point of fact the Germans had already developed their own turbo-superchargers by that time). The performance without the turbos, was judged to be inadequate and the large RAF order was cancelled *(Crown copyright)*.

A Curtiss S03C-1 Seamew on observation duties with the US Navy. Seamews were ordered by Britain as a possible Swordfish replacement operating from escort carriers. In the event, the Ranger engine proved so unreliable that the type was relegated to training or as radio controlled target drones. The fate of most US Navy S03Cs was similar. The aircraft illustrated is flying without its second crewman *(US Navy)*.

W5795, the prototype Mk. VI high altitude Wellington at Boscombe Down in April 1942. The Mk. VI, unlike the Bristol Hercules engined Mk. V, was powered by two Rolls-Royce Merlin 60s. The minute pilot dome can be seen just below the DF aerial *(Crown copyright)*.

A close-up of the original pilot dome fitted to W5795. It is just possible to distinguish the inner dome, hot air being forced between the two hemispheres to prevent frosting, which nevertheless often occurred *(Crown copyright)*.

D

E

A Messerschmitt Bf109E-3 of 11/JG54 which was forced down undamaged near Amiens on 2 May 1940. This aircraft was flown a few days later to Boscombe Down for evaluation, where this photograph was taken. The aircraft was built by Fieseler and still displays the *Gruppe* marking of JG54: the 'Lion of Aspen'. The aircraft was later allocated the RAF Serial AE479 and extensively flown in mock combat against Spitfires and Hurricanes *(Crown copyright)*.

The cockpit of the captured Bf109, AE479. The A&AEE test pilot thought the aircraft 'cramped'. The 'Revi' reflector sight with a small auxiliary ring and bead is well illustrated. The absence of any blind flying instruments is surprising since contemporary British fighters were so equipped. The compass appears superior to the British P4, though there is no provision for course setting and no directional gyro is fitted. The engine rev. counter is redlined at 2,450 rpm. The panel has been hastily annotated in English for the British test pilots *(Crown copyright)*.

LV633, the Avro York, *Ascalon,* which became the Prime Minister's (Winston Churchill's) personal transport. The A&AEE had to investigate a serious problem with the kitchen sink fitted to the aircraft *(Crown copyright)*.

A Piper L4, at the moment of engaging the bridle of the curious Brodie Suspension System. This photograph is a still frame from a ciné record of this remarkable proposal for operating light observation aircraft in jungle clearings. The development of military helicopters, plus the difficulty of operating the device, resulted in it being abandoned after evaluation at Boscombe Down. One of the present authors, Terry Heffernan, witnessed these hair-raising trials at Boscombe Down *(Crown copyright)*.

LANDING. STAGE 1

P9795/G, the paratroop carrying Barracuda tested at Boscombe Down in 1944. The trials were not entirely successful and the idea was not proceeded with. It seems incredible that four fully armed men could be carried in the small 'Cuda' floats. The aircraft is also displaying the original 1½ metre ASV Yagi radar aerials above each wingtip *(Crown copyright)*.

For comparison, a standard Barracuda I; the aircraft illustrated is the prototype P1767. The photograph, incidentally, reveals the 1940 Boscombe Down hangars (still in use in 1982) and the original control tower. Boscombe Down was a grass airfield until near the war's end, when a concrete runway was laid down *(Crown copyright)*.

A Bristol Beaufighter VIF, X7881. This night fighter displays the early 'metre' AI (Airborne Interception) radar aerials. The photograph was taken at Boscombe Down in November 1942; the following summer the A&AEE was required to investigate an unusual compass deviation occurring on Beaufighters when the guns in the nose of the aircraft were fired *(Crown copyright)*.

A Beaufighter cockpit; the reflector sight, fitted with a sunfilter, is to the right of the windscreen; the gun firing trigger set to 'safe' is on the right of the control wheel. The offending P4 compass can be seen mounted on the right hand cockpit wall in front of the group of four small gauges *(Crown copyright)*.

A very rare picture of the prototype Mosquito, W4050, still marked with the manufacturer's serial E-0234. W4050 came to Boscombe Down for initial handling trials in early 1941. Due to the photograph being taken on non-panchromatic film, the yellow overall finish appears dark. The aircraft in the misty background is a Westland Lysander *(Crown copyright)*.

The original file containing the proposals for the Mosquito. This file is typical of the thousands in the A&AEE archive and Public Record Office, London. Two dates are interesting; the first 1.10.39, when the file was issued, and the label stating the dossier is closed until 1991. (The present authors had the file de-classified for this book). The importance of the Mosquito is underlined by this file being graded an Historical Document *(Crown copyright)*.

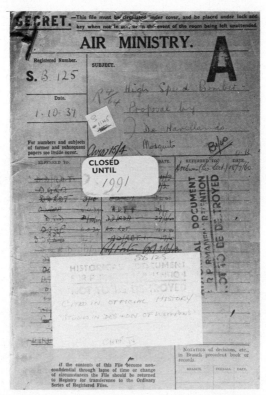

AM. 11083.

FIG. 2. NORMAL POSITION OF AIR BRAKES WHEN AEROPLANE IS STATIONARY. IN FLIGHT THE LOWER SET CLOSE

W5052, the first Mosquito night fighter prototype, tested an unusual annular airbrake to slow the aircraft when closing with a target, without the change of trim operating the flaps would cause. The photographs show the annular airbrake in its closed and open position. A&AEE tests disclosed excessive buffeting when the brake was used and the idea was abandoned *(Crown copyright)*.

AIRCRAFT AND ARMAMENT EXPERIMENTAL ESTABLISHMENT
BOSCOMBE DOWN

COPY No...*14*...

Gloster F9/40 - 2-W2B/23 engines

Preliminary handling trials

A. & A.E.E ref:- CTO/AM.77.
M.A.P. ref:- SB. 50809/DD/RDA
Period of tests:- 24th and 29th February 1944

Summary

Pilots from this Establishment have flown two of the prototype aircraft at the Makers' works and the following are the preliminary findings. Most flying was done on DG.205/G at 11,300 lb. and C.G. at 0.31 of the AMC, conditions corresponding to T.S.L. with an aft C.G. position.

(i) The aircraft is easy to fly and from the point of view of quietness, absence of vibration and fumes, etc. is very pleasant.

(ii) The controls are very badly harmonised as the rudder is immovable at ordinary level and diving speeds after the first few degrees of movement; the elevator is too heavy, whilst the ailerons are too light at low to moderate speeds. A directional oscillation of small amplitude is present in bumpy conditions and this must be eliminated before accurate aiming is possible. The elevator trimmer is much too sensitive and has an excessive amount of backlash.

(iii) The seat should be tilted back a few degrees, whilst repositioning of the throttles, the fuel shut-off controls, and some engine instruments, is desirable.

(iv) An emergency braking system is essential, and continuous reading fuel contents gauges are required.

(v) The minimum time restriction of 10 seconds on throttle movement from idling to max. rpm. should be eliminated, as should be the 5° maximum aileron movement at high speeds.

(vi) The aircraft appears to be statically stable stick fixed and also gives the impression of being dynamically stable.

(vii) The stick force per g in recovery from trimmed dives at 300 - 400 mph ASI is about 6 and in sustained turns at 300 mph ASI is about 8.

(viii) The rate of roll compares favourably with Spitfire performance.

1. Introduction.

1.1 It was considered desirable that A. & A.E.E. pilots should fly this type of aircraft at the Contractor's airfield in order to gain preliminary experience and impressions of this aircraft with its revolutionary mode of propulsion.

Another historic document from the Boscombe Down archive: the preliminary handling trials of the Gloster F.9/40 — the Meteor *(Crown copyright)*.

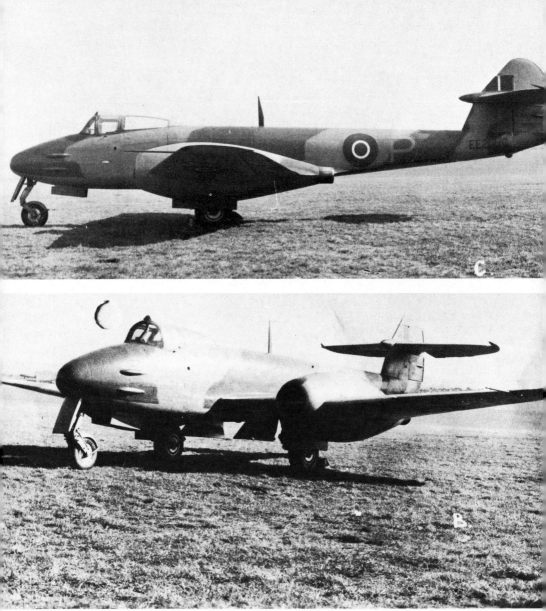

Two views of the third production Meteor I, EE212/G, which was extensively evaluated at Boscombe Down; the initial test flight by the A&AEE was on D-Day: 6 June 1944.

The Meteor displays the original 'framed' canopy and the rather rotund engine nacelles which are typical of early jet aircraft powered by centrifugal, as opposed to the much slimmer axial engines now universal. The small jet pipes betray the modest power of the 1944 Rolls-Royce Welland Is which offered only 1,700 lb static thrust.

The Meteor Is were the only Allied jet aircraft to enter service during the Second World War, mainly used to engage German V1 flying bombs, the first jet v. jet air combat *(Crown copyright)*.

The A&AEE conducted tropical trials of a Meteor II, EE336, powered by two Rolls-Royce Derwent engines. During the 300 hour trials, based at Khartoum, the effect of sand ingestion was investigated; EE336's engines were found to be undamaged *(Crown copyright)*.

For the sand trials, an Anson was used as a convenient wind machine *(Crown copyright)*.

The first production Vampire I, TG274/G, on the airfield at Boscombe Down in the autumn of 1945. This aircraft was extensively flown by A&AEE test pilots for, although the European war was by then over, the Pacific war was not. The aircraft ahead of the Vampire is a Hawker Tempest, one of the fastest piston engined fighters and which had shot down several Me262 jets in combat before the war with Germany had ended *(Crown copyright)*.

Rara Avis. The unique Boulton & Paul P.92/2. This, like the S.31 Stirling, was a half size scale model. It was to test a proposal to mount an airborne 37 mm cannon. The armament, not fitted to V3142, was to be mounted on the apex of the raised wing centre section. The model, V3142, was as far as the P.92/2 design ever got. It was highly unpopular with the A&AEE test pilots, due to the near impossibility of baling out. The photograph gives a good impression of the undulating and rough grass surface of Boscombe Down *circa* 1943, with aircraft dispersed far and wide *(Crown copyright)*.

Although test pilots tend to get the limelight, A&AEE observers also flew many long and hazardous hours in uncomfortable conditions in unheated, unpressurised, military aircraft, often prototypes. This photograph, taken on a test flight from Boscombe Down during the war, is typical. The aircraft is a Halifax *(Crown copyright)*.

tion of the cockpit (as had the Martlet I). Exhaust pipe modifications were recommended.

Although designed as a carrier aircraft, the Buffalo seems never to have served operationally in that role – the US Marines and RAF operating the type from land bases. The Fleet Air Arm did have a small number in service with No. 805 Squadron based in Crete in March 1941. It was reported that most FAA pilots there preferred the Sea Gladiator biplanes.

To be fair to the Buffalo, it should be mentioned that the Finnish Air Force had a number of early 339Bs which acquitted themselves well during the 'Winter War' against the Russians, though the Finnish pilots were not only very good, they were defending their country and the Russians were mainly flying biplanes at that time.

The Brewster Company followed the Buffalo with a dive-bomber, the SB2A Buccaneer, of which some 750 were supplied to Britain on Lease-Lend as the Bermuda; none was used operationally, indeed, one source describes the type as 'one of the most unsuccessful combat aircraft . . . in the Second World War'.[12] The Brewster Company ceased aircraft manufacture in 1944.

Martin Maryland

The Glenn Martin 167W was designed for the US Army Air Corps as an attack bomber and first flew in February 1939. In the event the type was not selected by the USAAF and manufacturers were free to offer the aircraft for export; it should come as no surprise to read that the French Government immediately placed substantial orders for the production version – the Martin 167F. As with the majority of French orders placed with American aircraft companies, the fall of France in 1940 caused the bulk of the order to be taken up by the RAF, 75 Martin 167Fs duly arriving by sea in June 1940. After assembly at Burtonwood, Lancashire, the 75 aircraft, now named Martin Marylands (the Glenn Martin factory was at Baltimore, Maryland), commencing with AR702, were designated Mk I, being powered by two single-stage, supercharged Twin Wasp SC3-G engines. They were three-seat reconnaissance/bombers, though the RAF rarely used the type for other than photo-reconnaissance purposes – a role they filled with distinction, mainly in the Mediterranean. The second Maryland of the original batch, AR703, was one of the few to remain in Britain and was on charge to the A&AEE for performance trials in early 1941.

The tests were to assess the performance with the aircraft fitted with an 'Anson' .303 turret in place of the original US manual dorsal armament.

The subsequent report[13] records that the 'Anson' turret reduced the performance to some extent, though it undoubtedly increased the aircraft's defensive capability.

Performance with the original dorsal armament:

Take-off run:	350 yards
Maximum speed:	294 mph at 9,000 ft
Maximum rate of climb:	1,310 ft/min
Service ceiling to rear:	27,250 ft

Performance with British turret:

Take-off run:	395 yards
Maximum speed:	282 mph at 8,800 ft
Maximum rate of climb:	1,260 ft/min
Service ceiling to rear:	24,600 ft

The report writers were critical of the layout of the cockpit and certain controls:

The flap operating lever can be easily fouled and has on several occasions vibrated forward and depressed the flaps.

The general arrangement of the instruments is not satisfactory. The blind flying instruments are not grouped together. The Pioneer compass is not satisfactory for navigation. [It proved impossible to set course by it] but it is to be replaced by a British P4. [The standard magnetic compass then fitted to practically all British aircraft.]

The ground handling of the Maryland was considered to be satisfactory. The aircraft did not swing on take-off and, once airborne, the harmonisation of the flying controls was good and the handling generally found to be good for a bomber but too heavy for defensive manoeuvring. Should an engine fail, the Maryland was easy to fly on either engine without heavy rudder load or excessive yaw. The aircraft was steady in the dive without vibration or any instability up to the maximum speed reached, 351 mph.

The Maryland has two celebrated sorties to its credit, the best known of which was the photo reconnaissance of the Italian fleet at Taranto for the Fleet Air Arm's famous attack on 11 November 1940. The other operation is little known but in some ways of greater importance. A small number of Maryland Is had been allocated to the Fleet Air Arm for use mainly as target tugs operating from Hatston in the Orkneys. One of these aircraft from No. 771 Squadron, flown by a volunteer crew, took off on 22 May 1941 in appalling weather – weather which, incidentally, had grounded the RAF – to fly to confirm, as the Admiralty had feared, that the German battleship *Bismarck* and heavy cruiser *Prinz Eugen* had sailed from their anchorage at Bergen, Norway, into the Atlantic to attack convoys. After a brilliant feat of dead reckoning navigation by Cdr. G. A. Rotheram, the pilot, Lt. N. E. Goddard, radioed that the warships had in fact sailed. On receipt of this vital intelligence, the Home Fleet steamed out eventually to engage and sink *Bismarck* on 27 May 1941.

Vought-Sikorsky Chesapeake

This single-engined dive-bomber had been selected for the French Naval Air Service; deliveries were well under way by the time of capitulation and, as a consequence, a number fell into German hands though it is doubtful if any were used operationally by the Luftwaffe.

The Chesapeake began life as the first operational monoplane in service with the US Navy, the original aircraft being designed by Rex Beisel who was later to design the Corsair. The prototype XSB2U-1 was selected after trials in April 1936 with an equivalent biplane version, also constructed by Vought. The result was an order for 54 SB2U-1 aircraft in October 1936, the type to serve as a carrier based dive-bomber.

The next batch for the US Navy was 58 SB2U-2s, virtually the same as the original -1 but with certain additional equipment, which were delivered at the end of 1938. The final US Navy version was the SB2U-3, 57 of which were delivered in 1940 and were the first to carry the US Navy's name 'Vindicator'.

SB2Us served aboard USS *Lexington*, *Saratoga*, *Ranger* and *Wasp* and, in addition, with Marines based on Midway, fighting the defence of that island in 1942.

The ex-French V-156-Bs, now named Chesapeake I, were transferred to Britain, the 50 aircraft being numbered AL908–AL957. The Chesapeake Is differed in some ways from the original French specification; they were fitted with four fixed forward firing guns and arrester gear. It was hoped to use the type on escort carriers but the take-off run was to prove too long for the small flight decks of the wartime escort carriers and the Chesapeake was relegated to Fleet Requirements Units for land based training purposes.

Two Chesapeake Is were evaluated at Boscombe Down – AL909 and AL913 – in late 1941. The first report[14] dealt with the maximum gross weight and CG position, the A&AEE writer complaining that:

> The aircraft arrived in this country with no available data as to operational uses or capabilities. Little loading data was available but the makers stated that the aeroplane was very critical to C.G. position. Tests were therefore made to determine the maximum weight for Service use and to what limit the centre of gravity could safely be moved.

As a preliminary, the aircraft was weighed with full fuel and oil and the figure of 8,360 lb recorded, the CG being at 30.6 inches aft of the datum, the design limit being 31 inches. The aircraft was then bombed up, first with a single 500 lb bomb, then two 500 lb bombs; the CG was now at 33 inches.

The test flights were undertaken with the maximum bomb and fuel load; the take-off performance was poor: 600 yards to lift off, 1,200 yards to clear 50 ft. (Since escort carriers typically had a flight deck of around 500 *feet*, one can see why the type was rejected for carrier use.)* Take-off performance apart, the Chesapeake did not handle well, 'unsatisfactory' being the word used in the A&AEE report, which recommended a maximum AUW of 9,000 lb which, at full fuel, necessitated a bomb load of only one 500 lb bomb. Since a single bomb suspended from one of the wings caused instability, the centre station was used. The normal aft CG limit was 31 inches with 31.5 inches allowed for short periods of flight. Although the original Vought SB2U had been, from the outset, designed as a carrier aircraft – it had folding wings – the A&AEE discovered that it was imprudent to use flaps to shorten the take-off since they were permanently interconnected with the undercarriage retraction; the latter could not be raised until the flaps were up. Few carrier pilots would have cared to ditch with the wheels down, so take-off flap was not recommended.

Performance and fuel consumption tests figures are given in the second A&AEE report,[15] the aircraft tested being AL913, at the maximum recom-

---

* The A&AEE take-off figures were taken in conditions of zero wind; even allowing for this, the performance was unsatisfactory for escort carrier service.

mended gross weight of 9,000 lb; a single 500 lb bomb was carried on the centre station:

Maximum speed:	222 mph at 9,900 ft
Maximum rate of climb:	500 ft/min from sea level to 11,600 ft
Service ceiling:	16,000 ft
Absolute ceiling:	17,000 ft
Maximum range:	1,170 miles
Endurance:	7 hrs 45 mins (max)

No British Chesapeakes saw action and the US SB2U Vindicators, which did, mainly in an anti U-boat role, had by 1942 been supplanted by other carrier dive-bombers, one of which was to become legendary: the Douglas Dauntless.

The Bell Airacobra

The Bell Airacobra was one of the first fighter aircraft to be fitted with a tricycle undercarriage and was considered, in 1939, when it first flew, highly unorthodox, being one of the very few military aircraft to be placed into production with the engine behind the pilot. The normal tractor airscrew was driven by a shaft which passed through a tunnel between the pilot's legs. One can imagine that the thought of that shaft transmitting 1,150 hp at around 2,800 rpm (the reduction gearbox was at the airscrew end) tended to pre-occupy the pilot's thoughts. (If it did not, there was also a petrol vapour burning heater on board.)

Whatever the disadvantages, mechanical and psychological, of the unconventional layout, it permitted a 20-mm Hispano cannon to fire through the airscrew boss, supplemented by two .50 inch Colt machine guns synchronised to fire through the airscrew arc and another four .30 inch Colts in the wings, giving the Airacobra a very effective armament.[16]

The Airacobra was immediately ordered in quantity by the USAAC as the P-39D and by that answer to the American aircraft salesmen's prayers – the French – whose orders were taken up by the British in 1940. A total of 675 Airacobras were spoken for, the first being delivered in July 1941, to be evaluated by the A&AEE and the RAF Air Fighting Development Unit at Duxford.

Four Airacobras, AH573, 574, 589 and 701, were tested at Boscombe Down between August and September 1941. The preliminary handling trials were prefaced by a criticism of the cockpit layout and means of entry. The method of entry was unique among contemporary fighter aircraft, being via car type doors on each side. These doors were complete with wind-down windows; only the right hand door had a handle on both inside and outside and was considered the 'normal' means of entry and exit. The left hand door could only be opened from the outside and was for emergency use; however, both doors could be jettisoned. The hood, on the other hand, was fixed and could not be jettisoned. Entry was difficult, there being a lack of handholds and a low fixed roof. With the engine running at its high idle speed of 1,200 rpm, essential to avoid severe vibration, the slipstream tended to shut the rearwards opening doors. The cockpit was considered suitable only for small to medium sized pilots, there being totally inadequate headroom for a tall man, to add to whose discomfort the bucket type seat was not adjustable.

In view of the above, it is not surprising that the A&AEE test pilot came to the conclusion that: 'Satisfactory parachute exit in the air could be difficult. . .'.

The forward visibility, in the hardly unlikely eventuality of heavy rain, was very poor, the report stating that the windscreen was 'completely obliterated' with no clear vision panel available. AP2064A, the RAF's Airacobra pilot's notes, simply advised the pilot when flying in heavy rain to:

(i)   lower [door] windows
(ii) reduce speed to 150 mph IAS
(iii) lower flaps ¼
(iv) select fine pitch
(v)   watch temperatures

Hardly a recommendation for a fighter in use in European winters – or summers.

The cockpit layout was further criticised by the Boscombe Down test pilots. For example, the aileron trim control could not be reached once the pilot was strapped in; the petrol cock was difficult to reach even with the straps released. The ground handling of the Airacobra was entirely dependent on the wheel brakes: 'If they fail it would be extremely difficult to control the aeroplane'. The nose wheel simply castored and could not be steered.

The tricycle undercarriage enabled the aircraft virtually to fly itself off the ground and the take-off was considered satisfactory, the aircraft unsticking at 100 mph, climbing away at 140 mph. The elevator was 'light, effective and responsive', though the ailerons, which were fabric covered, became heavy when the Airacobra was dived at over 300 mph.

The aircraft was found to be stable throughout the speed range. The stall was at 105 mph with flaps and wheels up and 88 mph with flaps and wheels down. There was no warning of the onset of the stall, though it was gentle, with no tendency for a wing to drop. Though not mentioned in the A&AEE report, the RAF's pilot's notes prohibited intentional spins. If the aircraft got into a spin unintentionally – not unusual in air combat – the recovery was normal: stick fully forward and full opposite rudder, which 'should be effective within two turns'. The notes, however, caution the pilot that in the spin he would be likely to encounter 'heavy rearward stick loads and under certain conditions of loading, violent oscillations may be encountered'.

The Airacobra's climb and level speed performance trials were conducted with AH754. This aircraft was fitted with a slightly different engine – an Allison V-1710-E12 – in place of the standard E4. The E12 had a different supercharger gear ratio: 9.6 to 1 instead of 8.8 to 1 for the E4. The propeller reduction gear differed also: 2 to 1 against the standard 1.8 to 1. The flight tests were made in June 1942 at an AUW of 7,830 lb. The performance was:

Maximum speed:	365 mph at 15,000 ft
Maximum climb:	1,845 ft/min at 12,500 ft
Service ceiling:	29,000 ft
Time to 10,000 ft:	5½ minutes
Time to 20,000 ft:	12½ minutes

The figures for Airacobras powered by the usual E4 version of the Allison V-1710 were obtained from trials with AH701 and AH753:[18]

Maximum speed:	355 mph at 13,000 ft
Maximum climb:	2,040 ft/min
Service ceiling:	27,000 ft
Time to 10,000 ft:	5.1 minutes
Time to 20,000 ft:	11.7 minutes

By the time these tests were made in August 1942, the RAF had rejected the Airacobra for European use; only one fighter squadron was ever equipped with the type: No. 601, 'The Millionaires' – so called because many of its original members were wealthy young men who joined 601 when it had been a fashionable pre-war R.Aux.A.F. 'weekend fliers' squadron, based at Hendon on the outskirts of London. No. 601 retained its Airacobras for only a month or two. The Allison engine, though acclaimed in America, had a very poor high altitude performance and the aircraft generally suffered from a high degree of unserviceability. The lack of altitude performance had relegated the Airacobra in RAF service to a ground attack role. The RAF order of 675 aircraft was terminated at 80, the remainder going to the USAAF.*

Later versions of the Airacobra, the P-39Q, were used in substantial numbers by the USAAF, mainly in the Middle East and in the Pacific. Over 5,000 Airacobras were supplied to the Soviet Union, where they were used mainly in a ground attack role.

North American Mustang

As we have seen, practically all of the American built aircraft which arrived in Britain in 1940/41 were either originally ordered for the US Air Force or Navy or for export – many for France. The fighters so acquired, with the exception of the Martlet, were outclassed by European designs and could not be used in their intended role. The reason for the lack of performance of American fighters was not for want of aeronautical skills; American transport aircraft were far ahead of the rest of the world. It was simply a lack of an appreciation of the conditions in which air combat was being fought, as for example during the Battle of Britain. That the Americans were soon to profit from the hard won experience of the RAF was to be reflected in the production of what was arguably the best all-round fighter of the Second World War – the North American Mustang.

The Mustang owed its existence to a British Purchasing Commission which was in America in April 1940, seeking a replacement for the RAF's Curtiss P-40 Tomahawks, the Allison engines of which were, as with the Bell Airacobras, relegating the type to low altitude and thus unsuitable for use against the Luftwaffe. Among the manufacturers consulted was the, then, relatively small North American Aviation Inc. of Inglewood, California. That company's president, J. H. 'Dutch' Kindleberger, had made a close study of the reports of air combat in Europe and was keen to produce a fighter. The only difficulty lay in the Commission's stipulation that, in view of likely military developments in France, any order was dependent on a prototype flying and being approved within 120 days; since North American had no fighters 'in stock', it meant starting with a clean sheet of paper.

* The US Army Air Corps (USAAC) changed to the US Army Air Force (USAAF) on 1st June 1941.

The design team, which had previously constructed only a single fighter (for Siam) began work; it was headed by Raymond Rice and Edgar Schmued, the latter having had the very useful experience of working in Germany for Messerschmitt.

In the incredible time of just 117 days the prototype, designated NA-73, was pushed out – on wheels borrowed from a trainer and without an engine. The Allison Company was to take a further six weeks to deliver the engine – a liquid-cooled V-12, 1,100 hp V-1710-39. When completed, the Mustang was revealed as a very purposeful looking fighter with exceptionally clean lines; what was not apparent to the casual onlooker was the laminar flow wings which, though at that time little used, can dramatically reduce drag. From the first flight on 26 October 1940, it was apparent that in the Mustang the North American Company had produced an outstanding fighter; it was eventually to be developed to one of the greatest of all as the P-51D, but that story is beyond the scope of this book.

The Mustang I went into production for the RAF (the USAAF showing little interest at that early stage) and the first aircraft (commencing AG345) arrived in Britain in November 1941, the type going into operational service with No. 2 Squadron as photo-reconnaissance aircraft in July 1942.

The first Mustang I which reached Boscombe Down in January 1942 for performance trials[19] was AG351. The test flights were somewhat delayed:

owing to the abnormally high temperatures due to coring [engine oil congealing due to over cooling] . . . during the winter months, tests had to be made with various types of blanks over the oil cooler and [engine] radiator.

The blanks had a pronounced effect on the maximum level speed:

Maximum level speed
without blanks: 370 mph at 15,000 ft
Maximum level speed
with blanks: 357 mph at 14,700 ft

It is not certain if this considerable difference was due to increased drag of the blanked off radiators or a loss of the 'jet' effect of the heated ram air leaving the radiator efflux – possibly a little of both.

The blanks had no measurable effect on the rate of climb which the A&AEE tests recorded as:

Maximum rate of climb: 1,980 ft/min at 11,300 ft
Service ceiling: 30,000 ft

The test pilots were complimentary about the handling of AG351: 'There is no appreciable tendency to swing [on take-off]. . . . Cross wind take-offs presented no difficulties in winds of up to 25 mph'.

The approach and landing of the Mustang with a cross wind component of up to 25 mph was:

not difficult but there is barely enough aileron control to effect the required sideslip,[20] with the tail wheel fixed [i.e. locked], as our pilots recommended.

Rudder alone was necessary to check the tendency to swing into the wind after touchdown.

AG351 was used for fuel consumption trials between May and August 1942.[21] The tests were made at an AUW of 8,300 lb, at which weight the still air range of the aircraft at 15,000 ft was 8.75 ampg at 180 mph IAS. The fuel capacity of AG351 was 130 Imperial gallons, which gave an estimated maximum range of 990 statute miles, equivalent to an endurance of 4.1 hours. It would seem from the A&AEE reports that AG351 – an early aircraft – had a slightly lower fuel capacity than the normal production Mustang Is which had a nominal capacity of 140 Imperial gallons, which extended their endurance and range to 4.5 hours and 1,080 statute miles, respectively. These figures make no allowance for combat; the A&AEE considered that the range would decrease by 80 statute miles for each five minutes at combat boost.

The very long range of the Mustang, which was outstanding for a single engined fighter, was later in the war to enable the P-51D Mustang to escort daylight USAAF bombers to Berlin and back.

The performance of the Mustang I was outstanding in other ways: the maximum level speed of AG351 was, at 370 mph, faster by some 13 mph than that of the Spitfire II and only 4 mph slower than the Spitfire V. The Spitfires, however, had a far better high altitude performance, the Allison engine limiting the capability of the Mustang as a fighter, as had been the case with the other Allison engined American fighters.

The Allison V-1710 was the only American designed, liquid-cooled V-12 engine to be produced in quantity and, although it had a certain aesthetic appeal, being beautifully proportioned and finished, it had little else to offer when compared with the Rolls-Royce Merlin. As is now well known, a decision was made to re-engine the superb Mustang airframe with a Merlin 61 engine; the result of that marriage is legendary: the speed shot up to 442 mph at 24,500 ft.

The USAAF soon realised the potential of the Merlin powered Mustang III and, with the similarly powered P-51D, they operated the type extensively with the 8th USAAF on daylight escort duties. 15,586 Mustangs were produced; incredibly the P-51 was put back into limited production in 1967–75 and many are still in service, some powered by turbo-prop engines: a most remarkable record for an aircraft originally designed and built in 117 days and thirty-seven years earlier.

The Consolidated Liberator

The B-24 Liberator was, with the Boeing B-17 Flying Fortress, the mainstay of the USAAF's daylight bombing force during the Second World War.

The B-24 was a later design than the B-17 and was easily identified by its large twin fins and the very high aspect ratio 'Davis' wing which offered high lift with low drag.

The Consolidated Aircraft Corporation had concluded a contract to supply the US Army with their Model 32 – later named 'Liberator' – in March 1939, the prototype XB-24 first flying on 29 December 1939. It should come as no surprise that the French ordered 120 B-24s but these, like most of the other types ordered for the *Armée de l'Air*, ended up in Britain, the original French order being supplemented by a further 165 aircraft. The first RAF Liberators were ferried across the Atlantic in March 1941. The initial half dozen or so were used as long-range unarmed transports, designated LB-30As, to fly ferry pilots to Canada to deliver aircraft such as Lockheed Hudsons and Catalinas back to Britain.

Drawing on British operational experience, the Consolidated design staff incorporated modifications to improve the B-24 as a bomber; increasing the defensive armament, fitting self-sealing fuel tanks and armour plating vital areas.

Twenty operational Liberator Is, AM910 to AM929, reached RAF Coastal Command during June 1941, where their very long operational range of 2,400 miles enabled them to fly anti-submarine patrols over the so called 'Black Gap' in mid-Atlantic, a gap caused by the inadequate range of existing aircraft based in the UK and Canada.

Three of the original Liberator Is, AM910, AM912 and AM929, were tested at Boscombe Down.

The first was AM912, though that aircraft's participation in the test pro-gramme was to be curtailed by an accident[22] which occurred on 16 April 1941. The aircraft had been performing in a satisfactory way but when the AUW was increased to 50,000 lb nosewheel shimmy was experienced which, even when taxiing at as low a speed as 20 mph, was so violent that the flight test programme had to be postponed while adjustments were made to the nosewheel hydraulic dampers. The adjustments effected no discernible improvement. The A&AEE then designed a nosewheel lock which was engaged when the aircraft was aligned on the runway for take-off after a very slow taxi. With this modification the B-24 was able to complete the take-off and landing trials but, after the last landing of the programme, the nosewheel collapsed completely when the aircraft was being slowly taxied over the, admittedly not particularly smooth, Boscombe Down airfield. The entire nosewheel structure was pushed up and rearwards, destroy-ing the underside of the Liberator's nose section. The subsequent report[23] noted that 'Crews should be warned not to occupy the nose turret or navigator's compartment during take-off or landing'. It was considered, from the evidence of the damage, that 'anybody [in the nose section] would have been killed although the speed was so low when the failure occurred'.

With the enforced exit of AM912, AM910 was used for the acceptance trials of ASV – Air to Surface Vessel – 1½ metre radar which, together with the formid-able anti-submarine offensive armament, was mounted on the definitive early Coastal Command Liberator I.[24]

The armament consisted of four 20-mm cannon and four airborne depth charges. The cannon were fixed and fired forward from a faired pod on the Liberator's underside. This armament was in addition to the three .50 Brown-ings, one each, hand-trained from the port and starboard beam positions, with a third in the tail. These guns only had a meagre provision of 100 rounds each, which the A&AEE considered as 'very poor'; they recommended that the guns should have at least continuous belt feed. (Later Coastal Command Liberators, the GR.IIIs, had power operated turrets.)

The ammunition for the offensive 20-mm cannon was considered satisfactory: 18 60-round magazines were situated in the bomb bay and the gunners could reload the four cannon in less than a minute. The bomb bay bomb crutches, which were specially manufactured by Consolidated to take British bombs and depth charges, were adjudged to be unsatisfactory and the armament specialists at Boscombe Down made recommendations to improve the existing design.

Another unsatisfactory aspect of the Liberator was a serious deviation of the Pioneer 1801 magnetic compass which was found to vary by 15°, dependent on the rate of charge of the aircraft's 24 volt accumulators! This was traced to the magnetic field of the battery charging generators.

The flight trials proved that the Liberator handled well in all conditions of flight from the glide to 300 mph. The characteristics with one or two engines shut down were considered good. Level speed measurements with AM910 at 5,000 ft and 45,500 lb AUW at 'combat emergency power' were 262.5 mph; normal maximum power gave 253 mph; maximum continuous cruise gave 216 mph. (Coastal Command had yet to change to knots.) The four engines were 1,200 hp Pratt & Whitney R.1830-65 Twin Wasp, 14 cylinder, two-row radials.

The flight trials also included dummy attacks against a floating target to represent a surfaced U-boat, and a Lancaster, used presumably to simulate that German long-range shipping predator – the four-engined FW 200 Condor – since this was the enemy aircraft most likely to be encountered over the Atlantic.

The low level attacks against the sea targets were considered 'easy and accurate'; of course the targets did not fight back, which U-boats certainly would; nevertheless the four 20-mm cannon were a formidable armament. The mock air combat against the Lancaster starkly revealed the inadequacy of the hand trained guns, the A&AEE report commenting that: 'against other heavy aircraft good results can only be expected from astern or almost astern attacks'. That would enable the Liberator I to use its 20-mm cannons.

The 1½ metre ASV radar was found satisfactory.

AM929, the final aircraft of the original batch of Liberator Is, was used at Boscombe Down for diving trials during September 1941.[25] Before the tests were undertaken, certain modifications were made to strengthen the tailplane which had limited the aircraft to a 'never exceed' speed of 275 mph. After the modifications AM929 was cleared for a maximum speed of 307 mph at an AUW of 47,000 lb. In the test dives the speeds actually recorded went over the limit slightly to 311 mph.

In the diving tests, AM929, in spite of its size (Liberators had a 110 ft wing span), was steady but it was concluded that, with a beam wind, aiming the fixed cannons in a dive would present difficulties, it being very hard to alter the aiming point once speed had built up in the dive. The rudders became progressively heavy from about 250 mph; by 300 mph they were virtually immovable, making corrections to the aiming point impossible. It was even difficult to get the big aircraft into the dive due to the heaviness of the controls and A&AEE recommended the use of the trimmers. Boscombe Down also cautioned that recovery from a high speed dive would require very high control forces and trimming would also be required for the recovery.

The early RAF Liberator Is were followed in 1942 by 139 Liberator IIs which were equivalent to the USAAF's B-24C; this version was slightly longer – 63 ft 4 inches to 66 ft – and had power operated .50-inch turrets. Many were supplied for Coastal Command's anti-submarine sorties. Two Mk IIs, AL505 and AL546, arrived at Boscombe Down in January 1942 for comparative compass trials.[26]

Deviation difficulties with the magnetic compasses installed in the Liberator I have already been recounted; the report on AM910 found the generators were causing large errors 'due to the magnetic fields of the generators'. This, one suspects, is only a partial explanation; the deviation experienced with the two

Liberator IIs' compasses was attributed to the standard American practice of using 'earth return' wiring for the entire electrical system of the aircraft. 'Earth return' wiring uses the metal structure of the aircraft for all the negative circuits; this is, of course, the case with cars, but cars do not normally carry magnetic compasses. The trouble with the system in aircraft is the very large currents which can circulate at different rates within the structure, due to imperfect bonding or differing conductivity of the various sections of the aircraft's structure; these currents created magnetic fields which affected the compasses. Tests with both British P4 and P9 and the much smaller US Pioneer Type 1809 and 1821 compasses showed significant deviation which varied with the electrical equipment switched on. No doubt the generators' 'magnetic field' on the early Liberators was partly a manifestation of 'earth return' wiring. British built aircraft used two-pole wiring to avoid the problem.

To rewire an aircraft as electrically complex as the Liberator was out of the question, so the A&AEE report[27] noted:

Once again it must be pointed out that the sole cause of all these [compass] deviations can be found in the earth-return system of electrical wiring used in American aircraft. If single [pole] wiring is unavoidable the only known solution is to fit a distant reading or remote indicating compass . . .

as was done on the Avro Lancaster when it was discovered that the cast iron bombs were causing compass deviations.

The Boeing B-17 Flying Fortress

During the Second World War, few aircraft (if one excepts the Stuka and Spitfire) could have received more attention from the popular press than the B-17 'Flying Fortress'; indeed, the very name owed its existence to a caption writer of the *Seattle Daily Times* on the occasion of the roll out of the prototype in July 1935. The name was a misnomer, for the early version supplied to the, then, US Army Air Corps was woefully inadequately armed; be that as it may, by 1941 over 100 'Flying Fortresses' had been delivered to the US Army.

In 1938 a British Purchasing Commission, which included Air Commodore Arthur Harris – later better known as 'Bomber Harris' – was not swayed by the hyperbole already surrounding the Fortress. The defensive armament then consisted of five single hand-trained .50 or .30 machine guns, two situated in blisters on the sides of the fuselage, one in a dorsal position and another in a ventral extension to the underside (the gunner in that position had to lie down to operate his gun). The fifth gun was mounted in the transparent nose. Air Commodore Harris commented that: 'so far from being a 'fortress' this aircraft is practically indefensible against any modern fighter'.[28]

The assessment was to be proved prophetic; however, circumstances alter cases and, with the desperate war situation in which Britain found herself in September 1940, approaches were made to the US Government to supply a number of B-17s. After a certain amount of political difficulty – the US Army Air Corps was by then urgently being re-equipped – 20 B-17Cs, AN518–AN537, were flown to Britain in April 1941, to enter service with No. 90 Squadron a month later as the Fortress I.

The operational record of those original B-17s was a fiasco. The aircraft were operated in daylight at a time when Bomber Command had decided to bomb by night. To avoid German fighters it was the intention to operate at 30,000 ft, flying not as a self defensive group, as envisaged by the Americans, but individually. A number of US 'advisers' was stationed at Polebrook, one of whom, a pilot, was to become the first US Army Air Force casualty of the war when the Fortress he was flying broke up due to losing control after severe icing. Ice caused other difficulties; the guns repeatedly froze solid; the windscreens iced over; there was trouble with the engines losing oil. These very high altitude raids revealed another problem which was to plague the 8th USAAF later in the war: 'contrails' – the exhaust gas condensing in the freezing atmosphere which, in a clear sky, gave away the aircraft's position to the waiting fighters.

When attacked the Fortress I was, for the unfortunate crew, highly vulnerable, for the tail was undefended. Losses from one cause or another forced the RAF to abandon the use of its dwindling force of B-17Cs over Europe. There were bitter recriminations from the Americans who considered with some justice, that the aircraft had been misused, which did not, however, prevent the USAAF from profiting by the lesson so expensively acquired by the RAF.

One of the original 20 B-17Cs, AN531, came to Boscombe Down in June 1941 for trials, the earliest of which was noise measurement.[29] The noise level to be measured was of course that to which the crew was subjected.

During the A&AEE performance and handling trials the noise level was found to be 'remarkably low' in comparison with the four-engined Halifax, then also undergoing trials at Boscombe Down. A brief investigation of the factors contributing to the B-17's low internal noise was undertaken; the propeller speeds were shown to be as high, or in some cases higher, than at corresponding conditions in the Halifax. The factors contributing to the low B-17 noise levels were determined by the A&AEE as follows:

a) The propeller discs were forward of the pilot's cabin.
b) There was a general absence of large transparent panels.
c) Such panels as there were were ¼″ thick.
d) The crew positions were thoroughly soundproofed but the A&AEE had doubts as to the long term serviceability of the cladding and criticised the difficulty of access to wiring, pipe and cable runs which the soundproofing material covered.
e) A final factor was the fact that the exhaust pipes of the engines were under the nacelles.

The question of the noise levels having been considered, a subsequent A&AEE report[30] dealt with the aircraft's handling.

The normal crew entry was via a small door on the starboard side, just in front of the tailplane; the flight deck crew had to negotiate a nine-inch catwalk through the bomb bay which had extremely limited headroom. (This arrangement was to be common on subsequent models and complicated by the fittings for the 'ball turret' which further impeded access, which is possibly the reason why most crew members, other than the rear and waist gunners, preferred to use the forward escape hatch in the fuselage floor, even if this did require a certain acrobatic agility.)

Once aboard, the pilot's view was criticised, except directly forward. Since the

B-17 was, from the outset, designed to operate at high altitude, the question of adequate heating was of some consequence and the A&AEE considered it to be 'excellent' in the 'static' crew positions: pilots, navigator and radio operator. The Boscombe Down test crews made flights with an outside air temperature (OAT) of −55°C in normal uniforms without flying boots or gloves. (It is difficult to equate this report with the published accounts of conditions encountered with the identical operational B-17Cs of 90 Squadron.)

As to the handling of AN531, the rudder, which on the B-17C was very large, was 'unmanageable' when the aircraft was taxied in a wind above 25 mph. It was recommended to be locked for taxiing on such occasions, using the engines' wheel brakes for directional control.

Take-off trials suggested that no flap should be used, since the flaps tended to accentuate a marked swing without conferring any noticeable improvement in take-off performance. There was ample power available; a safe take-off could be made even in the event of losing an engine; at 44,000 lb gross AN531 took off on three and climbed out 'comfortably'.

In flight control about all axes was good, the controls being light and effective, though there was a tendency for the elevators to become heavy at high speed and in steep turns. The B-17Cs did not have the waist gun position open all the time as did the later versions. The gunners were provided with transparent panels which were removed when action was imminent; when these panels were removed, the report noted − not surprisingly − that: 'considerable draught is caused'.

The trials included flying with two engines throttled back with the propellers in coarse pitch; even at 44,200 lb and 10,000 feet 'the flying characteristics were found to be exceptionally good. . . . [The aircraft] will just climb with any two engines out'. Asymmetric power caused no undue strain and the aircraft could be flown in that condition for long periods without tiring the pilot(s).

AN531 was dived by the A&AEE test pilots up to 315 mph − the Boeing limit was 305 mph − without any difficulty. Perhaps the Boscombe Down men were lucky: a month earlier, AN522, an identical B-17C, broke up after an unintentional terminal velocity dive, due to ice accretion, on a training flight. (It was on this flight that the US Army pilot was killed.)

The summary of the brief performance trials with AN531 gave the following figures:

At 49,300 lb AUW the take-off run was found to be:
    510 yds without flap
    540 yds with 12° flap
    515 yds with 17° flap

At 44,200 lb take-off AUW:

Maximum climb:	1,600 ft/min at sea level
Service ceiling:	37,000 ft
Absolute ceiling:	37,700 ft
Time to 37,700 ft:	42.7 minutes

At 49,300 lb take-off AUW:

Maximum climb:	1,300 ft/min at sea level
Service ceiling:	34,000 ft
Absolute ceiling:	34,700 ft
Time to 34,700 ft:	46.2 minutes

The A&AEE did not record any maximum level speed for AN531 but the report[32] does give figures for level speed at climb power settings: 2,300 rpm +39.5 inches Hg* manifold pressure; at 44,200 lb, 298 mph was achieved at 25,000 ft, which height was the maximum permitted at a manifold pressure of 39.5 inches.

After the RAF abandoned the idea of operating the B-17C as a daylight bomber, four of No. 90 Squadron's surviving aircraft went to serve in the Middle East; eventually five Fortress Is, including AN531, went to No. 206 and 220 Squadrons Coastal Command, where their long range of 3,160 miles was utilised for maritime reconnaissance, a role they fulfilled, based on Benbecula, until superseded in 1943 by the later and greatly improved Fortress II – equivalent to the US B-17E.

P-38 Lockheed Lightning

the pilots sent it climbing over eight miles straight towards the stratosphere, up to where even the highest-flying bombers couldn't go. They brought it scream-ing down out of the clouds like forked vengeance. They jammed down the throttle and flew it faster than any fighter before. . . .

The above is an extract from a 1943 Lockheed advertisement: even allowing for the natural copywriters' tendency to press their client's product, it is doubtful if today's Trade Descriptions Act would countenance the advertisement. The P-38 certainly looked formidable (so did the Westland Welkin) but, as the philosopher said: 'between precept and practice a shadow falls'.

The P-38 had its origin in a specification issued by the US Army Air Corps in February 1938 calling for a long-range interceptor fighter with a maximum speed of 360 mph at 20,000 ft. The Lockheed Company, which up to that time had produced only civil aircraft, tendered the P-38 design. It was, in many ways, revolutionary, with a tricycle undercarriage, the pilot sitting in a central pod, and the twin turbo-supercharged V-12 Allison engines being carried on two booms to which the wings and tail were attached.

The Allison V-1770 liquid-cooled engines were then untried, as was the highly secret General Electric Company's exhaust turbo-supercharger.

The prototype XP-38 crashed on landing in February 1939 but the design survived this unpromising start and the type went into production for the USAAC in late 1940. In March of that year, the British Purchasing Commission ordered 143 P-38s, armed with 37-mm Hispano cannon, replacing the 20-mm of the USAAC P-38s. The name Lightning was given to the aircraft destined for the RAF, a name adopted by the Americans. Unfortunately the turbo-superchargers of the Allison engines were considered by the US Government too secret to risk over Germany in 1940 and their export to Europe was forbidden. Thus the first three Lightnings delivered to the RAF, AE978, AF105 and AF106, were powered by conventionally blown Allison 1,150 hp engines. The performance of the aircraft with these rather moderate power plants was such that the RAF rejected the fighter and cancelled the remainder of the order. The rejects were completed with the turbo-engines and went to the USAAF.

* Inches of Mercury

At least one of the original three RAF Lightning Is – AF106 – came to the A&AEE in the summer of 1942 for brief handling trials.[33]

The entry to the cockpit required a ladder, due to the height of the wing from the ground, in part a consequence of the tricycle undercarriage, the A&AEE test pilots pointing out that: 'If the engines are running this [climbing onto the wing] is liable to be dangerous'. The view from the cockpit, despite the rather heavy frames, was considered 'reasonably good'. No bullet-proof screen was fitted.

The test flights were to be 'limited in scope due to the speed restriction of 300 mph IAS imposed as a result of accidents* that had previously occurred at higher speeds'.

An unusual feature of the Lightning, among many on this unorthodox aircraft, was the control column which was to the pilot's right, it being cranked with a half spectacle wheel, very different from the classic 'spade' grip of the Spitfire and Hurricane.

The pilots criticised the propeller pitch control as being 'too far forward for satisfactory operation'.

All the Boscombe Down flying of AF106 was made at a take-off weight of 13,860 lb with the CG on the datum point. Ground handling and take-off were satisfactory:

> The aeroplane flies itself off the ground . . . [there is] no tendency to swing. . . .
> The aeroplane is quite pleasant to fly. It is not particularly manoeuvrable for a fighter but in this respect it is comparable with other twin engined fighter types . . . with either engine stopped and the propeller feathered the aeroplane can be trimmed to fly with the feet off the rudder pedals. The general characteristics are good. The aeroplane will climb satisfactorily in this condition at low altitude and turns up to 45° [of bank] can be safely carried out with and against the stationary engine.

The stall with the aircraft clean was at 94 mph and 78 mph with flaps and undercarriage down. The A&AEE did not measure the level speed but it was, as noted, restricted to 300 mph – hardly electrifying by 1942.

The Lightning as used by the USAAF was to prove a tough and very useful escort fighter and long-range reconnaissance aircraft, fighting in every theatre during the Second World War. Perhaps its most celebrated action was the interception, by USAAF's 339th Fighter Squadron, of Admiral Yamamoto's Mitsubishi G4M 'Betty' 550 miles from the Americans' Guadalcanal base, enabling Lt. Thomas G. Lanphier to shoot down the Japanese Admiral's aircraft.

With hindsight, there is no doubt that the decision of the RAF to reject the Lightning I was correct, certainly with the ban on the turbo-supercharger. The de Havilland Mosquito was already showing promise and the developed fighter variants would outfly any mark of Lightning with ease. 9,942 Lightnings of all types were produced.

The Seamew

Of the American aircraft tested at Boscombe Down (and this chapter, of necessity, contains only a proportion), some are now legendary; some fairly well

---

* There is no record in the A&AEE files of any accident to a Lightning.

known; others less so. To end this chapter, here is the short report of an aircraft which is now only a footnote to the military aviation history of the Second World War – the Curtiss Seamew.

This small aircraft was designed as a Navy scout/reconnaissance machine and could be operated as either a land or seaplane. The US Navy's designation was SO3C-2. It was seen in Britain as a possible replacement for the Fairey Swordfish based on escort carriers. In the event, although 250 were ordered (some with arrester gear), it was soon apparent that the Seamew's single 520 hp Ranger engine was extremely unreliable; hardly a recommendation for an aircraft on reconnaissance duties over the North Atlantic. Only 100 are known to have been delivered to Britain (FN450–FN499 and FN600–FN649). One of the first batch, FN475, was the subject of handling trials at Boscombe Down during June/July 1943.[34]

By the time of the A&AEE interest in the Seamew, the aircraft, in both Britain and America, had been relegated to training duties, in Britain's case mainly to train FAA telegraphists based at Worthy Down.

The A&AEE test pilots found the cockpit layout of FN475 to be satisfactory in the main. Although the Seamew was, by military standards, a light aircraft, it was found to require high stick forces to effect a satisfactory three point landing if the CG was forward to any extent. It was recommended by the A&AEE to limit the permissible forward CG. On the other hand, if the CG was aft of the datum, the Seamew displayed a marked tendency to swing on landing to an extent thought dangerous for an inexperienced pilot. However, since the type was not to be used for pilot training, the fault was considered acceptable; the trainee telegraphists in the rear seat were presumably flown by tour-expired operational carrier pilots who could be expected to cope.

Handling in flight was adjudged to be only 'fairly good', though typical of a low, not to say under-powered, aircraft. The wings of the Seamew had automatic slats to aid low speed flight; the A&AEE recommended they be permanently locked shut since they actually caused a marked deterioration of the climb out, though it was conceded they did reduce the stalling speed. No figures were given as to performance but typically they were:[35]

Maximum speed:	190 mph at 7,500 ft
Cruise speed:	126 mph
Endurance:	8 hours

The Seamew, even in its humble rôle of trainer, was far from popular; the unreliable engine and difficult ground handling, caused by the narrow track undercarriage, all contributed, which is possibly the reason why many were converted as Queen Seamews: radio controlled gunnery target drogues for the Royal Navy. So ended the career of just one of the many intended Swordfish replacements.

If some of the aircraft described in this chapter were found to be wanting when used operationally, it should be realised that they were, in the main, designed at a time when the Americans were at peace and without direct involvement in the European war. When the United States did enter the war their aircraft industry rose to the occasion and it is doubtful if that war could eventually have been won without the tens of thousands of excellent aircraft 'made in the USA'.

CHAPTER SIX

The High Flying Wimpeys

The Vickers Wellington, universally known as the 'Wimpey', was the RAF's main night bomber until, during 1943, the four-engined 'heavies' took over that rôle. The nickname came from the 'Popeye' cartoon which was published in the *Daily Mirror*. Popeye had a rotund friend – 'J. Wellington Wimpey'; since the Vickers aircraft, like the cartoon character, had a certain well-fed appearance, the name seemed appropriate. At all events it stuck and 'Wellingtons' became 'Wimpeys' to Service and public. To a later generation the name has become synonymous with hamburgers: that too had its origin in the cartoon; J. Wellington Wimpey was usually depicted eating them.

The Wellington was designed by Barnes Wallis to Air Ministry Spec. B.9/32 and the prototype (K4049) first flew on 15 June 1936. The production Wellingtons entered RAF service in 1938, to become, as we have stated, the backbone of Bomber Command. They were soon in action when, on the second day of the war, 4 September 1939, 14 Wellingtons of Nos. 9 and 149 Squadrons made, with Bristol Blenheims, the first RAF raid of the Second World War, bombing German naval targets at Brunsbuttel in daylight. The Wellington continued to be used as a daylight bomber, the Air Staff (like the Luftwaffe during the Battle of Britain and later the USAAF Eighth Air Force) believing, wrongly, that bombers with gun turrets could defend themselves against opposing fighters. The RAF was the first to be disabused of the idea, on 18 December 1939 to be precise, when out of 24 Wellingtons attacking Wilhelmshaven in daylight, ten were shot down and three more badly damaged. After that débacle, Wellingtons, except those of Coastal Command, were used as night bombers, taking part in the first raid on Berlin, in addition to providing more than half the aircraft, 599 out of the famed 'thousand bomber' raid on Cologne, on the night of 30/31 May 1942.

Although the Wellington was phased out of Bomber Command's order of battle as the Stirling, Lancaster and Halifax became operational, it continued to fulfil many other service rôles, particularly the Mk XV and XVI which served with Transport and Coastal Commands; indeed, such was the success of the 'Wimpey' it remained in production throughout the war, the last being delivered in October 1945.

Of the 11,461 Wellingtons built, the most remarkable were a small number (64) of the Mks V and VI High Altitude Bombers. The first of these, known as Vickers Type 407, was built to Air Ministry Spec. B.23/39, which had called for a bomber to operate at 40,000 feet, at which altitude it was then (in 1939) considered to be immune from attack by either fighters or anti-aircraft guns.

For any heavy bomber to fly at 40,000 ft was, in 1939, no small achievement; for the Wellington it was an especially difficult proposition. The Wallis design utilised an ingenious geodetic structure of intersecting duralumin 'basket weave'. This form of construction, which had been used previously in the Wallis designed Vickers Wellesley, was not only light and immensely strong, it also possessed a very high degree of redundancy, there being many alternative stress routes. Although it could, and did, enable the Wellington to sustain incredible battle damage and still fly home, it had for high altitude operation one grave shortcoming: the structure was, apart from the engine nacelles, fabric covered. To fly at 40,000 ft the aircraft's crew compartment would have to be pressurised to some 7½ psi to give the cabin an apparent altitude of 11,000 feet. Clearly a fabric covered fuselage could not contain anything approaching that pressure.

When the original high altitude proposals were made in 1939, very little was known about pressurising an aircraft's cabin. To speed production, the design staff at Vickers decided that the 'stratosphere bomber' would utilise as many components from the standard Mk I Wellington as possible. The principal difference was the enclosing of the pilot, navigator and radio operator in a cigar-shaped pressure capsule 18 ft 3 inches long, with a diameter of 5 ft 5 inches; entry was via a 3½ ft circular pressure-tight door at the rear end. The working pressure was intitially 7 lb/sq inch, the structure having been proof tested up to more than double that figure at 15 lb/sq inch. The integrity of the cabin was, to some extent, compromised by the rather mundane requirement that the pilot needed to be able to see out; to achieve this essential facility the pressure vessel was pierced by a circular opening on the top, to which was fitted a double skinned perspex dome as the pilot's canopy. A second opening was made under the forward end and an optically flat window let in for the bomb aimer.

Thirty Mk Vs were ordered from Vickers on 1 March 1940 and work on the prototype, R3298, was proceeding without undue urgency until, just after the Dunkirk evacuation in May 1940, the then Minister of Aircraft Production, Lord Beaverbrook, demanded priority for the high altitude bomber. Some delay was then encountered with the prototype due to difficulties experienced by Bristol's in getting the specified engines, two turbo-supercharged Hercules VIII radials, right. Pending the eradication of faults, two standard Bristol Hercules IIIs were installed for the maiden flight from Weybridge in September 1941. Test flights up to 30,000 ft were made, though not without difficulty. The main problems were not aerodynamic or mechanical but simply the effects, largely unforeseen, of the intense cold at high altitude with outside air temperatures down to −40°C. At this temperature, which was to be by no means the lowest encountered during trials of the high altitude bomber (−71°C was later to be recorded) oil and grease in the control circuits and hinges for elevators, trimmers, ailerons and rudder, froze solid, making the controls all but immovable. Oil frozen into solid lumps was flung from the propellers; the hydraulics operating bomb doors and the rear turret (the only one fitted) ceased to function. The pilot's dome constantly iced over; the crew door to the capsule also froze solid. (Not that it would have made much difference to the crew had an emergency occurred, for on one test flight ice caused an engine to vibrate so badly the crew prepared to bale out; it took them ten minutes to depressurise the cabin and force open the iced up door, by which time the vibration had lessened and the aircraft was landed safely.) Although

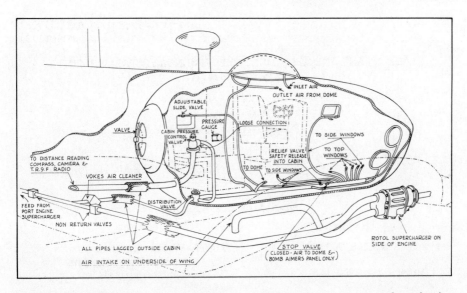

Original A&AEE diagram showing the pressure capsule and the arrangements for maintaining an apparent height of 11,000 ft. The high altitude Wellingtons were among the pioneer multi-seat aircraft to be pressurised.

there were no fatal accidents during the early tests, nevertheless the Wellington Mk V became known to the Vickers test crews at Weybridge as 'the flying coffin'.

A second prototype Mk V, R3299, was completed, powered by two turbocharged Bristol Hercules VIII air cooled radials; this aircraft was subsequently to be tested at Boscombe Down, though it was not to be the first high altitude Wellington at the A&AEE.

The first of the 30 production aircraft ordered in 1940 was W5795, which was completed at Vickers Foxwarren factory. Although ordered as a Mk V, W5795 was completed as the first Mk VI (Type 442). (Only three Mk Vs were to be built: the two prototypes, R3298, '99 and the only production Mk V, W5796, the first of the batch ordered on 1 March 1940. Of these, nine were cancelled and the remaining 19 (W5797–W5815) were completed as Mk VIs.)

The Mk VI, W5795, was the first multi-crew pressurised aircraft to be tested by the A&AEE. Unlike the Bristol engined prototypes, it was powered by two Rolls-Royce Merlin 60 engines, with two-stage superchargers, each offering 1,390 hp for take-off; these engines also had Rotol cabin blowers fitted to pressurise the crew compartment. Reproduced below is the A&AEE report on the handling trials of this interesting aircraft, which made a useful contribution to the then largely uncharted waters of high flight, a commonplace experience for today's package tourist, sipping duty free drinks 10,000 feet above the flights recorded by the A&AEE, under very different circumstances:

105

SECRET

3rd Part of Report No. A.A.E.E/703,h.
24 April 1942

AEROPLANE AND ARMAMENT EXPERIMENTAL ESTABLISHMENT.
BOSCOMBE DOWN.

Wellington VI W.5795.
(2 Merlin 60's.)
Preliminary handling trials.

A.&.A.E.E. Ref:– 4497/-A.M.39/37.

M.A.P. Ref:– Res. Air. 1781/01/D.D/R.D.A.

Progress of issue of report.

Report No.	Title.
1st Part of A.&.A.E.E./703,h.	W.5795 – Weights, Loading data and leading particulars.
2nd Part of A.&.A.E.E./703,h.	W.5795 – Night flying trials.

1.0. Introduction.

This aeroplane is the prototype pressure cabin Wellington fitted with 2-Merlin 60 engines. Apart from the engine installation there are only minor differences between this and the Hercules engined Wellington V. The cabin is of the full pressure type, the maximum differential pressure being about 7 lb./sq.inch, which, if the aeroplane were at 40,000 feet, would give a cabin 'height' of 11,000 feet. At first the engine life was limited to 20 hours but this was subsequently extended to 30 hours; of this period a considerable part was occupied by contractors' trials and wireless equipment tests. The remainder, approximately 10 hours . . . was utilised in handling, night flying and a full performance climb. This report deals with the handling tests made up to date, that is, between February and April 1942.

2.0. Condition of aeroplane relative to tests.

2.1. The initial tests were made with the aeroplane at a light load of approximately 27,700 lb, c.g. 69.0 in. aft of datum; bombs and camera ballast were added until a final weight of 32,325 lb, c.g. 71.4" aft of datum was reached. This weight is over the firm's quoted maximum all-up weight of 32,000 lb, but in fact corresponds to the probable service condition of the aeroplane, viz. pilot, and W/T operator in cabin, rear gunner in turret, full bomb load of 4500 lb, and full fuel and oil. 8750 rounds of ammunition were carried in the rear turret at all times. The design range is from 63.8" to 71.6" aft, u/c down and from 61.7" to 76.1" aft, u/c up.

2.2 The tests were begun with the standard Wellington rudder trimmer of 6⅜ inches chord having a range of 1.6" and 0.2" to left and right respectively. Whilst the tests were in progress, a larger trimmer of 8⅞ inches chord was substituted and the range was increased to 1.9 inches to the left and 0.5 inches to the right. Otherwise the controls and installation were as for the standard Wellington modified to suit the cabin layout. Anti-freezing lubricant to D.T.D.539 specification was used on the ailerons, elevators, rudders and trimmers.

3.0 Description of pressure cabin system.

3.1. The cabin is a parallel-walled chamber of circular cross section, having approximately hemi-spherical dished ends; the total length is about 18 feet and the diameter 5 feet. Entrance to the cabin is through a circular door (3½' dia.) in the aft end, the door being stowed against the starboard side of the fuselage outside the cabin and swung into place by the W/T operator when required. Locking of the door is effected by ensuring that correct register is obtained with the wedge-shaped clamping dogs around the periphery and then rotating the door through about 11½ degrees. A hemi-spherical perspex dome is provided over the pilot's head whilst two circular glass windows are situated at the lower forward part of the nose for the navigator/bomb aimer. In addition a number of smaller perspex windows are provided in the cabin for illumination and navigation purposes. All windows and the dome are of double sheets with an air space between the components.

3.2. The air for the cabin superchargers, which are mounted on the engine, is drawn from intakes situated below the wing at the rear of the engine nacelles; the compressed air pipes from port and starboard sides meet in the fuselage aft of the cabin and the common outlet line is led through an air cleaner to a distributing valve on the cabin floor at the aft end. There are three possible settings of this valve. The normal one delivers all the air to the cabin via the dome, bomb aimer's panel, and the windows. In the event of severe frosting conditions occurring, a small stop valve in the main supply line near the navigator can be closed thus shutting off the supply to the small windows and concentrating all the air on the dome and bomb aimer's panel.

The second valve position is one which feeds all the air to exhaust through the cabin control valve; the pipe connection to the latter is loose fitting and this means that if the control valve is shut and the distributing valve is set to exhaust, the cabin is under pressure without any air being passed to the windows, etc.

The third position, emergency, is intended for use in the event of the cabin being holed at high altitude. Under such circumstances, the supercharger compression ratio would fall and thus in addition to the loss of pressure, the cabin would become exceedingly cold. However, when the distributing valve is set to emergency an artificial back pressure is created on the cabin supercharger by a spring loaded valve, set to about 7½ lb/sq.in., inside the distributing valve proper. This restores the compression ratio to a little above normal and thus warm air is still fed to the cabin in spite of the leaks to atmosphere.

The actual cabin pressure is regulated by manipulating the control valve which passes the overflow air aft to the distant reading compass transmitter, cameras, and radio set. A circular wheel in the cabin door operates another valve which permits direct air connection from cabin to fuselage. This valve is used to let the cabin pressure down when it is desired to open the door.

3.3. *Entry.* The normal method of using the cabin is for the W/T operator, who does all the cabin control work, to shut the main door at a suitable height (say 7000 feet), set the distributing valve to give all air to cabin, shut the auxiliary valve on the main cabin door, and then regulate the cabin pressure by the control valve to maintain the desired altitude pressure inside the cabin. To let the pressure down the control valve and auxiliary door valves are opened and when the pressure difference across the cabin door is small, the latter is opened.

3.4. There are three crew positions in the cabin, viz. W/T operator at the rear, pilot near the centre, and navigator forward. The first two are seated on the port side whilst the navigator's seat is nearer the starboard side. A narrow passage is left along the starboard side.

4.0. Layout of aeroplane.

4.1. Entry to the aeroplane is by a door in the starboard aft side of the fuselage; sundry camera boxes incommode one on entering, but this is not a serious trouble. It is quite easy to walk up the fuselage to the cabin door though once inside the cabin the narrowness of the passage, and number of fittings, make it difficult to move about. All crew positions are rather cramped.

4.2. *View*.   The view on the ground from the pilot's cockpit is good to either quarter, abeam and to the rear, but is blind dead ahead owing to the length of the cabin. No practicable clear view system is provided with the present dome.

4.3. *Controls*.   There are a considerable number of small differences in the layout of the pilot's controls and instruments when compared with the standard Wellington; some of these are of considerable importance.

The engine instruments are now to the left of the blind flying panel; fuel control cocks are on the throttle box; the chassis and flap controls are below the b.f. panel and are too far away to reach with comfort; the throttle levers are longer and to open them fully, the pilot has to lean forward and down and in addition, the back of his hand fouls an electrical switch box during the opening; the emergency hand pump is on the pilot's left instead of right as heretofore and this makes it impossible for any other member of the crew to assist in the laborious process of pumping down the undercarriage; the trimmer box wheels are of a better design but being a little further back are harder to reach. Various electrical switches etc. have been repositioned but these are quite easy to reach. Flowmeters are provided, the dials and by-pass warning lights being to the right of the instrument panel. The blind flying instrument panel is, in relation to the pilot's head, higher and further forward; this constitutes a serious objection particularly when coming in to land with the seat raised to its full extent. Full movement of all flying controls can be obtained when dressed in flying clothing, though it should be noted that as the cabin is warm at all heights additional clothing is not required; observer's type harness is used by all the crew, the packs being stowed outside the cabin in the fuselage. Recommendations have already been made in the 2nd Part of this report, to reposition the chassis and flap controls, cockpit lights, throttle levers, A.S.I. etc., and of the remaining items, the emergency undercarriage lever is the chief one requiring repositioning. (To the right hand side as on normal Wellingtons).

4.4. *Other crew positions*.   The navigator who is situated in the nose, faces to port and has a large chart table folding across one of its diagonals. A periscope protrudes below the aeroplane and is intended to assist in backward searching, but the field and magnification is hardly suitable for this purpose, apart from its indifferent optical quality.

The W/T operator's position is at the rear of the cabin and the layout of his sets appears fairly normal; in addition it is his duty to operate the cabin pressure control valves, door, etc.

A rear gunner may be carried but he is unpressurised and for warmth has to rely upon electrically heated clothing.

4.5. *Escape Facilities*.   These are two exits in the fuselage, the normal entrance door and the bottom escape hatch forward of the door, apart from the emergency escape from the tail turret. With the present pilot's dome which cannot be jettisoned there is no way out from the cabin except through the main door, unless recourse is had to the axe. This could be of no value in flight since the parachutes are stowed outside the pressure cabin. If there is time to prepare for the escape in the event of the aeroplane being lost in the dark and it being necessary to abandon the aeroplane, the process would be the same as in any other aeroplane. A sudden emergency, such as a structural failure is a different proposition entirely. Freedom of movement in the pressure hull is very restricted and the progress of the crew aft must be slow. After emerging from the cabin the crew have to don their parachutes and then make their way further aft to one or other of the exits. The position would be considerably aggravated at height with the cabin pressure on when the crew would have to first fit and turn on their emergency oxygen supply, the W/T operator release the pressure and open the cabin door. Should the door be distorted by gun fire or splinters, the chances of escape would practically vanish.

5.0.   Handling.

5.1. *Taxi-ing.*   The view from the pilot's position is blind over an arc of approximately 15° to either side of dead ahead; the carburettor butterfly valves do not seem to follow the throttle levers very evenly and this tends to make taxi-ing difficult. As mentioned before, the throttle levers should be cranked back to suit small pilots.

5.2. *Take-off.*   As flown initially at a light load of 27,700 lb. (e.g. 69.0″ aft) there was, on opening the throttles, a slight tendency to port by the time the throttles were about ⅓ open. To counteract this swing, full trimmer, full right rudder, and a large differential throttle movement were necessary. At about 60 m.p.h. I.A.S., the port engine was running at + 11 lb/sq. inch boost whilst the starboard engine was indicating +3 lb/sq.in. boost. Not until the aeroplane was airborne was it possible to open the starboard engine up fully.

The load was increased by about 1000 lb. at a time until the aeroplane reached its maximum weight of 32,325 lb. (e.g. 71.4″ aft). In addition the rudder trimmer was increased in chord and range (see 2.2). Under these conditions the swinging tendency was much less than before and it was possible to open the starboard throttle very soon after the port throttle. The aeroplane was taken off and landed on a runway several times and found to be quite reasonable to handle during these processes.

5.3 *Climb.*   The aeroplane is markedly unstable on the climb with maximum engine conditions at 130 m.p.h. I.A.S., (a reasonable climbing speed which has not yet been checked by partial climbs.) At high altitudes, e.g. 30,000 feet, the ailerons and rudders become very stiff but the elevators and trimmers remain reasonably free.

It has been found on several occasions that the propellers tend to 'freeze' in their climbing pitch, the result being that they overspeed considerably on the early part of the descent unless extreme care is exercise. Usually they clear themselves and are behaving normally by about 25,000 feet. Further tests are being made with the thermostatically controlled bleed valves on the propeller.

5.4. *Level.*   The aeroplane is unstable in cruising flight at +4 lb/sq.in. boost, 185 m.p.h. I.A.S., going straight to the stall or dive when disturbed. Also it is extremely difficult to trim and has a more pronounced change of directional trim with speed than any other type of Wellington.

5.5. *Approach and Landing.*   On lowering the flaps the 'nose up' effect is less pronounced than on the normal Wellingtons. The flap indicator gauge cannot be seen comfortably on account of the stick position on the glide and ought to be repositioned. The actual landing is a little more difficult to judge than on a normal aeroplane of its size but once a pilot is familiar with the type this should present no difficulty. No trouble was experienced during the landing run except for the tendency to 'peck' on application of the brakes which is common to all Wellingtons.

6.0.   Single Engine Handling.

Brief handling only has been carried out with one engine throttled and the bulk of this has been at light load using the smaller rudder trimmer. At this weight and maximum cruising power on the live engine (2650, +7) and the propeller on the dead engine in fully coarse pitch it is possible to maintain height for a few minutes, but the foot load even with full trim is so great that the necessary physical effort cannot be sustained. With the starboard engine running and the port throttled, the foot load became excessive at about 140 m.p.h. I.A.S., even with an appreciable degree of bank; the corresponding speed for the port engine running is about 125 m.p.h.

At full load when the larger trimmer was in use, the conclusion reached after a very short test was that whilst it was doubtful whether height could be maintained at maximum cruising power with the 'dead' propeller feathered, the foot load was still very great and is the limiting factor at present.

Should an engine failure occur just after take-off it would be impossible to hold the aeroplane straight on one engine at anything less than 130 m.p.h. I.A.S. It is doubtful whether at speeds less than this the pilot could apply opposite trimmer or throttle back in time to avoid crashing. The general single engine performance of the aeroplane is inferior to that of the Wellington II or III.

7.0.   Miscellaneous Notes.

Most of the points enumerated under this heading have been gathered from a number of flights at light load to about 37,000 feet.

7.1 *Window Misting.*   It is found that the pilot's dome usually remains practically clear whilst the bomb aimer's panel sometimes acquires a light water or slushy condensation on the inside of the inner window. The sextant windows invariably freeze over at about 30,000 feet the part affected being the inner surfaces of the outer window.

7.2 *Engines.*   On the last full load climb, the automatic supercharger change occurred with only a slight shudder at 16,600 feet.

All immersed fuels [immersed fuel pumps] were on at the beginning of this climb but as fuel was streaming in large quantities from the port nacelle tank vent at 16,000 feet, the pumps were turned off for the remainder of the climb. The fuel pressure remained at 7½ lb/sq.inch. on each engine.

The periscope was tried by the observer at 26,000 feet but apart from inspecting the underside of the aeroplane, it was not much use, the vibration causing the ground to appear very blurred.

7.3. *Cabin Pressure.*   No difficulty is experienced in maintaining the cabin at full differential pressure, but it tends to become too warm for comfort. On occasions faulty oil seals in the cabin blower have produced unpleasant oil fumes which became so thick that the crew members could not see each other and were forced to don oxygen equipment to prevent nausea. This trouble is aggravated by the fact that the cabin supercharger tends to run too hot.

7.4 *Rear Turret.*   The rear turret has been operated normally at extreme altitudes but the guns have not functioned satisfactorily, and on most occasions have not fired at all.

7.5. *Pilot's Dome.*   This is the subject of a separate report, but in brief the present non-jettisonable hemi-spherical dome lacking a satisfactory clear view panel is suitable only for good weather conditions.

8.0.   Conclusions:

The handling qualities of the aeroplane at full load with both engines working are acceptable though not completely satisfactory, as the take-off swing is troublesome and the instability is unpleasant. The single engine handling is poor and a more powerful trimmer is required.

The A.S.I. flap indicator, and emergency hand-pump should be repositioned; the throttle levers and undercarriage and flap controls must be made more easy to reach.

A modified type of dome, jettisonable with clear view, should be developed as quickly as possible.

The sextant window de-misting, gun operation, oil fumes in the cabin are all points requiring attention.

The crew emergency escape facilities both in flight and on the ground are unsatisfactory.

The test flights described in that report were made in daylight and the problems of pilot's view through the dome were bad enough then. This was quickly apparent to the A&AEE testers who noted in a separate report:[1]

> The reduced view, together with a much increased tendency to swing on take-off when compared with other Wellington Marks, prompted us to assess at an early date the suitability of the type for night operation.

The night flights were made in the evening of 28 February 1942 during a full moon. There was, however, 10/10 cloud at 1,200 ft and a ground mist which reduced visibility to two miles and deprived the pilot of a horizon. For the night trials W5795 was flown at 28,000 ft (maximum load for type: 32,000 lb). The aircraft was fitted with a beam approach equipment; Boscombe Down airfield used 'Drem' lighting for the runway.

The report from the test pilots following the flights reveals several short-comings, apart from those noted during the daylight trials:

3.2. *Controls.* It is strongly recommended that the throttle levers be cranked back slightly as they are so far away from the pilot that he has to lean well forward and down in order to open them fully for take-off, thus momentarily losing his view – a very bad feature.

Similarly the undercarriage control is too far forward to reach without depriving the pilot of his view, whilst the safety catch is so far out of reach that it must be put to OFF before opening up to take-off. These undercarriage controls must be brought more within the pilot's reach.

3.3 *View.* The view from the pilot's dome, though not good, is adequate for take-off and landing in good weather conditions with an experienced night flying pilot. In bad weather during daylight however, it has been found that the dome becomes seriously obscured by rain and the difficulties of night flying would be aggravated considerably by such weather conditions.

3.4. *Lighting.* Lights in the cockpit cause serious reflections inside the dome and should be cut down to the minimum and shielded so that as little light as possible reaches the dome. In particular, the indicator lights which show whether the flowmeter is by-passed or not, must be provided with a switch in order that they can be turned off; the red chassis lights cause troublesome reflections even when dimmed and it is recommended that they be arranged to go out when the undercarriage is locked up.

The panel light for the top left corner of the dashboard and the lights for the pilot's switch panel on the starboard side of the cabin could be mounted, with advantage, on small universal joints to increase their range of movement.

The compass light, which is controlled by the same dimmer switch as the dashboard light, must be re-arranged as at present it scarcely illuminates its objective but directs a strong reflection from the compass glass into the pilot's eyes.

It was found to be very difficult to adjust either the trimmers before take-off or the blind approach controls, and it is strongly recommended that some form of lighting be provided on the pilot's left side for this purpose.

The landing lights were switched on once but owing to the reflection from the ground haze had to be turned off almost immediately; no comments on their effectiveness under normal conditions can be given.

3.5. *Instruments:* In this aeroplane the pilot's head is so high in relation to the instrument panel especially when landing with the seat fully up, that to see instruments placed at the top of the panel is extremely difficult. It is absolutely essential therefore

111

that the air speed indicator be placed where it is easily seen, i.e. at the bottom of the panel and not at the top, above the altimeter, as at present. The altimeter may be placed at the top without causing any difficulty.

4. Conclusions.

4.1. Subject to the lighting and instrument positions being rectified, normal flight and landing should present no undue difficulty in fair weather to an experienced night flying pilot. Under conditions of bad visibility, landing by night with the existing dome would be hazardous.

The shortcomings of the hemispherical pilot's dome as fitted to both the Mk V and VI high altitude Wellington prototypes was strongly criticised during day and night flying as 'giving an inadequate view in all conditions and became particularly bad in rain'.[2] The problem of rain on the dome was such that 'it is almost impossible to see forward . . . as the particles of rain obscure the perspex very badly. . .'.

Moreover, unlike practically all contemporary military aircraft, the Mk VI Wellington lacked a 'clear vision' panel which could be opened when landing in the event of the windscreen being obscured by rain or oil. The pressure dome had been designed to open a small amount by tilting it about the hinges on the left hand side, in order to give a clear view to starboard but, not unreasonably, the Boscombe Down test pilots complained that:

It [the dome] cannot be opened as designed because in attempting to do so, the dome comes out of its trunnions and cannot be closed owing to distortion. If the opening process is continued too far, the dome is liable to fly off. Furthermore, when it is opened the air [and the rain] blows directly on the pilot's face.

In view of the A&AEE findings, Vickers provided a modified dome fitted to the Hercules engined 1st prototype Mk V, R3298, which was tested at the A&AEE on 22–23 February 1942.

The modified dome differed from the original unsatisfactory one only in that in plan it was elliptical, not circular, though in transverse cross-section it was semi-circular. Although the sealing was slightly different, the unsatisfactory clear vision arrangements were the same as the first type of dome: the hood tilted to starboard and the pilot was expected to fly the aircraft peering through the resultant wedge of clear view to port. No air deflector was fitted.

After testing the modified dome, the pilots at Boscombe Down reported[3] that:

When closed the view forward and downward to the left is very much improved as compared with the original dome and in this position can be considered reasonable. Owing to the short stay of the aeroplane [R3298] at the Establishment it could not be tested in rain, but as the direct vision opening was the same as the previous one, little improvement could be expected in this respect.

The modified dome was only an interim measure, for the Royal Aircraft Establishment (RAE) was testing the final dome, the type 'D', attached to a Mk V Wellington cabin in a wind tunnel at Farnborough. The A&AEE report[4] summarised the findings of the RAE's wind tunnel tests which took place on 12 April 1942:

It is similar to the modified dome [as on R3298] . . . but an external deflector plate was fitted to the cabin outside the dome, extending from the forward

centre line round the starboard side. An inner skirting piece was fitted extending from just forward of the port beam to the rear; thus the clear view opening
was about ¼ of the circumference, positioned on the port bow. At 130 mph
airspeed with water injected into the air stream, a certain amount of air and
water entered through the opening but did not trouble the pilot as most of it
impinged upon his left shoulder [!].

At the maximum possible opening the clear view was considered
adequate and the amount of air and water entering was not regarded as
excessive.

The report concluded that, in addition, 'a jettisoning arrangement is essential'.

After the 'dome' reports, the Merlin 60-powered first production Mk VI,
W5795, was subjected to a full load climb test.[5] The aircraft took off at 32,500 lb
with maximum fuel and a 4,500 lb bomb load. The crew of four included an
A&AEE flight observer. The 'service ceiling', i.e. rate of climb of to 100 ft/min
(sea level climb being 940 ft/min), was established as 30,800 ft. The crew estimated the absolute ceiling to be 31,800 ft. At altitude the pilot encountered
difficulties with the propellers tending to freeze up. The subsequent A&AEE
report[6] on the flight concluded that: 'The climb performance of this aeroplane is
disappointing in view of its intended role as a high altitude bomber.'

In an attempt to improve the poor climb of the first Mk VI, W5795 had its
'standard' Wellington wingspan of 86 ft 2 inches increased by the addition of six
foot extensions.

On 12 July 1942 the aircraft took off from Boscombe Down at 1630 for a climb
to its ceiling, followed by level speed assessment. The pilot was Sqn. Ldr. C. C.
Colmore; his crew consisted of an A&AEE civilian technical observer, Mr. C. V.
Abbot. There were also on board an RAF navigator, wireless operator and a rear
gunner. After a normal take-off, nothing was heard from the Wellington which,
under the strict wartime radio silence orders, aroused no undue alarm. At 1940
hours, eye witnesses at Spondon in Derbyshire, 130 miles north of Boscombe
Down, saw an aircraft dive to earth from 'a great height'; the dive was at high
speed, the aircraft breaking up before hitting the ground. The aircraft was the
Wellington VI, W5795: there were no survivors. The cause of the crash was never
established but the time the eyewitnesses reported seeing the aircraft was consistent with the Wellington being at its briefed ceiling of 35,000 ft.[7]

Despite the crash, Mk VI production continued and the first batch of 27
aircraft, W5798–5815 and DR471–479, was completed during 1942. All of these
were Mk VIA: Mk V airframes converted on the production lines to Mk VI
standard with Merlin 60s in place of the designed Hercules VIIIs. One of these
aircraft, W5801, subsequently came to Boscombe Down for trials with a Sperry
bombsight.

The production of true Wellington Mk VIs continued, 35 being completed.

Two of the early aircraft, DR482 and '484, were to be evaluated at Boscombe
Down between December 1942 and January 1943.

DR484 was the first to be reported on by the A&AEE when 'Brief performance
trials and estimate of range' were made. This Wellington was one of only two
sub-variants of the basic Mk VI with the Vickers type number 431, being
pre-production prototypes equipped with 4,000 lb 'cookie' bomb gear. The nose
shape was altered from the earlier aircraft to allow for a forward escape hatch

from the pressure cabin, possibly as a consequence of the A&AEE report on the 1st prototype and its subsequent fatal crash. The unpressurised rear turret was regarded as impractical and had been removed and the tail faired over. The tailplane of DR484 was a Wellington 'Ic' type which was slightly smaller than standard. The revised 'D' or RAE tested elliptical pilot's dome was fitted. The engines were two Rolls-Royce Merlin 62s[9] with Rotol cabin superchargers.

In an attempt to improve the climb and ceiling, the aircraft was to be tested at a lower weight than the prototype Mk VI, W5795, the A&AEE report[10] stating:

> The aircraft is intended to be flown operationally at an all up weight of 28,440 lb corresponding to a load of 2,500 lb of bombs, 49 gallons of oil and 570 gallons of petrol.
>
> *Climb performance.* The maximum rate of climb was 1,300 ft/min at ground level. The service ceiling was found to be 34,000 ft and the time to this height on a full throttle climb is 50 minutes.

The best climbing speed was determined at 105 mph IAS below 30,000 ft but this was considered to be too low for prudent operational flying, the recommended climbing speed was 120 mph to 8,000 ft, decreasing to 100 mph up to 26,000 ft and as low as 90 mph at and above 32,000 ft. It was estimated that an operational altitude of 37,000 ft was possible over a target 400 miles from base. The test pilots reported that 'at this height the aircraft will be very tiring and perhaps difficult to handle'.

The maximum level speeds obtained on DR484 were:

MS gear at 11,400 ft: 376 mph TAS
FS gear at 32,000 ft: 300 mph TAS

The minimum comfortable speed when flying for maximum range was 115 mph IAS at 2,380 rpm −0.35 lb/sq inch boost; at 34,000 ft under those conditions the aircraft was estimated to have a fuel consumption of 2.4 air miles per gallon, which was approximately equal to a still air range of 1,100 miles.

The handling trials were the subject of a separate A&AEE report,[11] the aircraft being in the same condition as for the previous climb and range tests. The equivalent cabin height of 11,000 ft was easily maintained; the cabin heat was such that:

> no extra clothing, except for flying boots, was needed even for prolonged flight above 30,000 ft. The only difficulty met with was the closing of the [pressure] cabin door. The rim of the cabin on which the door closes is in such a position that mud and dirt collect very quickly from the feet of anyone entering the cabin. Considerable difficulty was encountered by an experienced man closing the door without assistance on the ground. . . .
>
> At 10,000 ft it was impossible for one man alone . . . to close the door. Thus it was necessary to close the door on the ground but leave the pressure control valve . . . open until pressurising was required.

The new forward escape hatch was thought to be large enough for crew men with chest (observer type) parachutes to be able to pass through, though in an actual emergency, it was considered that: 'the pilot and wireless operator would definitely have difficulty in getting forward owing to the restricted width of the passage [in the pressure cabin]'.

It would seem that the Mk VI was not a pleasant aircraft to fly, certainly not at 34,400 ft; the pilots at Boscombe Down, who were after all among the best and most experienced available, found that DR484, even flying level at that altitude, was:

> extremely tiring, for the pilot has no opportunity to rest . . . when the physical strain of the climb is taken into account it is probable that an operational pilot may find it necessary to cruise at 32,000 ft.

Although official interest in the Wellington Mk VI was by January 1943 waning, one further trial of the type was undertaken at Boscombe Down when DR482 was briefly tested.[12] This aircraft was similar to DR484 but had Merlin 60s and still retained a Frazer Nash four .303-inch rear gun turret. It achieved an absolute ceiling of 31,400 ft; time to service ceiling of 30,400 ft: 78 minutes. Maximum level speed at 31,000 ft was 271 mph.

The A&AEE undertook no further trials on the high altitude Wellington. By the time, early 1943, that the Mk VI was nearing operational status, the de Havilland Mosquito was showing a far greater high altitude capability, even the early unpressurised aircraft being able to fly at over 36,000 ft and to *cruise* at 340 mph. That was only the beginning: the Mk XVI Mosquito with a pressure cabin would lift 4,000 lb of bombs, the same as the Wellington Mk VI, but with a service ceiling of 36,000 ft and a maximum speed of 415 mph at 28,000 ft.

Of the 132 High Altitude Wellingtons originally ordered, only 64 were completed, none of which operated in the intended role; most were used as test aircraft or trainers for the radar bomber guidance system 'Oboe' with the highly secret No. 109 Squadron, based at Stradishall. One production Mk VI, W5801, is reported to have flown over enemy territory during the 'Oboe' test programme; if so, it is the only high flying Wellington to have done so.

Although never operational, the Mk VIs gave Vickers, Rolls-Royce and the A&AEE invaluable experience in high altitude flying which was to prove useful in the development of the pressurised Spitfire VI, built to intercept another high flier – the German Junkers Ju 86P.

CHAPTER SEVEN

Special Requirements

Spoils of War

Every aircraft type which saw service with the RAF and Fleet Air Arm (and some which did not) was, at one time or another, test flown at Boscombe Down. Strangely perhaps, very few of the many captured airworthy German aircraft came to the A&AEE, the reason being that a special enemy aircraft unit was formed at Duxford which evaluated these aircraft and flew them in a 'circus' which toured RAF bases for recognition and air tactics flights. However, at least one Me 109E-3 *was* test flown at Boscombe Down; this aircraft had been captured by the French and flown to England just before the Dunkirk evacuation. It was at the A&AEE for handling trials[1] early in June 1940. Since this is the earliest official British evaluation of the Luftwaffe fighter that was soon to oppose the Spitfires and Hurricanes during the Battle of Britain, it is here reproduced at length.

SECRET   Report A.&.A.E.E./755
                                                10th June 1940

AEROPLANE AND ARMAMENT EXPERIMENTAL ESTABLISHMENT
BOSCOMBE DOWN.

A.&.A.E.E. Ref: S.4487/38-A.S.66
A.M. Ref:-S.B.5860/R.D.T.4.

Messerschmidt† 109 Fighter.
Brief Handling Trials.

1.   *Cockpit.*

1.1 *Ease of entry and comfort.*   The cockpit is easy to enter but is rather cramped for a large pilot. The rudder pedals are not adjustable by the pilot but can be moved forward or backward by the rigger over a range of about two inches. They can only just be reached by a small pilot. The coupe‡ touches the head of a normal pilot when the seat is in the raised position. A tall pilot has to bend his neck even when the seat is in its lowest position. There is little noise when the hood is closed even when the side panels are open. The cockpit is very warm and the ventilation appears to be adequate.

1.2 *View.*   There is a blind area straight forward and this extends to about 20 degrees to either side of the nose when the aeroplane is on the ground. There is a

† As spelt in original.   ‡ Canopy.

D.V.* panel situated on the left hand side of the sighting panel. This is very easy to operate and allows the pilot a reasonable view to the left forward. There is no draught and little noise when the panel is open. It is of a good size and it is not necessary for the pilot to lean to one side in order to see through it.

1.3 *Seat adjustment and straps.* The straps are of the usual Continental pattern and are readily adjustable to fit various sized pilots. The seat can be lowered or raised by means of a lever situated on the left hand side of the seat.

1.4 *Brakes.* The brakes are operated by the toes as were the brakes on the 'Fury'.† Originally the brakes were difficult to operate, but wooden blocks have been added to raise the pedals and these are better but the braking system is not considered as good as the hand operated system. There is no locking device for parking.

1.5 *Controls.* All controls work with very little friction on the ground and there is no play. Longitudinal trim is effected by means of a movable tail-plane. The actuating wheel for this is positioned on the left hand side of the cockpit. It is easy to operate, does not slip, and can be moved over the whole range in about 18 seconds. Neither rudder bias nor aileron bias is supplied. The throttle box is not elaborate consisting only of the throttle lever and a butterfly nut for preventing slip. There is no mixture control lever. The engine mixture is controlled automatically by an aneroid. The V.D.M. airscrew control is easy to operate and does not slip. The flaps are controlled mechanically by a hand wheel and on the flaps themselves are markings which can be seen by the pilot. They are marked from zero to 40 degrees (fully down) in tens of degrees. On the lower right hand side of the dashboard is the undercarriage control. To the left are indicator lights while on the right is a mechanical indicator. The control is satisfactory and throws out after the operation is completed. The engine has two injector pumps and a control allows the pilot to use either pump or both. The radiator flaps are controlled by an arm on the right hand side of the cockpit. Each radiator flap has an indicator which protrudes through the wing. A further control which is unique inasmuch as it has not been seen before in this country is one which retards the ignition for the express purpose of heating the engine cylinders so as to burn oil off the sparking plugs if they should become oiled up. . . .

1.6 *Instruments.* The gauges and instruments are well marked and easily read. The oil and petrol pressure gauges have maximum and minimum markings. The compass is similar to the P.3. and is situated at the top of the instrument panel. The sole aid to cloud flying consists of an American-type turn-and-bank indicator.

1.7 *Illumination.* No night flying was carried out so it is not known what the cockpit illumination is like.

1.8 *Emergency exits.* For exit in the air the coupe hood can be jettisoned by pulling a single lever on the left hand side of the hood. There is no strong-point to support the aeroplane in the event of overturning on the ground and it is considered that a pilot would have great difficulty in extricating himself in that case since the rudder is very small and the hood would be on or very near the ground.

2.0 *Handling and flying qualities.*

2.1 *Ground handling.* Except for the poor visibility and the rather unsatisfactory brakes, taxiing presents no difficulties. The undercarriage is good and there is no tendency for the tail to lift when the brakes are full on.

2.2 *Take-off and initial climb.* There is a slight tendency to swing right on take-off and this changes to a tendency to swing left immediately the aeroplane is in the air.

---

* Direct Vision. † The 1931/9 Hawker Fury biplane fighter.

Both these tendencies are easily overcome by use of rudder. The tail comes up quickly and the forward view is then satisfactory. The undercarriage can be raised as soon as the aeroplane is off the ground and this operation has no noticeable effect on trim. The undercarriage retracts outwards and upwards and the whole operation takes about 8 seconds. The best speed for raising the flaps is about 125 m.p.h. A.S.I.R.

2.3 *Controls in level flight.* All controls are light, quick in response, and effective up to a speed of 250 m.p.h. after which they become extremely heavy. This is particularly so in the case of the elevator which is out of harmony with the other controls to start with, being noticeably heavier, and in the dive it becomes almost immovable. It is to be particularly stressed that the controls of this aeroplane are pleasantly light at all speeds up to about 250 m.p.h. and they then appear to tighten up very suddenly so that, as stated above, at high speeds they are practically immovable. It has been stated by experienced pilots who have flown this aeroplane that, in the event of attack from behind made by the M.E. 109, the attack can be easily broken off by the attacked by pulling up fairly quickly from a dive. The pilot of the M.E. 109 would never be able to recover quickly enough to follow owing to the heaviness of the controls.

2.4 *Stability.* The aeroplane is laterally, directionally, and longitudinally stable. The degree of directional and longitudinal stability is considered to be too high at normal speeds for a fighter but at high speeds the aeroplane becomes longitudinally neutrally stable. No tests were made to record phugoids.

2.5 *Control and stability at the stall.*
The stalling speed with flaps and undercarriage up is   130 KPH
                                                           (81 m.p.h.)
                                                           A.S.I.R.
The stalling speed with flaps and undercarriage down is 100 KPH
                                                           (62 m.p.h.)
                                                           A.S.I.R.
The aeroplane was not put through all the tests called for in A.D.M293 but the following remarks apply to the general behaviour of the aeroplane at the stall.

At the approach to the stall the left wing tends to drop and the control column has to be moved to the right. The nose also tends to turn to the left so that some right rudder has to be applied. The stall occurs with the control column just aft of the central position. Warning is given by a fore and aft pitching and a noticeable high rate of descent. If the control column is not moved from the above position the left wing drops followed by the nose. If the control column is pulled right back and rudder is applied to stop the turn, the aeroplane falls into a spin.

2.6 *Approach and landing.* The best gliding speed has been found to be 93 m.p.h. This is a little fast but is the best because the airspeed indicator is not well marked at the lower end of the scale and it is therefore easier to hold the higher speed constant. The aeroplane is easy to land. The attitude on the ground is steeper than most monoplanes, being comparable to a biplane. The ground run was not measured but did not appear to be unusually long and was estimated to be about the same as the Hurricane and Spitfire. There is no tendency to swing after landing. If the engine is opened up with the flaps and undercarriage set for landing the aeroplane becomes tail-heavy but can be held until retrimmed and climbs away satisfactorily.

3.0 *Aerobatics.*

3.1 *Loops.* It is impossible to execute a loop in the normal manner due to the heaviness and ineffectiveness of the elevator. If a normal loop is attempted, the aeroplane flicks over on the top of the loop. The only way in which a loop can be done is by winding the tail trim back. Even then great care must be taken to ensure that the aeroplane does not flick out of the loop on the top.

3.2 *Slow-rolls.*   It is very easy to slow-roll the aeroplane at speeds up to 250 m.p.h. but at higher speeds the controls are so heavy that difficulty is experienced. A great deal of rudder has to be used in the rolls and this is unusual in the modern fighter. Very tight rolls can be executed at speeds up to 190 m.p.h. Slight snatching of the ailerons is noticeable in rolls at speeds of 185–220 K.P.H.

3.3 *Half roll off a loop.*   This manoeuvre is difficult for the same reason as given in 3.1 above. When rolling off to the left the aeroplane has to be checked as it tends to flick out in the opposite direction. To the right the difficulty is overcoming a tendency towards a high-speed stall. Provided the control column is eased forward, however, the manoeuvre can be completed successfully.

4.0   *Summary of flying qualities.*

General reports on the handling of the aeroplane which were received before the arrival of the aeroplane itself led one to believe that numerous faults existed but these have been found to be untrue. The aeroplane is pleasant to fly at speeds up to 250 m.p.h. the only objection being the lack of space in the cockpit. This objection is a very real one in the case of a large pilot.

At speeds in excess of 250 m.p.h. the controls suddenly become very heavy and at 400 m.p.h. recovery from a dive is difficult because of the heaviness of the elevator. This heaviness of the elevator makes all manoeuvres in the looping plane above 250 m.p.h. difficult, including steep climbing turns. No difference was experienced between climbing turns to right and left.

In general flying qualities the aeroplane is inferior to both the Spitfire and the Hurricane at all speeds and in all conditions of flight. It does not possess the control which allows of good quality flying and this is particularly noticeable in aerobatics.

The A&AEE trials of the Me 109 were conducted by test pilots of the Establishment; the above report is dated 10 June 1940. On 9 June, the same aircraft was flown in mock combat against a Spitfire and Hurricane. The 109 was flown by Wing Cdr. G. H. Stainforth.[2] Although the report[3] of the trials is from a source other than the A&AEE archive, the dates suggest that the flight could have taken place from Boscombe Down.

INVESTIGATION OF TURNING CIRCLES OF M.E.109
SPITFIRE AND HURRICANE

A statement has been made that the M.E.109 is now turning inside the Hurricane in combat. It has also been suggested that this may be due to the fact that German pilots are able to withstand more high G.

Intention

To fly these fighters against each other under controlled conditions, recording accelerometers to be fitted to all aircraft, and pilot's accelerometers fitted for use of pilot.

Rudder modifications have been carried out on Spitfire and Hurricane to enable pilot to assume crouched position and so prevent 'blacking out'.

Programme

1. M.E.109 (W/C. Stainforth) to fly at 5000 ft. at three speeds 160, 200 and 240 m.p.h. Hurricane to start at same height 180° away from M.E.109 on same circle. Recording accelerometers to be run during high G part of turn for each of the 3 phases. Hurricane to choose his speed near those of the M.E.109 (±20 m.p.h.).

119

2. M.E.109 v Spitfire.
(Same conditions).

3. Hurricane v Spitfire.
(Same conditions).

4. Test of modified seating in Hurricane and Spitfire.

Pilots to fly at steady 6G in crouched position at 220–240 m.p.h. and report visual disturbance (if any).

Note

Crouching should raise the blacking out threshold by 1.5 to 2G.

REPORT ON INVESTIGATION OF TURNING CIRCLES OF M.E.109, SPITFIRE AND HURRICANE

by

Wing Commander G. H. STAINFORTH

1. I was flying at 2000 metres at 160, 200 and 240 m.p.h. In each case the Hurricane started behind the Messerschmitt and the Messerschmitt went into the turns as quickly as possible and tried to out-turn the Hurricane on the level or slight downward spiral at about 3–4G. Tightening up beyond a certain point resulted in the slots* opening unevenly and lateral flicking and slowing down of the rate of turn. The maximum rate of turn was obtained with the slots just about opening, either both just closed or both just open, and at the maximum rate of turn the Hurricane remained close to my tail. In each case the throttle was opened fully after the turn was started and for one or two turns the airscrew pitch was set to give 2600–2700 r.p.m., i.e. 11.30 on the clock-pace pitch indicator, as for take-off.

2. I then started two or three more runs on the tail of the Hurricane, and was out-turned within about one complete turn. Attempts were made to fly straight away in order to leave the Hurricane far enough behind to turn round quickly, gaining height to make an attack before the Hurricane was close enough to turn on to my tail; but this took too long, as the Messerschmitt only gained about one mile in about 30 miles and so the turn was made too close, with the result that the Hurricane succeeded in getting on my tail straight away.

3. The Messerschmitt appears to be only slightly faster than the Hurricane; in fact the Hurricane was not apparently flying at full throttle.

4. These runs were then repeated in exactly the same way against the Spitfire as follows:–

1, 2 and 3 at 160, 220 and 240 m.p.h.

We then repeated the first run with the Messerschmitt starting on the Spitfire's tail but the Spitfire out-turned the Messerschmitt almost as easily as the Hurricane did. A converging attack was then made, each aircraft attempting to get on the other's tail. The result was the same, the Spitfire quickly gaining the advantage and getting on the tail of the Messerschmitt. Increasing the speed in a downward spiral would not have had any advantage as the opposing aircraft would also have done the same. The rate of

* Automatic slots fitted to the leading edge of the wings.

turn obtained was the maximum possible in every case. The effect of putting flaps down about 10° was tried but this had little, if any, effect.

5. It was found that if an attempt was made (a) to dive on the opposing aircraft at high speed, pulling up at it when it started the turn, or (b) an attempt to dive away from it in trying to escape, and then pulling up to turn round at it was made, the slots would open singly even at very high speeds, with the result that the aircraft did a violent flick, almost on its back, and a spiral dive.

6. Water temperature remained very high during these tests – over 120°C.

7. Although the aileron control was very good up to moderate speeds – the aircraft is generally extremely unmanoeuvrable owing to –

- (a) Its large turning circle.
- (b) Impossibility of tightening up the turn, owing to the uneven opening of slots, and the tendency of the wings to stall unevenly, resulting in flick, and the slowing down of the rate of turn.
- (c) Extremely heavy aileron control at high speed.

8. No advantage was found in attempting to flick during the turn in order to turn 180° rapidly (with slight loss of height, the object being to pull up from underneath the opponent from a favourable position) because a tight pull-up could not be done for the reasons described above.

9. The pilot of the Spitfire reports that he had no difficulty in 'sitting on' the Messerschmitt's tail, but could, in fact, have tightened up his turn quite a lot more and got well on the inside. He was at +5 boost – almost full throttle.

9th June, 1940

A series of comparative Spitfire/Me 109 flights also took place with the same Messerschmitt later (July 1940) at the RAE Farnborough, when the pilots were G. H. Stainforth and Stanford-Tuck.

With only the evidence of the two reports on the relative merits of the Hurricane, Spitfire and Me 109, one might come to the conclusion that the German fighter was not really such a very difficult proposition for RAF pilots. During the Battle of Britain, the Me 109 was to prove superior to the Hurricane and very evenly matched with the Spitfire I. It is true that during wars, human nature being what it is, the evaluation of the enemy's weapons tends to be perhaps subject to prejudice and a little less objective than if, say, comparing two fighters of the same country. The Luftwaffe evaluated, at about the same time, a captured airworthy Spitfire I and a Hurricane which were duly test flown in mock combat against an Me 109E. The test pilot, Hauptmann Werner Mölders, even at that early stage of the war an 'ace', reported, as quoted by Alfred Price in his authoritative book *Spitfire*:[4]

It is very interesting to carry out the flight trials at Rechlin* with the Spitfire and Hurricane. Both types are very simple to fly compared with our aircraft, and childishly easy to take off and land. The Hurricane is very good-natured ... but its performance is decidedly inferior to that of the Me 109. ...

* Roughly the German equivalent of RAE Farnborough.

The Spitfire is one class better. It handles well, is light on the controls, faultless in the turn and has a performance approaching that of the Me 109. As a fighting aircraft, however, it is miserable. . . .

One wonders if that view of the Spitfire, written before the Battle of Britain, was the one held after, for as Alfred Price pointed out:[5]

When the crunch came . . . during the Battle of Britain in the late summer of 1940, most of the fighter v fighter combats took place at altitudes between 13,000 and 20,000 feet. . . . In that height band the performances of the Spitfire I and the Messerschmitt 109E were rather more equal than either nation's trial had suggested.

Including the Kitchen Sink

The test flying of captured enemy aircraft was one of the more unusual tasks undertaken during the war years at Boscombe Down but perhaps *the* most unusual was concerned in part with the performance of a kitchen sink.

The sink in question was no ordinary appliance but a Very Special Sink fitted to a Very Special Avro York, LV633, the acceptance trials of which, sink included, were the subject of an A&AEE report.[6]

To begin at the beginning: there was, during the war, a general agreement that the Americans would manufacture Allied transport aircraft, the British industry concentrating on combat and trainer machines. This was, by and large, the case but by the time the Lancaster had gone into service, the Experimental Department of Avro's, at the instigation of Roy Chadwick, decided to utilise the tail unit, wings, power plants and undercarriage of the Lancaster, married to a capacious rectangular fuselage which had twice the cubic capacity of the Lancaster, to form a high wing monoplane transport: the Avro Type 685, later to be named York.

The project had no official backing – it is doubtful if its existence was admitted, certainly in the early stages of construction. Because of the large number of standard Lancaster parts and fittings incorporated, the prototype York, LV626, was completed and test flown by 5 July 1942 – only five months after the decision to construct it had been made. The performance of the prototype was good enough for its existence to be made known and for the Air Ministry to place a development contract for three further prototypes. The first, LV626, after its early flight trials with Avro's, was tested at Boscombe Down; but it is the acceptance trial of the third prototype, LV633, which is the more interesting, for this aircraft, unlike its fellows which were being completed to a very low order of urgency, was the subject of a greatly upgraded priority, for it had been selected to be used as the personal transport of no less a person than the Prime Minister, Winston Churchill.

LV633, to be named *Ascalon**, was fitted out, by wartime standards, to quite a high degree of comfort, the accommodation including two cabins, bedroom, a conference room, toilet and galley – which brings us to the kitchen sink, the A&AEE report finding that, when airborne: 'water, instead of draining from the sink, was blown upwards in a fine spray when the plug was removed.'

* *Ascalon* was the name of the spear with which St. George slew the dragon.

Clearly unacceptable. The A&AEE boffins considered the problem to be essentially aerodynamic; the offending drain was a simple pipe which ran from the kitchen sink to a point outside the York into the slipstream beneath the fuselage. It is not recorded if a wind tunnel was resorted to but a complete cure to the reverse flow sink was effected by simply cutting the outside end of the drainpipe at an angle of 45°.

There was a secondary problem with the washbasin in the dressing room, Compartment H. When the plug was removed: 'there is a loud whistle from the wash basin'. It seems the occupant had to live with that one.

The aircraft's unexpected, and to some extent embarrassing, high priority had resulted in a lack of time for refinement, which caused the A&AEE to criticise other points: for example the desk in the private cabin – Churchill's – 'had a lock of the type that can be opened with almost any key'.

The Boscombe Down trial raised another point which might well have caused *Ascalon*'s illustrious passenger more immediate concern than the lack of security of his desk; it was put as follows:

> One small but possibly important point was that from Compartment 'G' [Churchill's bedroom] a very good view was obtained of the flexing in flight of the cover plate over the wing joint. On the Lancaster the amount of flexing on the plate has alarmed even experienced operational crews.

Even the experienced crews of the A&AEE found that, in addition to the disquieting view from the bedroom, the noise level of the York was 'in general excessive, such that continued conversation is tiring'. The sole exception appeared to be the dressing room, Compartment H, which was considered to be 'satisfactory', apart from the aforementioned whistling washbasin.

The first prototype York, LV626, had a standard Lancaster tail unit with the familiar twin fins. The third, *Ascalon*, as tested at Boscombe Down, had been fitted with an additional third fin on the fuselage centre line *à la* Manchester, as were all subsequent production Yorks. This fin, which had presumably been added to give improved directional stability to the rather slab-sided design, was considered also to reduce the rolling tendency which was apparent on the prototype when flown in rough weather. However, when LV633 was flown in really bumpy conditions: 'It is considered that passengers in the rear compartment might easily suffer from air sickness'. While on that delicate subject, it should be noted that 'The cold air ventilation system appeared to be adequate'.

Since the unpressurised aircraft could operate up to 11,000 ft, the cold air ventilation would be distinctly fresh but comprehensive cabin heating was also installed with no fewer than fourteen outlets, including 'at the base of the settee in the main cabin ... at head level in the sleeping compartment and in the aft washroom at the wash basin'. To reinforce the local heating arrangements, Boscombe Down recommended that electric points should be provided at all the bunks, especially in the private cabin – Churchill's – 'so that an electric warming pad could be plugged in'.

When one considers that this aircraft was constructed in haste in a factory geared for the exclusive production of bombers, which do not, in the nature of things, require the workforce to include skilled cabinet makers and upholsterers, the standard achieved by Avro's in fitting out *Ascalon* was fairly good – a point the A&AEE report concedes; nevertheless it concluded that:

GENERAL SUMMARY OF EQUIPMENT AND LOCATION DIAGRAM

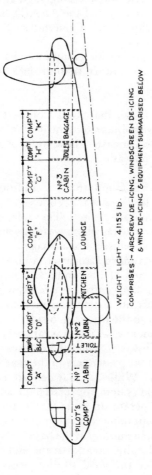

WEIGHT LIGHT ~ 41155 lb.

COMPRISES :- AIRSCREW DE-ICING, WINDSCREEN DE-ICING & WING DE-ICING & EQUIPMENT SUMMARISED BELOW

PILOT'S COMPARTMENT
- FLYING INSTRUMENTS
- INSPECTION LAMP &
- CONTROL LOCKING GEAR
- RADIO COMPLETE (TR1154/5 TR1196, R1124 & 5)
- 2 HAND FIRE EXTINGUISH
- STOWAGE FOR SPARE VALVES
- 1 AXE
- NAVIGATORS FLYING
- 2 ANGLE POISE LAMPS
- INSTRUMENT PANEL
- STOWAGE FOR PENCILS ETC
- 1 PERSPEX STOWAGE
- AIR POSITION INDICATOR
- 1 SIGNAL PISTOL & CART'S
- AIR MILEAGE UNIT
- 2 CUPBOARDS UNDER
- DRIFT METER
- NAVIGATOR'S POSITION
- SEXTANT DOME
- 4 PORTABLE OXYGEN &
- SIGNALLING LAMP
- STOWAGES
- ASTROGRAPH
- 4 OXYGEN ECONOMISERS
- ASTRO COMPASS
- 6 SEA MARKERS &
- FLARE CHUTE
- STOWAGE
- AUTO CONTROLS

Nº 1 CABIN
- 2 BUNKS 5/w MATTRESSES
- ESCAPE LADDER IN ROOF
- 8 HEAT REGULATORS
- 4 SETS CURTAINS
- 3 ROOF LIGHTS
- 4 OXYGEN ECONOMISERS

Nº 3 CABIN
- ENTRANCE HANDRAIL &
- CURTAIN
- 2 HAND FIRE EXTINGUISH
- 2 ROOF LIGHTS
- 1 BUNK 5/w MATTRESS
- 1 HEAT REGULATOR
- OXYGEN GAUGE
- 1 TABLE & CHAIR
- BELL SWITCH FOR STEWARD
- LAMP ON WALL
- 2 SETS CURTAINS
- 1 OXYGEN ECONOMISER
- 1 CURTAIN (WARDROBE)

FWD. TOILET
- 2 TIP-UP WASH BASINS
- 2 MIRRORS
- 2 SHELVES WITH RAILS
- 2 GLASS HOLDERS
- 2 TOILET ROLL HOLDERS
- 2 HAND RAILS
- 2 ELSANS
- 2 LEATHERETTE BAGS
- 2 OXYGEN ECONOMISERS
- 2 ROOF LIGHTS
- 2 CURTAINS & RAILS

Nº 2 CABIN
- ESCAPE LADDER IN ROOF
- 4 BUNKS 5/w MATTRESSES
- 8 HEAT REGULATORS
- 1 CURTAIN & RAIL
- 3 HAND RAILS
- 3 ROOF LIGHTS
- STOWAGE ENTRANCE
- STOWAGE WITH 5 SHELVES
- 1 OXYGEN REGULATOR & GAUGE

AFT TOILET
- 1 ELSAN
- 1 TOILET ROLL HOLDER
- 1 OXYGEN ECONOMISER
- SINK & 5 DRAWERS
- TOWEL RAIL
- 1 MIRROR
- 1 SHELF
- 1 GLASS HOLDER
- CLOTHES LOCKER & CURTAIN

KITCHEN
- 1 SINK
- 1 WATER FILTER
- ELECTRIC CONTROL PANEL
- 2 GALLON URN
- REFRIGERATOR c/w
- LARGE MAID BOX
- UNDER SINK ON FLOOR
- 2 RACKS
- 1 OXYGEN ECONOMISER
- 1 LIGHT IN ROOF
- HAY-BOX c/w TINS & DRAWERS
- 1 AXE
- 1 PHONE
- 1 FIRE EXTINGUISHER
- CURTAIN & RAIL
- 1 CUPBOARD ABOVE
- HAY-BOX

LOUNGE
- OXYGEN GAUGE
- 2 BUNKS 5/w MATTRESSES
- 6 HEAT REGULATORS
- 6 ROOF LIGHTS
- 6 SETS CURTAINS
- 2 HANDRAILS

BAGGAGE COMP'T
- W/T EQUIP'T (R3003 TR1196)
- 1 FAN
- 1 FIRE EXTINGUISHER
- 1 ROOF LIGHT
- DESERT EQUIP'T STOWAGE
- 15 OXYGEN BOTTLES
- DR COMPASS
- 2 LIGHTS
- RATION BARREL
- DINGHY PACK

The Boscombe Down drawing showing the cabin arrangement for Winston Churchill's personal York, LV633 Ascalon. The offending wash basin was in Compartment 'H'.

the impression is that it has been finished to austerity rather than luxury standards. Allowance must of course be made for the fact that the interior furnishing has obviously been rushed and that much of the poor workmanship is due to the shortage of time and suitable materials. Nevertheless as this aircraft is bound to attract a considerable amount of attention if it goes abroad, it is felt that a better advertisement of the capabilities of the British aircraft industry for interior decoration and furnishing should have been provided, unless it is the intention to lay stress on the war austerity prevailing in this country.

To complete the record as far as Boscombe Down's involvement with this unusual aircraft was concerned, the acceptance trials of other than the fittings was straightforward, the report noting that the testing was to a high order of priority, which of necessity precluded any extensive evaluation. The tests were made between 30 April and 14 May 1943 with 16 flights totalling 31 hours 20 minutes. Two flights were long: one of 7 hours 30 minutes and another lasting 4 hours 10 minutes.

The four Merlin 22s conferred a maximum cruise of 244 mph TAS at 13,000 ft. Maximum still air range with 2,478 gallons of fuel at 10,000 ft was estimated at 2,950 statute miles at 170 mph IAS. 'It was thought improbable that this aircraft would operate above 15,000 ft'.

No defects occurred 'which have not been experienced already on Lancasters and the maintenance was straightforward'. However, the cockpit windscreen wipers were tried in light rain and failed to clear the screen and it was thought desirable to fit sunblinds to the extensively glazed cockpit roof.

As to *Ascalon*'s subsequent career, shortly after the trials at Boscombe Down, the aircraft was delivered to No. 24 Squadron, Transport Command, then based at Northolt on the western outskirts of London, from where, on 25 May 1943, it took off for Gibraltar to pick up the Prime Minister and Allied commanders for Algiers and Tunis, returning with Winston Churchill to Northolt on 5 June having flown a trouble free maiden trip of some 5,000 miles. A week later *Ascalon* took off for an extended tour of the North African front with its most illustrious passenger, H.M. King George VI. *Ascalon*, was followed by a small number of production Yorks, mostly fitted up as VIP transports: MW102 for the C-in-C South East Asia Command (SEAC), Lord Louis Mountbatten; MW107 for the use of Field Marshal Smuts and MW140 for the then Governor General of Australia, the Duke of Gloucester. It was not until May 1944 that production York transports were issued to RAF Transport Command; the first fully York equipped squadron was No. 511, based at Lyneham, which received its aircraft during 1945. In all, 257 Yorks were constructed, the last, PE108, being delivered in April 1948.

The York is best remembered for its role during the post war Berlin Airlift when six squadrons of RAF Transport Command flew 29,000 sorties to the German capital carrying 230,000 tons of supplies – often coal, which was to become apparent years later when the last of the Yorks were scrapped and it was found that practically every one had coal dust lodged in its innermost recesses.

The Pride of Lt. Brodie

The Second World War offered, if nothing else, an unparalleled opportunity for inventors: many were called and many were chosen; one feels that in stating that the Brodie Suspension System was one of the more improbable, one is on fairly secure ground. Indeed, secure ground – or rather the lack of it – was the whole point of the American Lieutenant's brainchild.

The Brodie System was originally devised in 1940 as a method of operating light observation aircraft from ships by landing and retrieving them suspended from a suspension wire running between two outriggers on the ship's bow and stern. These seaborne aircraft thus were unique in that the 'arrester hook' was on top. It is very difficult to be truly original and the Brodie suspension was no exception; the basic concept had been tried before, in 1931, when the US Navy had fitted their airships, USS *Akron* and *Macon* with suspension points to launch and retrieve modified Curtiss F9C Sparrowhawks. The system had not been a total success then and, after the loss of USS *Akron* and *Macon* (unconnected with the operation of the Sparrowhawks), the idea had been abandoned.

To return to the Brodie System, the aircraft, a modified Piper L4, had two hooks disposed about the C of G, one hook facing forward for engaging the suspension wire on landing, the other aft facing for take-off.

Considering the complications of using the Brodie System in a seaway, it is hardly surprising that it was not used in its intended shipboard role but was apparently considered ideal for use in the jungles of the Far East, when the whole device could be dropped to troops on the ground. It was evaluated by the A&AEE during October 1945, using a Piper L-4, locally modified by the

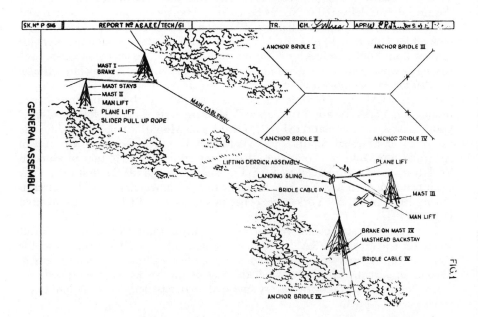

The layout of the Brodie suspension system was far from simple as can be seen in this war-time drawing which formed part of the instructions for setting up this totally impractical idea.

engineering staff at Boscombe Down. One of the authors of this book, Terrry Heffernan, was a trials officer for the tests, and the relevant parts of the subsequent A&AEE report[7] are reproduced.

The American Brodie Suspension System.

Erection and Operation of Suspended Runway.

The object of these trials was to test the erection and operation of the Brodie Suspension System and to assess the usefulness of such a device.

1.2 The complete equipment was packed in 54 crates, 35 of which contained the equipment required, and 19 contained spares.

1.3 Originally it was intended that assistance and guidance in the erection and tests be given by American Engineers and pilots, but this assistance did not materialise. The services of unskilled R.A.F. personnel and civilian technicians had to be utilised in erecting the gear and conducting the tests, a handbook of instructions and a film only being available for their guidance.

1.4 A Piper L.4 aircraft was allotted for these tests and was suitably modified, at this Establishment, to take the special hook.

2. *Description.*

2.1 The system consists principally of a 500 ft. main cableway held taut by bridle cables supported on masts. This provides a smooth, straight runway for landing and launching the aircraft which is suspended by a special hook from a trolley.

2.2 The take-off gear consists of a trolley and a sling. The trolley takes the form of a rolling block in which is incorporated an emergency release mechanism operating when the block reaches the end of the cableway.

2.3 The landing gear consists of a separate trolley fitted with an arresting brake mechanism. A wide and deep sling with three loops to facilitate landing on is attached to the landing trolley.

3. *Field Work (Erection).*

3.1 *Site.* The site must be carefully chosen, as on this depends the speed of erection and the safety of the aircraft. The three main factors to be considered are:–

(a) The physical features of the country.
(b) The direction of the prevailing wind.
(c) The nature of the ground and vegetation.

The nature of the ground greatly affects the speed of erection due to the amount of work required for boring the anchor-plate holes and driving in the anchor rods.

7. *Ground Observations on Flight Trials.*

7.1 A day was selected when conditions appeared reasonably suitable although the wind component along the cable way was only 3 m.p.h. The rig was prepared and inspected, and was found satisfactory. Ciné cameras were set up at salient points. Prior to 'landing on', the pilot made the dummy runs, which gave the operators an opportunity to get set. The arresting brake was pre-set to 90 lb/sq.in. and set for automatic operation. A successful 'landing on' was made, the centre loop of the sling 'engaging' and the aircraft being brought to rest after a run of approximately one third of the cable length.

7.3 The rig was prepared for a take-off and second landing-on. An inspection of the hook attachments was made and a ground check of the restraining cable release trip carried out.

7.4 After the engine was started, hoisting operations were commenced. Since a full team was not available, this operation was carried out using a light van to apply the effort. The hooker experienced no difficulties in attaching the take-off sling and avoiding the revolving propeller. It was found necessary to taxi the aircraft forward approximately its own length to ensure that the rudder would not foul the landing sling when commencing the run. After lowering the hooker, the pilot opened up to take-off power and gave the signal to release the holding back cable. The cable release did not operate the first time due, possibly, to the new condition of the line imparting a twisting motion and causing the release unit to rotate about its longitudinal axis. When the holding back cable release was operated successfully the aircraft appeared to accelerate rather slowly and it was observed that the aircraft's attitude was considerably nose down with elevators depressed. A little over half-way along the cable-way, the pilot operated the aircraft release, the aircraft falling heavily to the ground.

8.   *Flight Trials. Pilot's Report.*

8.1 *Landing On.*

8.11 Initial flights were made to assess the stalling and handling characteristics of the aeroplane, the pilot flying solo from the front seat. In this condition some difficulty was experienced in trimming the aircraft at slow speeds, as with the trimmer in its fully aft position the aircraft remained nose heavy and some backward pressure was required on the control column. Whilst this was not serious, it was considered desirable to be able to trim out the aircraft during the approach. Ballast of 100 lb. was stowed in the rear seat.

8.12 Tests made on the slow flying characteristics of the aeroplane showed that 1800 rpm gave a steady speed of 50 mph ASI with adequate control. At lower speeds, whilst the general control of the aircraft was adequate, a loss of height could not be quickly regained without advancing the throttle, since any reduction of speed also occasioned a reduction of rpm (fixed pitch propeller).

8.13 Preliminary flight tests through the structure under the wire were made to obtain familiarity. With a little practice no difficulties were experienced in passing down the centre of the gear providing that the wind was steady and at not too large an angle. Rough air made the flight under the wire somewhat difficult.
    The estimation of height during the approach presented some difficulties particularly during the final approach, since no suitable aiming points or marks could be established. It was found advantageous, however, to remove a forward side panel to give a clear view of the ground forward and downward. The sag in the cable was a deterrent to flying too high during the practice runs. Finally it was considered that the hook-on could be satisfactorily made by making the approach slightly downhill and running in on the final part of the approach from about 2–300 yds. at such a height that the mass of fitments at the ends of the centre wire coincided. This helped in maintaining the height during the run and avoided getting low and attempting to climb up to the sling – a noticeable tendency during practice runs.

8.14 The final practice runs were made up to the sling – the control was pushed forward and the aircraft passed under the wire at a low height.

8.15 During the run in which the hook-up was made, the aircraft was flown into the sling, and the engine was not throttled back until it became obvious that the hook had engaged. The nose of the aeroplane tended to rise though not sharply, and the control column was instinctively pushed forward but whether this had any restraining influence on the rate of rise of the nose is not known. The behaviour of the aircraft at the end of the landing run was not unpleasant.

8.2 *Take-off.*

8.21 The aeroplane was hoisted into position and after various formalities one unsuccessful attempt at take-off was made. It had been decided previously that the signal for the release of the aircraft to start the take-off run should be made from the ground when everything was set and engine running at take-off rpm. This was satisfactory and was given in full view of the pilot.

8.22 Acceleration from the start was surprisingly poor and a measure of doubt existed as to the successful outcome of the test. It was fully realised from the outset that the position of the elevator should be as in the position of the approach and during the landing on stage. The tail trim of the aeroplane had not been altered and the pilot was conscious that the position of the elevator was an important feature. That the subsequent photographs of the take-off showed a large degree of down elevator was quite astonishing to the pilot and can only be attributed to the poor acceleration and the instinctive tendency to put the elevator down as in a normal take-off.

8.23 An arrangement had also been made whereby one person stood to the side and about halfway along the run and another at the ¾ distance. This was to enable the pilot to estimate his position along the wire, the intention being to release at the ¾ mark. It is considered that the position of release should be pre-determined and a signal given from the ground at say approximately ⅞ distance.

.3 It is considered that with practice there is no great difficulty with 'hooking on'. For the take-off, more power in the aircraft is required to obtain a greater acceleration along the wire. The necessity of holding the elevator in the neutral or slightly up position regardless of the pilot's natural inclinations is pointed out as an important feature of the take-off.

9. *Conclusions.*

9.1 Although tests were curtailed due to the aeroplane being damaged in the first attempt to take-off, it is considered that a light aeroplane could be operated successfully from the Brodie suspended runway.

9.2 The Piper L.4 aircraft with Continental engine is slightly under-engined for safe take-offs in light winds on the suspended runway.

9.3 Pilots should have some preliminary training to enable them to master the technique required to land or take-off.

9.4 The erection of the apparatus is very much a civil engineering job, but can be carried out by inexperienced R.A.F. maintenance personnel with technical supervision. The time taken by inexperienced personnel is however considerably greater than that inferred in the descriptive handbook (i.e. 24 hrs. for 9 men). Personnel trained in the erection and maintenance of this apparatus would therefore be required.

9.5 It is not considered that the weight of this gear could be substantially reduced.

9.6 Daily and periodic inspections of the structure and operating gear would be essential but this should be fairly straightforward, apart from the need to check periodically that the jointed masts remain vertical. (A theodolite was used to carry out these checks during the tests.)

9.7 The Brodie gear is packed for dropping by parachute with an experienced crew on enemy held territory. Except, however, in those cases where it is impossible

129

to level the ground into some form of runway, it would appear to be more economical to drop a crew with the necessary equipment (e.g. dismantled Bulldozer) to clear a short runway for the operation of a light aircraft.

On marshy or rocky ground it would be very difficult to make satisfactory anchorage points for the cables.

The Brodie System was not adopted in this country. Interestingly, after the war it was discovered that the famous German woman test pilot, Hanna Reitch, had tested a very similar system using a glider: that too proved impractical.

The A&AEE conclusion that the dropping of a small bulldozer to clear a runway was a far simpler and more practical proposition was fulfilled during the Korean war and later in Malaya to operate Auster aircraft used for artillery spotting. The need for light aircraft for Service use disappeared when efficient military helicopters became available, able to operate from a small clearing in even the most dense jungle.

Beast of Burden

The Fairey Barracuda, a naval torpedo/dive-bomber, was not, it is fair to say, universally beloved of the men who flew the type; whatever its shortcomings, however, few service aircraft have been required to carry a larger variety of external equipment: radar antennae, torpedoes, rockets, bombs, lifeboats and, surely the strangest of all, beneath each wing a container to carry two men – fully armed marine paratroopers, to be dropped in the forthcoming operations against the Japanese in the Far East.

The containers were approximately eight feet long, two feet wide and three and a half feet deep – which must have been a tight fit for two men wearing service parachutes. The paratroopers sat facing each other, each with a double 'bomb door' beneath him. These doors were opened remotely by the pilot and were supposed to close automatically when the men had jumped, though since the doors constituted the entire floor area of their cramped compartment, 'fell' might be a more accurate word.

The prototype and sole paratroop Barracuda, fitted with the 'Cuda' floats, as they were known – 'floats' being a cover name – was a Mk II, P9795/G, which arrived at Boscombe Down in July 1944 for handling trials to discover how the 'floats' affected its performance *vis-à-vis* the standard Barracuda carrying the equivalent weight, i.e. 6×250 lb bombs.

The first part of the A&AEE trials was to assess the take-off; P9795/G was powered by a single 1,640 hp Rolls-Royce Merlin 32. At an all-up weight of 13,650 lb (the floats for the early trials were dummies, ballasted to the equivalent of four men), the Barracuda required a take-off run of 390 yards in zero wind. At that time – 1944 – the A&AEE take-off trials of carrier borne aircraft assumed a minimum wind of 20 knots, into which the 'Cuda float' Barracuda unstuck in 203 yards, which was only about 50 yards longer than a standard aircraft at the same AUW.

After the take-off trials, brief handling flights followed with the Cuda floats augmented by a container slung in lieu of a torpedo, for arms and ammunition to be dropped with the men. The handling trials were made both with floats ballasted and with them empty.

At full load (13,650 lb) the unstick speed was 70 mph and the bulky floats appeared to have remarkably little effect on the general handling; indeed, the fin stalling which was a defect of the normal Barracuda was 'much less noticeable' with P9795. The floats and container caused no vibration even when the aircraft was dived up to the maximum permitted speed of 300 mph. The A&AEE report noted:[8] 'As in general for the type there is insufficient elevator control movement to stall the aircraft with flaps and undercarriage down'. A baulked landing was possible but the climb away performance was considered 'poor'.

After the first handling trials the working floats were fitted and the remote operation of the doors was tested.

The actual operational drill when dropping supplies and men was for the pilot, presumably after warning the parachutists over the intercom, to actuate the automatic drop using his bomb selector; the sequence of events was as follows:

Doors open: port rear man dropped; one second later starboard rear man; after a one second delay the arms container fitted to the Barracuda torpedo station dropped; another one second and the port front man left, followed a second later by the starboard front paratrooper joining the drop.

A flight with empty floats was arranged to test the door opening and closing sequence. In practice the doors proved troublesome, as reported by the observer who could see both the port and starboard doors from ports in the fuselage under the wings. At 140 mph all the doors opened correctly but, instead of automatically closing, remained half open. Thinking that the slipstream could be preventing the closure, the Boscombe Down test pilot reduced his airspeed to 90 mph, at which point the port doors closed but the starboard pair remained obstinately open, even with the ASI at 80 mph. To reduce speed still further, full flap was

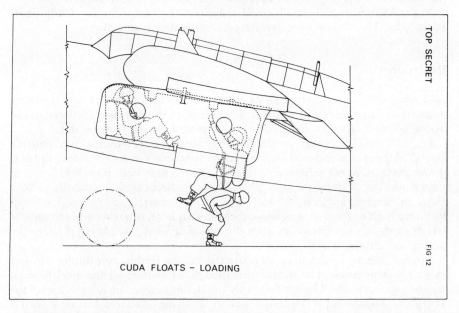

TOP SECRET

FIG 12

CUDA FLOATS – LOADING

It is difficult to reconcile the 'Top Secret' classification with the actual drawing, which is reminiscent of the work of W. Heath-Robinson, showing the recommended method of entry to the paratroop-carrying 'Floats'.

selected and speed reduced to an indicated 72 mph when the Barracuda, not surprisingly, stalled, closing the starboard doors but leaving a gap of about one inch. Finally the aircraft was dived to 250 mph and yawed from side to side, which finally completely shut the doors.

The test was repeated; this time the starboard doors closed but the port pair did not: after stalling, violent sideslips caused the doors to open and close. On landing, the door mechanism worked perfectly. (It would of course.)

On yet another flight, one set of doors refused to open, the other side refusing to close. Strangely, opening and closing the doors did not affect the handling, though with the floats empty and with all the doors closed, there was considerable vibration from the floats which was transmitted to the airframe when the aircraft dived at speeds above 250 mph, increasing markedly with speed to the point where 250 mph was considered the maximum prudent with empty floats. This vibration had not occurred with the ballasted dummy floats, the conclusion being that the loaded weight acted as a damper.

The A&AEE report somewhat summarily concluded:

> The handling qualities of the Barracuda II with loaded 'Cuda' floats and a container fitted are satisfactory.
> The operation of the doors of the . . . floats is erratic: they failed to open once in eight attempts, and failed to close five times in seven attempts.
> There is considerable vibration in the dive with empty floats fitted. . . .

In spite of the erratic behaviour of the doors, live drops with four paratroopers were successfully made at the then sister establishment of the A&AEE, the Airborne Forces Experimental Establishment at Beaulieu, in March 1945.

As far as is now known, P9795/G remained the one and only 'Cuda float' Barracuda. The 'floats' were certainly never used operationally.

Deviation

All ferrous structures, be they ships or parts of aircraft, exhibit a characteristic magnetism, the polarity of which is dependent on the direction, relative to the magnetic pole, in which the structure was placed during construction.

Because of their size and the fact that they are – or were – built almost entirely of steel, ships exhibit induced magnetism to a most marked degree; if they did not, the magnetic mine of the Second World War would have been pointless. It was in the countering of those weapons that scientists discovered a great deal about ships' induced magnetism. Not only was it found possible to say if a given ship had been built in the northern or southern hemisphere, it was possible to state at which yard, in some instances even the actual slipway, simply by plotting the magnetic 'signature' of the vessel.

Aircraft, being in the main constructed of non-ferrous duralumin, do not exhibit a large amount of magnetism though, of course, all the steel fittings, engines, guns, etc, do. Though relatively small, this magnetism does influence the aircraft's compass but it is a simple matter to 'swing' the aircraft, that is turn it through 360° and plot the compass readings against known magnetic headings. The errors thus revealed are displayed on a 'deviation' card placed by the compass which shows the pilot that if, for example, he wanted to fly due east – 90°

magnetic – he would have to add or subtract the amount of deviation for that particular heading as shown on the deviation card.

The deviation of an aircraft's compass is fairly constant, though it will differ between apparently identical machines; it is, however, usual to 'swing' aircraft fairly frequently, certainly after any major repair or engine change. With Second World War military aircraft, the armaments could create quite strong magnetic fields. Bombers had an additional problem in that the bombs they carried, being made largely of cast iron, could cause large compass errors which could not be compensated for since, obviously, once the bombs had been dropped the magnetic anomaly they caused dropped with them. The problem was solved by bombers carrying a remote reading compass with the sensing unit placed as far away from the bomb bay as possible, usually somewhere in the tail of the fuselage. (The unit fitted to Lancasters was just inside the rear crew door.)

The guns, particularly 20-mm cannon with which many fighter aircraft were armed, caused compass errors but, when mounted in the wings, as was usually the case with single-engined aircraft, were sufficiently far away from the compass to cause little influence. In any case, since the armament was the same for each wing, the magnetic field tended to cancel out. This was not the case with one aircraft type – the Bristol Beaufighter – which had a deviation error caused by its armament which was sufficiently serious for the A&AEE to be asked to solve the problem in the summer of 1943.[9]

The aircraft which arrived at Boscombe Down was a Beaufighter VI, JM119, armed with four 20-mm cannon. These formidable guns were grouped in the nose of the twin-engined Beaufighter, quite near to the pilot's P4 compass.

Beaufighters of RAF Coastal Command were at that time being used extensively in an anti-shipping role, the cannon armed Mk VI proving capable of destroying surfaced U-boats crossing the Bay of Biscay when on passage to or from their bases on the French Atlantic coast. It was soon discovered at Boscombe Down, that after firing the cannon a large deviation appeared on the standard P4 magnetic compass; a serious defect for a long-range aircraft which had to navigate over water well out of sight of land.

The only other direction indicator available in the Beaufighter was the gyrocompass which, although unaffected by magnetic fields, was subject to 'precession' errors, particularly after violent manoeuvres and, even in straight and level flight, required to be checked against the P4 compass and reset at roughly ten minute intervals.

JM119 was a brand new Mk VI. The guns had never been fired. At Boscombe Down the aircraft's compass was carefully swung on 12 headings, 30° apart, with the Beaufighter jacked up in flying attitude. The maximum deviation throughout the 360° did not exceed ½° – a figure, incidentally, lower than average.

The aircraft then had its cannon fired into special stop butts, 100 rounds on North, South, East and West by headings. The firing was repeated four times with a 12 point compass swing between each 100 rounds. The P4's deviation after firing was now up to 30°, the actual figure being dependent on the heading of the aircraft when the cannon fired and the number of rounds fired.

Following a most thorough investigation at Boscombe Down, it was found that the magnetic anomalies were caused by the mild steel blast tubes surrounding the cannons' barrels becoming magnetised by the percussive shock of the cannon fire.

(If a length of mild steel is hammered the molecular structure of the metal is disturbed and will rearrange, becoming magnetised with a strength and magnetic polarity appropriate to the position of the steel relative to the earth's magnetism when the hammering takes place.)

The Beaufighter's blast tubes were being magnetised by the action of the guns; moreover this effect appeared to have a very slow decay, leaving the unfortunate pilot with a compass having a large, and largely unknown, deviation, it being difficult under combat condition to remember on which magnetic heading the cannons were last fired.

An obvious remedy would have been to fabricate the blast tubes from a non-ferrous metal, Mu-metal or even hard-drawn copper, but supply difficulties rendered this impractical.

The A&AEE investigation with JM119 had revealed that, irrespective of how many rounds had been fired on East, West or Southerly headings or how large the resultant deviation, it could be restored to the original ½° deviation by firing a short burst of five rounds with the aircraft on a Northerly heading.

Interestingly, the Germans, at about the same time, were having a similar problem with the prototype V1 flying bombs. These missiles, which for cheapness were constructed from mild steel sheet, were going off course after launching at Peenemunde, due to the vibration imparted to the airframe from the simple pulse jet. The resultant induced magnetism was deviating the compass sensing unit which controlled the V1's direction gyros. The solution was in essence the same as that proposed by the A&AEE, though instead of firing guns on a Northerly heading, the V1s were, prior to launching, placed in a small non-magnetic building aligned precisely on the heading that the missile would shortly fly and then beaten with wooden mallets, the induced magnetism being then the same as that of the desired magnetic course: to London.

Following the A&AEE trials with JM119, Coastal Command Beaufighter pilots were briefed to fire at least five rounds on a northerly heading after any attack. One can only conjecture just how they could ascertain this direction when over the sea on a cloudy day with the P4 compass up to 30° adrift, or what happened if, in the heat of battle, they ran out of ammunition.

CHAPTER EIGHT

The de Havilland Mosquito

On 20 September 1939, just seventeen days after Britain had declared war on Germany, Geoffrey de Havilland wrote a letter to the Air Member for Development and Production, Air Marshal Sir Wilfrid R. Freeman. The letter[1] is of considerable historical significance and is here reproduced.

THE
DE HAVILLAND
AIRCRAFT CO., LTD.

Hatfield   Herts.
Aerodrome England

GdeH/ELC   20th September 1939.

Air Marshal Sir Wilfrid R. Freeman,
       K.C.B., D.S.O., M.C.,
Air Member for Development and Production,
Air Ministry,
Berkeley Square House,
Berkeley Square,
LONDON W.1.

Dear Freeman,
    We have stopped all civil design and want to put our whole design staff on to war work. From former conversations with you, and using the experience we have gained in very quickly producing types which have to compete with others from all over the world, we believe that we could produce a twin engine bomber which would have a performance so outstanding that little defensive equipment would be needed.
    This would employ the well tried out methods of design and construction used in the 'COMET' and the 'ALBATROSS' and, being of wood or composite construction, would not encroach on the labour and material used in expanding the R.A.F. It is specially suited to really high speeds because all surfaces are smooth, free from rivets, overlapped plates and undulations. It also lends itself to very rapid initial and subsequent production.
    The brief specification would be as follows:

    Rolls-Royce Merlin 100 octane engines.
    1,500 miles range.
    Two 500 lb. or six 250 lb. bombs.
    Pilot and observer.

Maximum speed 405 m.p.h. at 20,000 feet.

Cruise on weak mixture 320 m.p.h.

Take-off would be well within the extended limits allowed for bombers.

Landing without fuel and bombs would be on a wing loading of 30 lbs. per sq. ft.

The principal objects which would be achieved by this type are shortly as follows:–

1. Its production would absorb a class of labour and material which is outside and additional to that used in the main aircraft production.
2. The smallest possible call would be made on 'Embodiment Loan' stuff etc., owing to its simplicity and to the fact that it relies mainly on performance for its defences.
3. It makes use of a design staff which has had much experience in very quickly producing aircraft types to meet specific and competitive needs.
4. The wood or composite construction allows of the minimum time and man-hours being spent on making jigs etc.
5. The existence of a type of bomber having the highest performance possible and capable within a year of going into production forms a kind of insurance against surprises emanating from the enemy's design resources. If a prototype were undergoing trials in, say, nine months, without detracting from the main production plans, it would be a platform for future plans, the value of which can hardly be exaggerated.
6. This type of construction permits mixed grades of timber to be used with safety.

We have arranged a provincial location and are moving our design staff to it. We should be able therefore, to start on this project forthwith.

We feel such confidence that the existence of this type or a closely similar one will be a valuable asset in a year's time that we very much hope you will be able to give it your support. If this is the case we should have to discuss the minimum equipment with the people concerned.

Yours sincerely,

(Signed) G. de Havilland

P.S. I am anxious to get this preliminary proposal in to you without delay, but will just add that it has been based on the availability of Merlin engines. Were it possible to use Sabres the same performance and range could be obtained with 4,000 lbs. of bombs, crew of three and two guns.

The aircraft proposed was, of course, to be called 'Mosquito' and it is generally acknowledged to have been one of the truly great aircraft of the Second World War, and one of the very few that was to prove equally effective in bomber, fighter and photographic reconnaissance roles.

The idea of a bomber able to fly at a speed which would enable it to operate unarmed was one with which the de Havilland design staff had toyed for some time. The concept hardened into a definite proposal in the summer of 1938. It was nurtured by the performance of the company's D.H.91 Albatross airliner, a wooden monoplane of outstanding aesthetic appeal and with an actual performance on as little as 1,280 hp that would have enabled a bomber version to carry a 6,000 lb bomb load from Britain to Berlin at 210 mph.

The Albatross had four 525 hp de Havilland Gipsy Twelves; the unarmed bomber proposal was to be designed around two Rolls-Royce Merlins. By October 1938, a design team led by Geoffrey de Havilland and including R. E. Bishop and C. C. Walker, began a detailed study.

Informal contact was made with Sir Wilfrid Freeman, as is revealed in the letter quoted above 'From former conversations with you'. Sir Wilfrid was unofficially encouraging but he was not in a position to order a prototype, the letter of 20 September being the first formal proposal; the concept of a 400 mph unarmed wooden bomber was, to say the least, received with less than acclamation at the Air Ministry.

In the Public Record Office in London there is an undated Air Ministry memorandum[2] which refers to de Havilland's proposal; this paper notes, *inter alia*:

> The information provided by the firm is somewhat scanty and is not such that reliable estimates can be made. It is, however clear that their performance estimate is optimistic. . . .

The Air Ministry man then corrected de Havilland's figures based on two Rolls-Royce R.M.2.SM Merlins and a bomb load of 1,000 lb. The AUW was increased by the man from the Ministry to 19,500 lb; the maximum speed was reduced from 404 mph at 20,000 ft to 250 mph at 18,500 ft. The maximum continuous weak mixture cruise at 15,000 ft was raised slightly from 322 mph to 325 mph.

The memo also displays doubt as to the unarmed concept, for it appears that de Havillands had been asked to hedge their bets and to provide a revised estimate of performance using, as the Air Ministry put it, 'defensive armament on Hampden lines'; that is: one fixed and one hand-trained .303-inch gun forward and twin .303-inch guns in dorsal and ventral positions. De Havillands considered that such armament – which one can be certain was a heresy to the design team – would reduce the maximum speed to 340 mph at 20,000 ft. The Ministry revised this to 315 mph at 18,500 ft; both agreed that the rate of climb would be reduced by 600 ft/min.

After further doubts in official circles, the Air Ministry agreed to accept the firm's radical proposal for an unarmed bomber. There was no obvious enthusiasm and it is probable that the main factor in saving the Mosquito was the simple fact that it did not require scarce aluminium and could be built by woodworking sub-contractors, principally furniture makers, which tapped a source of skilled labour likely to be under-employed in a war economy. The official acceptance of the de Havilland proposals is dated 29 December 1939 and a specification, B.1/40, was drawn up shortly afterwards. B.1/40 called simply for an unarmed, twin-engined, two crew bomber, 50 of which were ordered on 1 March 1940.

The de Havilland design team, convinced of the potential of their aircraft, unofficially amended the design to enable it quickly to be modified on the production lines for fighter or photo-reconnaissance duties, a decision which was to be proved farsighted.

The deteriorating military situation in France which was to culminate in the Dunkirk evacuation placed the whole B.1/40 programme in jeopardy; the project was, for a time, omitted from the Air Ministry forward production programme but production of the prototype, W4050, continued despite a lone Ju 88, on 3 October 1940, destroying most of the materials stockpiled for the first batch of production aircraft. Fortunately the prototype was undamaged in the raid and, in a total time of only eleven months from the start of the detailed design work,

W4050 was ready for its maiden flight. The Company number for the aircraft was simply D.H.98 but the highly appropriate name Mosquito was by then adopted.

Captain de Havilland took off from Hatfield for the first time in the bright yellow prototype on 25 November 1940. It bore the experimental number E-0234. Its early trials confirmed the promised 400 mph with a fighter-like aerobatic capability, Geoffrey de Havilland performing upward rolls with one engine feathered for the benefit of the assembled Hatfield staff and guests.

The spirited performance of the prototype had one unforeseen effect; the Air Ministry, whose interest in the bomber was already waning, now wanted the Mosquito as a fighter! The contract was amended to twenty bombers and thirty fighters. The third prototype, W4052, was completed armed with four 20-mm cannon and four .303 Brownings in the nose.

The fighter prototype first flew on 15 May 1941, followed by W4051 in June 1941 as the prototype photo-reconnaissance variant; thus Geoffrey de Havilland's prediction became fact.

W4050 (still marked E-0234) came to the A&AEE in early 1941 for Performance and Brief Handling trials;[3] the trials were to prove brief indeed for, after only eight and a half hours testing at Boscombe Down, the fuselage failed, presumably on the ground since the damage was extensive enough that it: 'necessitated the reconstruction of the aeroplane'.

Before the failure, the aircraft was tested at 16,770 lb without 'armament or other operational equipment and was only lightly loaded' (thus vindicating the Air Ministry's upward revision of de Havilland's original estimate of 15,500 lb AUW in operational trim).

The de Havilland test pilots had warned the A&AEE that some buffeting would be experienced at 'normal speeds' and modifications were in hand to alleviate the problem. The A&AEE pilots reported that:

(a)   The aeroplane is pleasant to fly. The aileron control is light and effective, the elevators are rather heavy but effective and the rudder is heavy. Take-offs and landings are quite straightforward.

    The behaviour at the stall is not vicious; either with flaps up or down. Warning of the stall, which occurs at 105 m.p.h. A.S.I. with flaps up, and 90 m.p.h. A.S.I. with flaps down, is given by buffeting.

    Buffeting in normal flight, which has no direct connection with the buffeting near stall, was observed at speeds of 170 m.p.h. A.S.I. and higher speeds, but was not considered serious at the speeds at which the Mosquito was flown, up to 320 m.p.h. A.S.I. If attention had not been drawn to the buffeting by the Firm's pilot, it is likely that adverse criticism would not have been made.

    No tests were made with the nacelle extensions fitted.*

    Longitudinal instability was found to be present on the climb, in level flight and on the glide. The instability is not serious with the present C.G. position (0.32 A.M.C) [Aerodynamic Mean Chord] but it would be a handicap if the Mosquito is flown at night or for long distance work.

(b)   The performance climb was made with the radiator flap in the closed position. The climb had to be interrupted by a section of climb at a higher speed than the best climbing speed because of inadequate cooling. It was continued to 30,000 feet and the Service ceiling is roughly determined as 34,000 feet.

    The best rate of climb in M.S. blower is 2880 feet/min. at 11,400 feet and in F.S. blower is 2240 feet/minute at 18,100 feet.

* These had been proposed to alleviate the buffeting.

(c)   The top speed in F.S. blower is 388 m.p.h. at 22,000 feet.

There was an addendum to the report[4] which included the stall characteristics:

2.7   *Stalls*. The stalling speed is
flaps and undercarriage up 105 m.p.h. A.S.I.
flaps and undercarriage down 90 m.p.h. A.S.I.
       With flaps and undercarriage up a general buffeting is apparent at 110 m.p.h.
A.S.I., and this is the only warning of the approaching stall. At the stall the nose
drops followed almost immediately by the right wing. It is not vicious and
control is regained quickly when the speed is increased.
       With flaps and undercarriage down more pronounced buffeting is noticed at
100 m.p.h. A.S.I. and here again this is the only indication of the approaching
stall. At stall the nose drops sharply followed by the dropping of either wing.
Although a little more violent than with the flaps and undercarriage up, the stall
cannot be described as vicious. . . .

The prototype's approach and landing was also reported upon.[5]

       The approach speed with flaps and undercarriage down is 110 m.p.h. A.S.I.
The approach is reasonably steep when full flap is used. Lowering the
undercarriage makes the aeroplane nose heavy and lowering the flaps makes
it tail heavy. With half flap, there is a long float after approaching at 120 m.p.h.
A.S.I. There is adequate control if the engines are used down to a speed of
130 m.p.h. during an approach with flaps up, but as soon as the engines are
throttled back there is a rapid sinking.
       The landing itself is reasonably straightforward. There is adequate elevator
control right down to the point of touch [down] and the aeroplane settles down
on three points very smoothly. The shock absorbing qualities of the
undercarriage are excellent and the brakes can be applied firmly without the
tail rising.
       Baulked Landing. The flaps rise too rapidly from the full down or the 25°
position, and may be a source of danger at heavier loads, in view of the sharp
nose down couple. This can be overcome with larger flap jacks which should
definitely be fitted as early as practicable in production.

The same report also reviewed the cockpit layout – at that time often haphazard
in British aircraft – and the question of routine maintenance:

1. *Cockpit layout.*

   1.1. *Ease of entry and comfort.*   Entry is by ladder through a hatchway in the floor
of the cockpit. Because of the proximity of the airscrews, it is deemed inadvisable for
anyone to enter the aeroplane while the engines are running. It is necessary therefore
for the pilot to get into the aeroplane before starting the engines, and this is an
unsatisfactory state of affairs if the aeroplane is ever to be employed as an interceptor
fighter. Two doors form the hatchway, an inner and an outer, and the outer door can
only be opened and closed by means of a square key. It is recommended that some
means be provided on the aeroplane for opening the outer door without the use of the
key so that in the event of a crash anyone can get into the aeroplane to rescue the
crew. There is no external handle for opening the roof emergency exit. The inner door
also requires a handle on the underside. The pilot's seat is on the left with the
Observer on the right slightly behind him. The seating is a little cramped, but because
the heating system is very good, it is not necessary for the crew to wear much flying

clothing. With the low slung pedals the pilot's seating position is a little upright for maximum comfort on long flights. The pedals are also rather close together. There is a good range of seat adjustment, but when right down the seat is too low and the handle is almost out of reach. With his eye at a comfortable height, the pilot's head is rather ·near a cross tube in the roof. It is thought that the pilot might sustain injury even though his Sutton Harness is done up. The Firm are proposing to put padding on the cross tube, but this may not be a complete solution to the difficulty.

Special test instruments are at present suspended below the dashboard on the right-hand side and therefore no attempt has been made to enter the nose of the aeroplane in flight, so that no assessment can yet be made of the comfort of the bomb aimer's position.

1.2 *View.*   The pilot has a good view all round except immediately downward, this latter being restricted by the wing. Blisters are fitted on each side and they give a good field of view astern. In the armour plating behind the Observer's seat is a peep-hole made of bullet-proof glass, and this is an excellent feature. The aeroplane has not been flown in very bad weather for long periods, but during an early flight a snow shower was encountered. The pilot on this occasion reported that the view forward through the windscreen was poor, but the direct vision opening gave greatly improved visibility with little draught. It is essential however, that the direct vision panels be made to either hinge upward or backward because, hinging forward as they now do, they give added obstruction to the view through the front windscreen and offer a dangerously sharp corner to the pilot's face. A modification is in hand by the Firm.

1.3. *Controls.*   All aeroplane controls work freely on the ground without undue friction. The control column is provided with a spectacle type hand grip and mounted on this is the brake control actuated by the right-hand thumb. The airscrew, throttle, and mixture controls are conveniently situated on the left side of the cockpit but are stiff to operate. The bomb door and undercarriage actuating levers, are all positioned on the dashboard to the right of the pilot. This aeroplane is not in the final production stage as regards cockpit layout so that one blower gear control is mounted on the pilot's left and the other behind him next to the Observer. The fuel cocks are also mounted next to the Observer. The elevator trim wheel is too free and requires damping. It is also positioned too low for a short pilot. The rudder trimmer which is mounted forward in the roof, is provided with a crank obviously intended to give movement over a wide range. Although this movement would no doubt be necessary for flying with one engine dead, only a very small part of the available range is used for normal flying on both engines and it is therefore recommended that in addition to the crank a small knurled knob be provided for fine adjustment. The radiator flaps are at present controlled by two small electrical switches on the dashboard in front of the Observer. These are not labelled but the Makers state that in production aircraft the flaps are to be thermostatically controlled. The ignition switches are not satisfactory. They are difficult to reach round the control column, and the bolt on the connecting link between the engine switches and the electric master switch fouls the inboard switches of each engine, so that it is difficult to avoid switching off both magnetos together.

The undercarriage actuating lever, while satisfactory, might, it is thought, inadvertently be moved to the up position by a large pilot getting in or out of the seat. The type of lock used on the Battle is suggested as a much safer arrangement.

1.4. *Brakes.*   The brakes are operated pneumatically. They are controlled by a thumb lever on top of the control column and appear to work very efficiently. A pressure gauge is required.

1.5 *Instruments.*   An assessment of the instrument lay-out is difficult at this stage because in this aeroplane there are many test instruments which would not normally be fitted. One or two criticisms can be made however. The engine boost gauges are too low. With constant speed airscrews fitted an indication of boost is probably the most important point for the pilot to watch and the gauges should be much higher. The radiator thermometers are also too low. The undercarriage indicator is unsatisfactory although the principle on which the lights work is good. There is no light for the tail wheel, and no dimming switch nor changeover switch is provided. At dusk the green lights are too bright and in the day the screen is opaque so that the lights cannot be seen in direct sunlight.

The warning horn is not loud enough and a proper switch for switching it off will be required. Apart from the warning light and the horn, no other indication is given to the pilot that his wheels are not down. In the reconnaissance type the observer can be sent forward to see if the main wheels are in the down position, but he cannot be sure that they are locked. This cannot be done if the guns are fitted in the front compartment, and some form of mirror or viewing panel is desirable.

1.6. *Emergency Exits.* Emergency exits are provided in the floor and the roof. The normal means of abandoning the aeroplane is by opening the entrance hatch and dropping through, but in the event of this not being possible, the cockpit roof can be jettisoned. An outside handle is required to enable the crew to be rescued in a crash. It has been found that the observer's feet foul the inside door of the hatch and it is recommended that heel recesses be provided under the observer's seat. The pilot wears a normal seat type parachute, but the observer wears a harness with a separate parachute.

4. *Maintenance.*

3.1. *General.* There has been little opportunity for a complete examination of the aircraft and the information given is preliminary only.

3.2. *Engines.*

3.21. The existing exhaust system masks the ignition plugs and the magnetos to a marked degree; the latter cannot be inspected without removing the exhaust tail pipes and magneto air ducts. The plugs are very difficult to remove or replace even with a special spanner.

The system is being re-designed and the question of accessibility of these items is being considered by the Firm.

3.22. An access panel in the lower portion of the bulkhead is required to facilitate the removal of the rear attachment nuts of the carburettor air intake which at present are most inaccessible.

3.23. Handles for hand turning gear were not delivered with the aircraft and it has therefore not been possible to establish whether or not complete rotation for hand starting is possible.

3.24. The flexible drive to the electric R.P.M. indicator generator should be shortened or adequately supported to prevent sagging.

3.3 *Fuel System.*

3.31. Pressure filling for the fuel system has not been provided for on this aircraft in which the balance pipes between each pair of tanks is of 1″ petro-flex. It has been agreed that this is too small even for the existing method of filling and the size is to be increased to 2″ dia.

3.32. An unusual provision in each tank connection is a 'Petroflex Shut Off Union' which automatically shuts off the petrol flow when the pipe union is disconnected and opens the valve when the connection is remade. These seem to work extremely well.

3.4. *Undercarriage.*

3.41. The layout of cables for undercarriage door operation is open to criticism. The flexible cable is led through and around a small eyebolt instead of around a pulley and this is likely to lead to trouble. A modification is required.

3.42. *Hydraulics.* The hydraulic pipework generally needs laying out more neatly and accessibly particularly under the hand pump and in the bomb nacelle where many of the unions are hidden behind a cluster of pipes. A similar criticism is made regarding the pipes behind the passenger's seat where the joints could be repositioned and made accessible.

3.43. The ground warning device for the undercarriage external locks should be rearranged so that it is obvious when the engines are running. At present the red fabric is blown into the undercarriage nacelles out of sight except when the engines are idle.

3.5. *Elevators.*

3.51. The elevator mass balance weight is too close to a tail plane bracing strut on its starboard side. The constructors state that it is equally close to the retracted tail wheel but as the airframe had been dismantled before this was disclosed it was not possible to check this. Any offset through slackness or damage will cause a jamb with the elevator up or down which it may be impossible to release. The layout of this balance should be re-designed.

3.52. The elevator trimmer tab jack and its chain and sprocket should be protected from mud and stones.

3.6. *Rudders.*

3.61. It is not possible to use a grease gun on the rudder trimmer tab jack. This should be repositioned or an angled nipple should be fitted.

3.7. *Stowage.* It is not known if a First Aid stowage is a requirement on this aircraft but no such fitting is provided.

3.8. *Jacking points.* All jacking points should be clearly marked.

Following the above tests the fuselage of W4050 failed on 24 February 1941. It was given temporary repairs at Boscombe Down by de Havilland staff, sufficient for it to be flown back to Hatfield for a full rebuild, returning to Boscombe Down in March. W4050 now had a new fuselage and the engine nacelles had been extended experimentally. The extensions were fairings which projected beyond the trailing edges of the wings which, pending a redesign, prevented the operation of the flaps, therefore all the testing at that stage had to be conducted with the flaps locked in the 'up' position.

The A&AEE report[6] noted that the aeroplane was still 'very difficult to trim accurately in level flight'; on the other hand, the nacelle extensions seemed to have alleviated the vibration: 'This vibration was previously attributed to the engines, but it is evident now that it was, in fact, due to turbulence round the tail, and this had been cured by the extended nacelles. The aeroplane is very much more pleasant to fly now with the longer nacelles'.

The A&AEE report, under 'Recommendations', considered that:

The extended nacelles improve the handling qualities of the aeroplane considerably, and it is recommended that they be fitted to all production aircraft. It is understood that approximately 20 aircraft are being produced with the original short nacelles, and, because there would be considerable delay if the modifications were insisited upon, it has been agreed by this Establishment that these first aircraft will be accepted by the RAF with the short nacelles.

The prototype returned to de Havillands mainly for the temporary nacelles to be removed, an increase in elevator balance and the fitting of fuel tanks which would enable the AUW to be increased to the then maximum overload of 19,500 lb. The aircraft returned to Boscombe Down on 3 May 1941 but a second fuselage failure soon occurred.

The handling tests completed before the second fuselage failure amounted to only 20 flights which logged a total of 12 hours 45 minutes. The stability of W4050 was described as 'unpleasant in bumps and turns'. This lack of stability was not enhanced by the radiator's flaps which, being thermostatically controlled, opened automatically without any prior warning, causing 'a sharp change of trim to tail heaviness', the A&AEE report commenting that the flaps could open at full throttle when the pilot first sighted an enemy aircraft: 'The change of trim is a serious matter which should receive consideration'.

The wing flaps also gave cause for criticism: 'The wing flaps rise too rapidly and the [resultant] change of trim is very sharp'. The flaps were unsatisfactory during that vital phase of flight, the approach to a landing: 'As the flaps go down the aeroplane becomes tail heavy and there is insufficient longitudinal trim for the overload case. When engine is used to assist the approach the tail heaviness increases'.

The A&AEE test crews found the cockpit to be 'too hot at low and medium altitudes and fumes enter during taxying'. The seat became 'uncomfortable after 1½ to 2 hours and the pilot then starts to fidget'. The A&AEE recommended that the seat should be able to be tilted back some 10°.

Although twin engined, the prototype had only one generator fitted. The A&AEE pointed out that: 'In the event of failure [of engine or generator] it is doubtful if the accumulator could supply enough current for the wireless'.

Following its second structure failure, W4050 does not figure in any further A&AEE reports but one is pleased to be able to report that this prototype of one of the most famous wartime aircraft is preserved at Salisbury Hall, near Hatfield where it was built.

The prototype fighter variant, W4052, officially referred to as 'Mosquito N.F.II', 'N.F.' standing for night fighter, was tested at Boscombe Down during the summer of 1941, the first relevant A&AEE Report[6] being dated 23 August 1941.

This aircraft was powered by two Rolls-Royce Merlin 21s of 1,230 hp. The prototype had the now standardised extended engine nacelles and a larger span tailplane of 20 ft 9 inches, compared with the 19 ft 5 inches unit fitted to W4050. As tested the night fighter scaled 18,400 lb, with a C of G 12 inches aft of the datum, this being the maximum permissible for the fighter. The stability – essential for a night fighter which requires to be a stable gun platform – was considered superior to the prototype bomber, W4050. (The bomber was tested at 17,800 lb AUW, C of G 14 inches aft of datum). Although the stability was favourably commented on in level flight, on the climb at 170 mph, the ideal speed, the aeroplane was found to be unstable longitudinally. The climb apart, W4052 was also unstable when gliding at 140 mph with undercarriage and flaps down; when these speeds were increased to 185 mph for the climb and 150 mph when gliding with engine throttled the aircraft was 'just stable'.

The stability was commented on by the A&AEE testers:

> The results are consistent in that the larger tailplane and more forward position of the c of g [essential due to the nose armament] gives increased stability, but the stability is not sufficiently improved by the slightly larger tailplane to be satisfactory.

The possibility of weight increase – inevitable with service aircraft – and the C of G moving further aft led the A&AEE to recommend an increase of the order of 20 to 25 per cent to the size of the tailplane, adding that such a modification should be made as soon as possible for flight testing.

Pending the modification, W4052 was flown[7] at a maximum level speed of 376 TAS at 21,800 ft. During these tests a performance climb terminated abruptly when *both* engines cut out at 23,750 ft.

W4052 was presumably landed safely, for a later report[8] states that the aircraft was tested with two different sizes of tailplane in response to the A&AEE recommendations. The tailplanes had an area of 88 and 98.5 sq ft. respectively (the prototype W4050 had a tailplane of 83 sq ft).

The larger of the two tailplanes was tested first and the aircraft showed an improvement in stability, but not as great an improvement as expected, the report pointing out that:

> Some improvement is, however, necessary if any rearward movement of the c of g takes place and the larger tailplane should be fitted unless some other more convenient means to improve the [longitudinal] stability can be found.

The smaller tailplane was also tested. With the C of G 17.9 inches aft of the datum:

> the aeroplane was so unstable in all conditions of flight . . . no records could be obtained.

With the larger tailplane the C of G – other load factors being the same – was found to be 18.6 inches aft of datum, this being due to the simple fact that the larger tailplane was, of course, itself heavier. In this condition, as noted above, though there was some improvement, the aircraft was still unstable on the climb, at maximum speed in level flight and neutrally stable in level cruise; if the cruise was increased above 280 mph IAS, tail buffeting occurred but was 'not severe'.

The A&AEE considered that for a night fighter which, other considerations apart, would have to be flown extensively on instruments and A.I. radar, even the small improvement in stability conferred by the larger tailplane was desirable and that the consequent increase in buffeting must be accepted.

The large 98.5 sq ft tailplane was also recommended by the A&AEE for fitting to the proposed Mk I photo-reconnaissance Mosquito should the cameras fitted cause the C of G to extend beyond 17.9 inches aft of datum.

While the A&AEE was investigating the stability of the prototype N.F.II, a second night fighter – an early production aircraft, W4070, was also tested to investigate the relative drag imposed by the application of night fighter black finish. The test[9] arose because de Havillands had discovered that one of their production night fighters (W4082) showed a marked maximum speed difference when the aircraft was finished with the matt black paint considered essential by the RAF for any service aircraft operating at night. De Havilland found that W4082 was 26 mph slower with a matt, as compared with a smooth (i.e. eggshell) finish; this was an unexpectedly large figure.

W4070 arrived at Boscombe Down in March 1942, finished by the makers with a matt finish to RDM/2A Spec. The maximum level speed at 21,400 ft (AUW 18,530 lb) was 358 mph TAS. The paint was then stripped and the aircraft repainted with a smooth black finish to DTD308. The level speed was then measured by the A&AEE and found to be 366 mph TAS at 21,400 ft: a difference of only 8 mph. The 'matt' speed was, in point of fact, 6 mph faster than when W4082 was tested by de Havillands and the 'smooth' speed 12 mph slower; even allowing for inevitable differences between seemingly identical production aircraft, this was a large difference. De Havilland put the discrepancy down to the fact that W4070's matt was less matt than the paint on their test aircraft and the A&AEE 'smooth' paint was smoother than the finish Hatfield applied to W4082!

While the finishes were being evaluated the prototype night fighter, W4052, was flown with an interesting airbrake placed peripherally round the fuselage, just aft of the wing trailing edge. The brake had been developed by de Havillands for possible use on night fighters to give pilots the ability of rapidly reducing the speed of their aircraft when in range of a target, following an interception. The A&AEE report noted:[10]

Such a brake must not affect control adversely by causing excessive change of trim or other undesirable characteristics. With the former requirement in mind the designers had departed from the conventional wing air brake flap arrangement, by fitting the brake around the fuselage.

To this end, W4052 was so fitted and flown to Boscombe Down for evaluation. Alas the aims of the design staff at Hatfield were not, it would seem, fulfilled:

By throttling back the engines when flying at 250 mph A.S.I. the aeroplane lost 100 mph in 45 seconds without the use of the air brake. Use of the air brake under otherwise identical conditions reduced this time to 30 seconds. When the brake was applied, considerable buffeting was experienced on the elevator and rudder controls. The aeroplane became slightly tail heavy when the brake was applied, but this could easily be held on the controls; the change of trim at 250 m.p.h. I.A.S. was from 1 division nose down to 1.1/10 divisions nose down.

In its present form the air brake is not considered acceptable as the braking effect is not sufficient and the buffeting experienced is excessive.

The airbrake was not used on any production Mosquitos.

It is not the intention, in the present volume, to discuss the operational career of the Mosquito or, indeed, to enumerate the 27 major variants of the basic design. However, two Mosquitos were of particular interest: in October 1942 the A&AEE tested a Mk VI (HJ662/G) which was a multi-role aircraft: intruder, long-range fighter and escort fighter.

The aircraft was tested at an AUW of 20,835 lb. (It was flown in the intruder role with 2 × 250 general purpose bombs suspended from hard points beneath the wings. Diving and handling tests were also made with the bombs replaced by 2 × 315 lb containers.) The report of this developed production Mosquito reflects the improvement in the basic design when compared with the early machines, the A&AEE reporting that:

> The aircraft is exceptionally manoeuvrable. The controls are effective, well harmonised and reasonably light even in dives to 425 m.p.h. A.S.I. If yaw is applied in the dive, wing drop occurs in the direction of the applied yaw.
>
> The aeroplane is longitudinally and directionally stable under all conditions of flight, except on the glide with flaps and undercarriage down when the aeroplane is neutrally stable longitudinally, and in level flight at low speed when there is a tendency to slight instability.
>
> Laterally the aeroplane is stable. . . . Handling tests made with . . . containers under the wings in lieu of 250 lb bombs showed no detrimental effect on the flying qualities and no buffeting was felt on the ailerons or tail surfaces.

In early 1943, by which time the Mosquito was in very active service with the RAF, the A&AEE was to test a Mosquito bomber, a Mk IV. This aircraft was then highly secret, as reflected by the suffix to its serial – DK290/G – which required it to be guarded 24 hours a day.

DK290/G had been modified to carry 'certain stores', these being the Barnes Wallis bouncing bombs 'Highball', a smaller version of the 'Upkeep' dambusting bomb dropped by Lancasters. Highball was an anti-shipping weapon and was not used operationally but is of interest; there exists in the Imperial War Museum film archives some spectacular footage of trials of the bomb, or rather bombs – two were carried – shot at Reculver, which has since been shown on television. But in 1943 the A&AEE report[12] guardedly stated that 'A number of Mosquito B. Mk IV aircraft are being modified to carry certain stores in the bomb-bay'.

DK290/G was only modified for a mock-up installation to assess the aerodynamic effects of the Highball bombs which weighed 1,100 lb each and required the aircraft to fly (like the 'Upkeep' Lancasters) with the standard bomb doors removed, a streamlined fairing being built round the edges of the bomb bay to lessen drag and possible buffeting.

The A&AEE report on the flight trials of DK290/G is here quoted at length:

2.   *Condition of aircraft relevant to tests.*

2.1. *General.*

For the present series of tests two 'mock-ups' of the stores were carried in the bomb-bay.

2.2. *Loading.*   The envisaged maximum take-off weight is 21,000 lb., with two stores and full fuel. However, the mock-up stores only weighed 28 lb. each, and with the maximum amount of ballast which could safely be stowed internally, the take-off weight during the tests was 19,555 lb. with the centre of gravity 18.3″ aft of the datum point (undercarriage down). This is some 1,500 lb. lighter than the take-off weight will be in service. The anticipated effect of the heavier weight on handling is discussed in paragraph 5.

3.   *Scope of tests.*

Brief handling trials, including dives to the limiting speed of 390 mph ASI were carried out, particular attention being paid to the behaviour of the aicraft on the approach to and at the stall and in dives.

4. *Results of tests.*

The take-off and initial climb, the stall, response to controls and the characteristics of the baulked landing etc., were identical with those reported on for stores removed. . . . The stability and behaviour in dives, although also in general similar, are however, given below:–

4.1. *Stability.*

4.11. *Longitudinal stability.*   Under all conditions of flight, when the airspeed was changed by ± 10 mph from the trimmed speed and the control column released, the aircraft executed gentle phugoids, the amplitudes of which increased in magnitude at a slightly more rapid rate than that experienced with the stores removed.

4.12. *Directional stability.*   Under all conditions of flight, when approximately 20° yaw from the trimmed path was applied in either direction, and the rudder bar then released, the aircraft quickly returned to the original course.

4.13. *Lateral stability.*   Under all conditions of flight, when approximately 30° bank was applied to either port or starboard and the aileron control released, the aircraft continued to fly in a banked attitude, the angle of bank increasing steadily and the nose dropping into a spiral dive.

4.2. *Dives.*   Two dives were made to the limiting speed of 390 mph ASI, one at full throttle, and the other at 1/3rd throttle setting.

Dive 1 (Full throttle).   The aircraft was trimmed for all-out level flight (zero elevator trim) at 10,500 feet, and a dive made at full throttle to 310 mph ASI. A gradually increasing push force was required on the control column as the speed increased, to hold the aircraft in the dive. The maximum force to hold the aircraft in the dive at the limiting speed was slightly less than the corresponding force required with the stores out. As before, recovery was easy, a push force having to be maintained on the control column to prevent excessive accelerations. At the limiting speed, 10° of yaw could be applied easily in either direction, without any ill effects on the other controls.

Dive 2. (1/3rd throttle).   Trimmed for all-out level flight at 10,000 feet, the engine was throttled back and a dive made to the limiting speed of 390 mph ASI. The push force on the control column required to hold the aircraft in the dive was not as great as in the full throttle dive. Recovery was quick and easy, there being less push force needed on the control column than that required in a similar dive with the stores removed.

At the limiting diving speed, 10° yaw could be applied easily in either direction, without any ill effects on the other controls.

4.3. *Airframe vibration in flight.*   With the stores in, the airframe vibration was much less marked than that reported previously with stores out. Since the vibration experienced previously may have been contributed to by a defective magneto setting up an engine vibration, this was again checked with the stores out. This test showed the magnitude of the vibration to be much less. It can therefore be concluded that with or without the stores in situ, vibration is not present to any greater degree than that which occurs on a normal Mosquito IV, and in no way reacts unfavourably on the pilot.

5. *Effect of weight on handling.*

As pointed out in para. 2.2. the tests were made at a weight approximately 1500 lbs. less than the typical Service load envisaged. The effect of this increase in weight can however be estimated from previous handling tests made on this particular aircraft at weights of 19,300 and 20,670 lbs. with c.g. at 18.3″ aft of datum. . . . It was found that the only effect of the increase in weight was to increase the acceleration obtaining at the peaks and troughs of the phugoids, there being no apparent deterioration in longitudinal stability. However, during the recent tests with the modified fuselage, both with and without stores fitted no appreciable accelerations have been observed during flight in phugoid motion and it is apparent that the modifications to the aircraft have improved the longitudinal stability to some extent.

6. *Conclusions.*

   The handling characteristics of this aircraft are satisfactory under the conditions tested.

   Although the aircraft was not tested at the full Service weight of 21,000 lb. . . . it is concluded from other tests made at this Establishment . . . that little difference in the handling characteristics will occur, and therefore the aircraft in its modified form is considered to be satisfactory for Service use at full load with stores fitted.

Such was the versatility of the Mosquito, there can be little doubt that, had it been required to drop 'Highball' in action, it would have performed the operation with the same distinction as the many and varied tasks that the 'wooden wonder' undertook.

The Mosquito continued to serve with the RAF post-war, the last Service sortie being flown by a photographic reconnaissance PR34A, RG314, of No. 81 Squadron on 15 December 1955 during the campaign in Malaya.

When production ceased in 1950, a total of 7,781 Mosquitos (including Canadian and Australian built aircraft) had been delivered: an outstanding record for a wooden aircraft which so very nearly never went into production at all.

CHAPTER NINE

A&AEE Reports 817 and 819

Entry into the Jet Age

The Gloster F.9/40, the prototype of the RAF Meteor, was the first, and indeed, only operational Allied jet aircraft to see service during the Second World War and, although it was to be the first jet to be tested by the A&AEE, it was not the first to fly from Boscombe Down: the paradox is simply explained. The preliminary handling trials of the F.9/40 were based at the Gloster Company's airfield at Moreton Valence.

The test flights of this aircraft, DG205/G, the fourth prototype, were the culmination of many years of struggle by the man who, against a background of delay, disappointment, lack of official encouragement and inadequate funds, had developed the jet engine: Wing Commander (later Sir) Frank Whittle. Whittle's first engine, the 860 lb thrust W.1, had powered the purely experimental Gloster E.28/39 (W4041) which had first flown from Cranwell on 15 May 1941 – the first flight of a British jet propelled aircraft. The logical development of that aircraft was the F.9/40, a twin-engined fighter which was to be named Thunderbolt, though the name was later (in March 1942) changed to Meteor, when the earlier name was allocated to the American P.47.

The F.9/40 project began in 1940, even before the first flight of the E.28/39, as an Air Ministry specification for a twin-engined jet fighter. Two engines were chosen, for the very simple reason that the early jets developed insufficient power for a single engine to offer a worthwhile performance increment over the contemporary piston engined fighters. By the beginning of 1941, the detailed design was complete and, on 7 February 1941, the Ministry of Aircraft Production placed a contract for twelve pre-production prototypes (DG202–213); in the event, only eight prototypes were to be built, the first being DG202/G.

If the F.9/40 jet engines were revolutionary, the same could not be said of the airframes; the Gloster design team, led by W. G. Carter, had produced a conventional monoplane, the only feature of which, engines apart, appeared in 1941 to be in any way forward looking was the tricycle undercarriage.

The power plants installed in DG202/G were Power Jets Whittle W.2Bs, manufactured by the Rover Company; these were non-flight engines, offering only 1,000 lb static thrust, suitable for ground handling only. It is now a matter of historical fact that the Rover Company and Frank Whittle were not, at that time, enjoying a fruitful relationship and already negotiations were in hand to transfer the jet engine's production to Rolls-Royce. After taxi trials, which commenced at Moreton Valence on 3 July 1942, DG202/G was returned to the factory for the fitting of the Rover built flight engines, the W.2/500s, but these engines proved 'troublesome', which was to delay the first flight. In the meantime, the fifth prototype, DG206/G, with two Halford H.1 engines which each developed 1,500 lb static thrust, was prepared for flight.

Thus, no doubt to the disappointment of the Power Jets staff and in particular their chief designer, Frank Whittle, who had so doggedly pioneered the jet engine, DG206/G became the first of the prototypes to fly, which it did on 5 March 1943, powered by the rival Halford engines, though it must be said that these engines owed a great deal to Whittle's design. The first flight of the original prototype F.9/40, DG202/G, powered by two Whittle/Rover B.23s, each rated at 1,526 lb static thrust, was not until 24 July 1943.

By that date, the difficulties between Power Jets and the Rover Company had been resolved by Rolls-Royce taking over Whittle's jet engine production – in exchange, it is said, for a tank engine factory, the deal being concluded in a Clitheroe pub, over a five shilling (25p) wartime dinner between S. B. Wilkes of Rovers and Lord Hives of Rolls-Royce. The first Rolls-Royce jet engine produced was the centrifugal W.2B/23 Welland of 1,700 lbs s.t.; two were fitted to the fourth prototype Meteor, DG205/G, being, in June 1943, the first Rolls-Royce jet engines to fly. This power plant was the one selected for the production Meteor Is which were to be built at the rate of 80 a month. As a matter of historical interest, DG204/G, the third prototype, was flown with yet another early jet, the Metrovick F.3/1 of 2,000 lb s.t.; this was the first British axial flow engine and was later developed into the Beryl. DG208/G flew with Rolls-Royce W.R1s which had a 2,000 lb s.t., and DG209/G with a later development by Rolls-Royce, the W.2B/37, which was to be the prototype of a truly seminal engine, the Derwent which, when developed in the Nene, would power most of the early jets worldwide.

The first jet to be flown by the A&AEE was the fourth F.9/40 prototype, DG205/G, powered by the two Rolls-Royce W.2B/23s. Because of the historical importance of the initial handling trials of this, Britain's first operational jet, the relevant A&AEE Report[1], is here reproduced in full.

MOST SECRET   1st Part of Report No. A.&.A.E.E./817

AEROPLANE AND ARMAMENT EXPERIMENTAL ESTABLISHMENT
BOSCOMBE DOWN

Gloster F9/40 — 2-W2B/23 engines
Preliminary handling trials

A.&.A.E.E. ref:– CTO/AM.77.
M.A.P. ref:–   SB.50809/DD/RDA
Period of tests:– 24th and 29th February 1944

Summary

Pilots from this Establishment have flown two of the prototype aircraft at the Makers' works and the following are the preliminary findings. Most flying was done on DG.205/G at 11,300 lb and C.G. at 0.31 of the AMC, conditions corresponding to T.S.L.* with an aft C.G. position.

* T.S.L – Typical Service Load
        (i.e. crew fuel and armament for a representative operational sortie)

(i)   The aircraft is easy to fly and from the point of view of quietness, absence of vibration and fumes, etc. is very pleasant.

(ii)   The controls are very badly harmonised as the rudder is immovable at ordinary level and diving speeds after the first few degrees of movement; the elevator is too heavy, whilst the ailerons are too light at low to moderate speeds.
A directional oscillation of small amplitude is present in bumpy conditions and this must be eliminated before accurate aiming is possible. The elevator trimmer is much too sensitive and has an excessive amount of backlash.

(iii)   The seat should be tilted back a few degrees, whilst repositioning of the throttles, the fuel shut-off controls, and some engine instruments, is desirable.

(iv)   An emergency braking system is essential, and continuous reading fuel contents gauges are required.

(v)   The minimum time restriction of 10 seconds on throttle movement from idling to max. rpm. should be eliminated, as should be the 5° maximum aileron movement at high speeds.

(vi)   The aircraft appears to be statically stable stick fixed and also gives the impression of being dynamically stable.

(vii)   The stick force per g in recovery from trimmed dives at 300–400 mph ASI is about 6 and in sustained turns at 300 mph ASI is about 8.

(viii) The rate of roll compares favourably with Spitfire performance.

1.   Introduction.

1.1 It was considered desirable that A.&A.E.E. pilots should fly this type of aircraft at the Contractor's airfield in order to gain preliminary experience and impressions of this aircraft with its revolutionary mode of propulsion.
Accordingly four pilots carried out five short flights and the following report deals with their assessment of the aircraft. It is stressed, however, that some of the conclusions arrived at may be modified as experience is gained, and this report should be regarded therefore as tentative.

1.2 A preliminary letter was sent to DD/RDA on 12.3.44 giving the essence of this report.

2.   Condition of aircraft.

2.1 The Gloster F9/40 is a low-wing metal monoplane with a tricyle undercarriage, and is powered by two W2B/23 engines giving a nominal static thrust of about 1,600 lb. at 16,900 rpm. The horizontal tail surfaces are placed some distance above the line of the fuselage. The control surfaces are fabric covered except for the ailerons on DG.205 and the elevators on DG.208; the ailerons are fitted with balance tabs whilst the other controls have normal adjustable trimmers.
Most flying was carried out on DG.205/G, but some flights were made on DG.208/G.

2.2 According to the Firm, DG.205/G was at about T.S.L., the weight being approximately 11,300 lb and C.G. at 0.31 of the AMC., a position nearly at the aft C.G. On this aircraft the aileron balance tabs were working normally; in addition to lengths of cord on both sides of the rudder trimmer some was attached to one side of the fin along almost its whole length about 6–8″ from the leading edge.

3.   Handling.

3.1 *Cockpit layout.*   This is fairly reasonable, though the following points are made:–

151

(a)   The sitting position would be more comfortable were the seat tilted back a few degrees.

(b)   View is fairly good but elimination of the heavy horizontal frame above the windscreen is highly desirable.

(c)   The throttle positions might be improved slightly by moving them downwards and forwards as they are felt to be rather high. This would bring them closer to the trimmer controls which would be advantageous.

(d)   The controls for the fuel pressure shut off valves could, with advantage, be placed in front of the pilot as these are important emergency controls and ought not to be on either side of the seat at the rear where access is rather difficult.

(e)   More satisfactory fuel contents gauges are required, preferably of the continuous reading type so that a close check on the fuel available may be kept more readily than can be done at present with the 'double-push' button type.

(f)   A re-grouping of the instruments, in order that the principal engine instruments are together, would be an improvement.

(g)   The form of individual rudder pedal adjustment is not liked and seems unnecessary.

3.2 *Engines.*   The starting and use of these is simple and only the following points require comment:–

(a)   The throttle controls are too stiff.

(b)   Restriction of 10 seconds on minimum time for opening up from idling to maximum rpm is a serious disadvantage and unless engine development renders it unnecessary, some form of automatic delay of the throttle opening for use with sudden throttle lever movements would be a necessity for Service use.

(c)   The throttle lever movement has little effect for the first half but near the maximum power position the control is very sensitive. A more even balancing of the engine response to throttle movement would be helpful.

3.3 *Taxying.*   Generally straightforward, though the response to throttles is much slower than with conventional aircraft. On DG.205/G the castoring of the nose wheel was very stiff, possibly due to the fairly aft C.G. and hence reduced leverage of the nose wheel about the castoring axis.

3.4 *Take-off.*   It is advisable to run up to take-off rpm before re-releasing the brakes to avoid the 10 second throttle delay affecting the run. Take-off is straightforward and easy, without any tendency to swing, and the run is fairly short, though the initial climb is poor. The latter might be improved with experience.

3.5 *Climb.*   The aircraft was climbed at full throttle until an engine surge occurred at 13,000 ft. To the pilot this was in the nature of a back-fire, but its effect on the aircraft was not very noticeable. An increase in speed or decrease in height or power stopped the surge for the time being.

3.6 General flying.

3.61 *Controls.*   These are very badly harmonised and must be improved. The elevator is the most acceptable of the three, as this is sensitive, but it is heavy for a fighter aircraft (see para. 5 for measurements). The rudder, particularly on DG.208/G is very heavy indeed at moderate speeds and upwards, and can only be moved a degree or two either way; within this range the response of the aircraft is good. The ailerons are very light and effective but completely lack feel and self-centring qualities up to about 200–250 mph ASI. Above that speed they become heavier, being satisfactory around 300–350 mph ASI, but are a little heavy at 400 mph. A limitation of 5° movement at this speed is imposed and clearly this must be raised for Service use.

In bumpy conditions a directional oscillation is most apparent and this can be induced in calm air by applying a little rudder and then centralising the control. These

152

oscillations are fairly rapid ($^3/_4$ – 1 per second) and though the amplitude is small the movement is quite pronounced whilst the decay is very gradual in still air. Clamping the rudder pedals firmly does not seem to affect the motion appreciably. This feature is considered serious and must be eradicated otherwise aiming accuracy will be impaired.

3.62 *Trim.* The elevator trimmer is extremely sensitive, 45–60° of wheel movement being adequate for all flight conditions, whilst there is an excessive amount of backlash, etc. amounting to about 40° wheel movement in the circuit. This control must be improved. The rudder trimmer is rather less sensitive than the elevator trimmer and is regarded as acceptable. No aileron trimmer is fitted. There is hardly any change in longitudinal trim with engine and the change with flaps and undercarriage is very small. A left wing low tendency at low speed changes to right wing low at high speed, but owing to the lack of aileron trimmer, this cannot be trimmed out.

3.63 *Stability.* No dynamic stability tests were made but the aircraft gives the impression of being longitudinally stable.

3.64 *Dive.* At present the limiting speed is 400 mph ASI. The acceleration in the dive with power on is normal at low or moderate speeds but rapidly becomes greater as speed is gained; deceleration on recovery is slow. (see para. 5.1 for forces in dive).

3.65 *Single engine handling.* This seems to be very good as at 150 mph ASI the aircraft can be held on the rudder without retrimming, with only a moderate foot load when one engine is throttled right back and the other is at climbing power.

3.7 *Approach and landing.* This process is straightforward and easy, the approach speed used being 120 mph ASI for gliding turns, reducing to 95–100 mph ASI when coming over the aerodrome boundary. A fair amount of buffeting is present with undercarriage down. The latter is fairly soft with good shock-absorbing qualities whilst the brakes are smooth and positive in action.

The brakes are operated by air contained in a bottle but no compressor is fitted, nor is there an emergency system; The latter is an essential requirement, particularly with a tricycle undercarriage.

3.8 *Baulked landing.* On opening the throttle from 110 mph ASI with flap and undercarriage down, the aircraft lost about 100 ft. in height before commencing to climb away; part of this loss might have been due to unnecessarily slow opening of the throttle.

4. Noise, ventilation, etc.

4.1 The aircraft is comparatively free from engine noise but at higher speeds aerodynamic noise is appreciable.

4.2 There is no vibration and this is a most commendable feature (though ironically, it makes the pilot much more aware of atmospheric 'bumps').

4.3 The cockpit is comfortably warm up to 13,000 ft., the highest altitude reached, but some additional ventilation will probably be required low down in warm weather.

4.4 No fumes were noticed.

5. Quantitative measurements.

These are approximate and no calibrations are available, but are quoted to give some indication of the static stability, rolling capabilities, control forces, etc.

5.1 *Static stability, engine on:*

ASI mph	Elev position degrees	Trim position units down	Remarks
160	$+1\frac{3}{8}$	$+1\frac{1}{4}$	Statically stable stick fixed
200	$+1\frac{7}{8}$	$+1\frac{1}{8}$	but stick free rather
300	—	$+\frac{7}{8}$	indeterminate probably owing
350	$+2\frac{3}{8}$	$+1\frac{5}{8}$	to poor circuit (see
395	—	$+\frac{3}{4}$ to $+\frac{7}{8}$	para. 3.62)

5.2 *Stick forces in dives and turns.*

Height: 10,000 ft. Accelerometer readings quoted

Trimmed speed mph ASI	Recovery at 4 g from trimmed dive		Steady turns at 4 g	
	Stick force lb.	Stick force per 'g'	Stick force lb.	Stick force per 'g'
300	15	5	24	8
350	17	$5\frac{1}{2}$	—	—
395	17	$5\frac{1}{2}$	—	—

5.3 *Time to roll from 45° port bank to 45° starboard bank.*

ASI mph	Applied aileron	Stick force lb.	Time secs.	Rate of roll degree aileron degrees/sec.	Remarks
200	5°	10–15	3–4	5	These rates compare
340	5°	10–15	$2\frac{1}{2}$	7	favourably with Spitfire performance.

6. Conclusions.

(i)   The aircraft is easy to fly and the comparative quiet and freedom from vibration make it very pleasant in these respects.

(ii)   The control harmonisation should be improved by lightening the rudder considerably and the elevator moderately; the ailerons should be made heavier at low speeds.

(iii)   The directional oscillation should be eliminated.

(iv)   An improved, less sensitive, elevator trimmer, free from backlash, is required.

(v)   Some re-arrangement of the pilot's controls and repositioning of the seat is advisable.

(vi)   An emergency braking system is necessary.

(vii)   The 10-second minimum time restriction on pilot's throttle opening should be abolished.

(viii) The rolling performance seems very good for a twin engine aircraft but the restriction to 5° maximum aileron movement at high speeds should be eliminated.

7.   Postscript.

An additional flight made on 16th March on DG208/G without the aileron tab balance has brought out the following points:–

7.1 The ailerons are heavy at speeds above 300 mph ASI but are reasonably effective; at 350 mph ASI and up to 400 mph a vibration or snatch is felt on the control column in the lateral plane and though silent, the snatch is most noticeable and is particularly unpleasant.

7.2 In bumpy conditions the directional oscillation is accompanied by a rolling motion and the aircraft tends to fly in a series of left and right hand banked turns.

Before the prototype had flown, the first of the twenty production aircraft were on the Gloster Company's line; the haste to get production under way, in contrast to the years of official indifference, was no doubt due, in part at least, to intelligence reports of the progress in jet propulsion being made in Germany.

The first twenty production aircraft bore the RAF serials EE210 – 229 and were named Meteor Is. The first, EE210, was, as part of an Allied agreement, shipped to the USA (an early Whittle jet engine had preceded it). A Bell YP-59A Airacomet was received in 1944 in exchange. Of the remaining 19 production aircraft, fifteen went to the RAF and four were retained for testing and evaluation at Moreton Valence. These Meteor Is, EE209, EE211, EE212 and DG208, were to figure in A&AEE reports.

The immediate pre-occupation of the testers was to assess whether the modifications recommended by the A&AEE had improved the marked directional instability from which the prototype had suffered. The tests were conducted on 6 June 1944 (D Day! One must commend the objective detachment of the A&AEE). The subsequent Report stated:

1.1 In the first Part of this Report certain aspects of the controls and the aircraft, notably a directional oscillation, were the subject of special comment. Since then the firm has been working along several lines to improve the various items criticised. As a certain amount of progress had been made, arrangements were made for pilots of the Establishment to fly the modified aircraft.

1.2 Three pilots from this Establishment visited Moreton Valence on 6th June and made six flights on [the] four aircraft.
      The findings are:–

(i)   EE.212 alone is considered satisfactory from the above aspect, but the rudder now seems ineffective for small movements and heavy for large movements. The lower part of this control is metal covered and an 0.3 to 1 ratio combined gear trimmer and balance tab is fitted. The other controls are fabric covered.

(ii)   The 5° increase in wing tip dihedral has made no apparent difference to the directional oscillations which are still present on the other aircraft.

(iii)   Locking the aileron geared tab has made this control too heavy for a fighter. The elevators also are rather heavy, with the possible exception of the metal covered control on DG.208.

(iv)   The increased power available in EE.209 [this aircraft had RR W.2B/23s fitted] has improved the performance appreciably, especially on take-off.

(v)   A thorough investigation of the handling qualities of a representative aircraft should be made as soon as possible, as several features are present which should be explored more fully.

Less than a month after the report had been written, the first two Meteor Is had been delivered to 616 Squadron at Culmhead, to convert the pilots from their Spitfires. By the end of July 1944, 616 Squadron was posted to Manston in Kent to intercept the V1 flying bombs. The squadron was still mainly equipped with Spitfires but had a flight of seven Meteors. On 4 August 1944, F/O Dean made history by bringing down a V1; his guns had jammed and he formated on the missile at 365 mph and succeeded in tipping it over with his wingtip. F/O Dean was flying EE216 and the sortie was the first ever jet v jet combat – though admittedly a little one-sided. By the end of August, 616, now completely converted to the jets, had shot down – conventionally – 13 V1s.

The German jet fighter, the Messerschmitt Me 262, was by then being used operationally against the USAAF 8th Air Force B-17s and B-24s, and Meteors were being prepared for genuine jet v jet combat over Europe. Prior to moving to a continental base, four Meteors were used with the USAAF in exercises, flying against P-47 Thunderbolts and P-51 Mustangs for the Meteor pilots to gain experience of manoeuvring against high performance fighters and to give the US piston engined escort fighter pilots some idea of what to expect when confronted by the German jets. Useful as these joint exercises undoubtedly were, in point of fact the Me 262 was, in many ways, a far superior aircraft to the Meteor, which was still considered by the A&AEE to be distinctly underdeveloped and rushed into service when, firstly, the V1s appeared, followed by the Me 262. Prior to that, the official policy towards jet propulsion had been vague, an attitude which seems to have persisted even after the aircraft were operational.

On 5 October 1944, two months after the operational début of the Meteor I, Wing Commander J. W. Truran, then Senior Handling Technical Officer in the Performance Division at Boscombe Down, wrote a minute to the Superintendent, Mr. Scott-Hall. In this confidential memorandum,[2] Wing Commander Truran welcomed the fact that the Meteor testing was at last to be based on Boscombe Down:

It seems more than clear [he wrote] after talking to the pilots, that although they did not realise it at the time, they were working under severe handicaps by having to carry out their tests at the firm [Moreton Valence]. . . . The chief objection in the case of the Meteor aircraft is that the pilots were asked to fly four aircraft, all in slightly different form, and having flown each one once were then asked to render a report. Since the jet propelled aircraft is such a new feature there is no doubt that a pilot requires some little time in which to get used to them, and comments which were made, therefore, at the time of their visit and which were incorporated in their reports, are no longer agreed to in all details although generally speaking there is agreement within broad conclusions reached.

There appears to be a complete lack of information from the Ministry of Aircraft Production as to the future operational role of the Meteor. We all know, of course, that there is considerable political pressure being put on the operation of jet propelled aircraft, but from the performance of this aircraft [Meteor I] it would appear that it is operationally unsuited to any particular role in the present theatres of war. The reasons for this are that the rate of climb is too low to make it suitable for interceptor work and the directional control is unsatisfactory for low level attack work. It would assist our trials considerably if we had some guidance from [the] Ministry of Aircraft Production as to the proposed use of these aircraft.

In the light of this frank letter, it is of interest to consider the actual performance of the Meteor I, powered by two 1,700 lb s.t. Rolls-Royce Welland Is:

Armament:	Four 20 mm Mk III Hispano cannon
Maximum speed:	385 mph at sea level
	410 mph at 30,000 ft
Initial rate of climb:	2,155 ft/min
Service ceiling:	40,000 ft

For comparison, the performance of the contemporary Me 262A-1a, *Schwalbe* (Swallow) was

Armament:	Four 30 mm Mk 108 cannon
Maximum speed:	500 mph at sea level
	538 mph at 29,560 ft
Initial rate of climb:	3,937 ft/min
Service ceiling:	37,565 ft

The Meteor I had a marginally better ceiling and, it must be said, far better engines; the Me 262's Junkers Jumos were underdeveloped, with very poor reliability and short life (about 11 hours). In the event, the expected jet v jet conflict never arose, the war ending before sufficient Meteors were available on continental bases – an essential prerequisite due to their limited range.

The figures for the Me 262 would not, of course, have been available, in detail, to the A&AEE in 1944; the adverse comments about the Meteor in Wing Commander Truran's memo were possibly made with the rather better performance of Britain's second jet fighter in mind. That aircraft had also been under test at Boscombe Down: the de Havilland E.6/41, 'Spider Crab', later to be re-named Vampire.

The project, known simply as the D.H.100, had begun when Major Halford, the engine designer working with de Havillands, had been one of the few witnesses to the early flights of the Gloster Whittle E.28/39 at Cranwell. As Sir Geoffrey de Havilland put it in his autobiography *Sky Fever*:

> Halford was enthusiastic about the engine [the Whittle W.1] and . . . was invited to design a production jet engine of greater thrust, suitable for a jet fighter, and it was decided that Bishop*, our chief designer, should at the same time get out plans for a single seater fighter 'plane. The result of the combined effort was the Vampire.

The fundamental difference between the Meteor I and the D.H.100 Vampire was, whereas the former had been built as a conventional twin-engined fighter, able to accept such jet engines as would be available (including at least one example (EE227) flying with Rolls-Royce Trent turbo-props), the Vampire, like the Spitfire, was designed around a specific engine, the engine in question being the H.1, later to be named Goblin, designed by Major Frank Halford. Though it is true that this excellent power plant was a variation on the Whittle centrifugal

---

* Roland Bishop, de Havilland's Chief Designer who was also responsible for the Mosquito.

turbo-jet, it promised 2,500 lb s.t. – an increment over the Whittle W.2/500 engines of some 1,000 lb thrust. This increase in power was due in part to a revision of the combustion chambers which, in the Halford engine, fed the turbine directly, instead of the reversed flow of the Power Jet/Rover W.2/500s and Rolls-Royce Wellands which powered the F.9/40 prototypes and Meteor Is. (The next Rolls-Royce engine, the Derwent, would use the same arrangement of the combustion chambers as the de Havilland H.1.) The power output of the H.1 was considered just sufficient for a small single-engined fighter and, since it was all 'in House', the airframe was designed around it.

The experimental Gloster E.28/39 and the Heinkel 178 were, of course, also single-engined, but these aircraft had a simple direct entry to the turbo-jet compressor with a long, tailpipe running the length of the fuselage. The de Havilland design consisted of a short nacelle containing the engine and cockpit with the wings attached, the tail unit being carried on two slender booms, thereby achieving a very light airframe with a short efficient tailpipe. The problem of air entry to the compressor was solved most elegantly with neat intakes at each wing root, with a bifurcated pipe to the engine. The D.H.100 could be said to be the first true British jet fighter, in that its shape was a consequence of its jet propulsion, rather than jet engine being adapted to suit a conventional airframe, as was the case with the Meteor. The net result was the first Allied jet fighter to exceed 500 mph in level flight, which the prototype LZ548 – the first flight of which was on 26 September 1943 – later achieved.

The second prototype D.H.100, MP838/G, was the one evaluated at the A&AEE in April 1944, becoming the first jet-powered aircraft to fly from Boscombe Down. The relevant Handling Trial Report[3] makes an interesting comparison with that of the Meteor. It is here reproduced.

TOP SECRET   1st Part of Report No. A. & A.E.E./819
                                                                              1 June 1944

AEROPLANE AND ARMAMENT EXPERIMENTAL ESTABLISHMENT
BOSCOMBE DOWN

De Havilland E6/41 MP.838/G
(Halford H1A)

Handling Trials

A.&A.E.E. ref: CTO/AS.84
M.A.P. ref: SB.56746/RDL1(d)
Period of tests: April 1944

1.   Introduction.

The aircraft dealt with in this Report is a jet propelled single seat fighter built to specification E6/41 and powered by a single Halford H1A engine. The aircraft was sent to this Establishment for tests to assess its suitability as an RAF fighter. To-date, owing to the limited time available and the pre-occupation of the aircraft in other tests, only a few flights have been made to assess handling characteristics. This Report is therefore of a preliminary nature only, a comprehensive Report being impossible, and the comments are liable to modification in the light of subsequent experience.

2. Condition of aircraft relevant to tests.

2.1 *General description.* The pilot's cockpit and engine are situated in a central nacelle, and air is supplied to the compressor from an intake in the leading-edge of each wing root, the jet nozzle being set in the tail of the nacelle. Two out-rigged booms carry the tailplane and fins and rudders, and the construction is of metal stressed skin throughout, except for the forward portion of the central nacelle which is of plywood monocoque. Armament consists of four forward firing 20 mm guns mounted in the belly of the nacelle. The aircraft has a tricycle undercarriage.

The salient features of the aircraft were:

A Halford HIA engine
Compressor air intake in each wing root leading-edge
Support for wing drop tank beneath each wing outboard of tail booms
4 × 20 mm. guns in nacelle belly, muzzles sealed, ejection chutes open.
Camera gun aperture in nose of nacelle
Sliding cockpit hood
Whip aerial above nacelle, type 90 aerial beneath port wing
Retractable tricycle undercarriage with twin contact anti-shimmy nose wheel
Rubber skids on tail booms
Pitot-static head on starboard fin

Normal split trailing-edge flaps were fitted to the wings, extending from the ailerons to the nacelle.

All control surfaces were metal covered and the ailerons and rudders were fitted with geared balance tabs.

A trimmer tab was provided on the elevator only, and a length of elastic rubber cord was attached to a crank in the elevator control circuit acting so as to move the control column forward.

2.2 *Loading.* The aircraft was flown at the following take-off loading:

Weight (lb)	Centre of gravity position
8495	6.5 ins. aft of datum
	0.272 SMC

The above centre of gravity position is with undercarriage down. Retracting the undercarriage moves the centre of gravity about 0.1 ins. aft.

This loading was based on the information available at the time, and should represent approximately the normal loading of the type with full fuel, oil, ammunition, etc.

2.3 *Airframe limitations.* The following airframe limitations were applicable throughout the period of tests:

*Maximum diving speed	510 mph ASI
Maximum speed with flaps down	200 mph ASI
Maximum speed with undercarriage down	170 mph ASI

3. Tests made.

The aircraft has been flown at the above loading and an assessment made of the controls and flying qualities. As stated in para. 1 it has not been possible to carry out complete tests since the aircraft was also engaged on other urgent work, consequently this Report is based on the results of a small number of flights and may be subject to later modification and amplification.

Comments are also given on the cockpit layout, view, etc.

* This was based on the maximum speed covered by contractor's trials up to the time of these tests.

4. Cockpit Layout.

Taken as a whole the cockpit of this aircraft is one of the best among modern single-seat fighter aircraft, being comfortable and well laid-out with all controls and instruments readily accessible.

4.1 *Ease of entry and comfort.* Entry to the cockpit was gained direct from the ground via a retractable footstep on the port side of the nacelle, and was satisfactory, though it required rather more effort from a man of short stature due to the height of the footstep. The step was automatically retracted by a spring when the pilot's weight was removed, thus ensuring retraction of the step before flight. Though advantageous the device has disadvantages during maintenance work, but these can be easily overcome by making up a suitable distance piece for insertion on the ground.

The sliding hood was operated by a rotating handle position just below the starboard coaming of the cockpit, and operated easily on the ground. Its operation in flight was not investigated.

The seating position was comfortable and the latest type of seat harness was fitted which had a quick-release box similar to that employed on parachutes. A large diversity of opinion exists among pilots as to whether the new type is an improvement over the long-established Sutton harness.

No cockpit heating was provided on this prototype aircraft on which the hood was provided with sealing but no cabin pressurisation; as production aircraft will have pressure cabins any criticism is relevant only to this particular aircraft. This aircraft was pleasantly warm up to 15,000 ft. and a ventilator was provided. With the hood sealed the ventilator operated in the normal manner.

With the sliding hood closed the noise level was low, and what noise there was seemed mostly aerodynamic, there being practically no noise from the engine. The increase of noise with speed was very slight. On one occasion the hood was opened whilst gliding, but with the hood about three-quarters back a very high pitched note developed which was so uncomfortable as to require immediate closing of the hood. On the whole the general absence of noise in flight was a most striking feature.

4.2 *View.* On the ground and in the air the view directly forwards was very good for an aircraft of the single-seat fighter category, but taken generally the view was disappointing. The windscreen and side panel frames were thick and compared unfavourably with other modern fighter windscreens. The hood was situated rather far back in relation to the pilot and a view sideways was directed at the front edge of the hood which gave a blind spot of approximately 4 ins width. This was caused by the thick frames of the windscreen and hood and the forward portion of the hood which was opaque where two layers of material were pressed together.

Upwards and forwards there was considerable obstruction to view from the top frames of the windscreen and hood. The view to the rear could be considerably improved; no rear view mirror was fitted and it was only just possible to see the rudders. No clear view panel was provided.

On the whole the view in the forward hemisphere was good except where obstructed by the canopy framework, and by modern standards the rearwards view was bad. Whilst it is fully realised that a pressure cabin imposes limitations on hood design it is considered that an improvement over the existing view should be made.

4.3 Control layout.

4.31 *Flying controls.* The flying controls were laid out in conventional manner and full control movement was easily obtainable on the ground and no excessive friction or play in the various circuits was present. The control column was of the vertical grip split type. It is thought that the more usual spade grip would be better, as it provides for a wide range of personal preference in the manner of holding the control column.

The rudder was controlled by pedals of the pendulum type and the pedals could be easily adjusted for leg length by lifting them separately and dropping them into one of a number of slots.

A set of locking struts was provided for the control column and rudder pedals and it was not possible to sit in the cockpit with the locks in place. An alternative method of locking the rudders and elevators was provided, which consisted of pins inserted in the tail booms. Red flags were attached to these pins, and it is understood that they are normally used for rigging purposes.

The elevator trimmer was operated by a fairly large hand wheel mounted on the inboard side of the throttle box on the port side of the cockpit, level with the pilot's thigh. The control was satisfactory in position and operation, showed no tendency to slip, and the gearing was satisfactory. A trimmer position indicator was mounted on the instrument panel and was satisfactory.

4.32 *Engine controls.*   The engine controls were situated in a box on the port side of the cockpit and consisted of a throttle lever and a fuel cock control, which were well placed and satisfactory in operation. The throttle was positioned at the top of the box and moved lightly and easily in the conventional manner. The control showed no tendency to slip or creep, and though no friction damper was fitted such a device did not seem necessary. No gate was provided on the quadrant at the take-off position, but it is understood that one is to be fitted; this is most desirable.

The fuel cock control lever projected from the bottom of the throttle box and moved from the rear to the front of the segment to turn the fuel on. There was little chance of the control being misused, as the lever had to be moved through about 140° and the 'Off' and 'On' position were clearly marked. This single control lever operated all tanks.

4.33 *Hydraulic controls.*   The undercarriage control projected from the rear of the throttle box and was satisfactory and easy in operation. Before the undercarriage could be set in motion the lever had to be moved slightly outboard to clear the gate at the 'Up' and 'Down' positions. A safety device was incorporated in the system which prevented operation of the undercarriage when the weight of the aircraft was on the wheels. It is thought that such a device is most unsatisfactory on any aircraft and in particular on an aircraft with a tricycle undercarriage and low drag, as in the event of the brakes failing it is impossible to stop the aircraft quickly by dropping it on its belly, and consequently serious damage may result from a collision. It is suggested that this lock be replaced by a mechanical trip device operated by the pilot.

The undercarriage indicator was of standard pattern and was positioned low on the port instrument panel and was not readily seen, while in strong sunlight it was not easy to see whether or not the lamps were lit. A red warning light was positioned in the centre of the instrument panel and lit if the throttle was closed when the wheels were not locked down.

The flaps were operated by a lever in the rear of the throttle box and inboard of the undercarraige control. There were three positions 'Up', 'Neutral', and 'Down'. Any desired flap position could be obtained by returning the lever to 'Neutral'. The control was satisfactory in siting and operation. The flap positon indicator was suitably mounted inboard of the undercarraige indicator on the lower port instrument panel; the scale was marked in 10° divisions and was open and easy to read. The take-off position (30°) was marked in red.

4.34 *General.*   The brakes were operated pneumatically by a lever on the forward side of the control column and differential braking was available in the normal manner by moving the rudder pedals.

The hydraulic hand pump was situated on the floor of the cockpit on the left of the seat and the emergency system selector valve was positioned beside the pump. The selector valve was a little inaccessible but could still be reached. Two emergency methods of lowering the undercarriage were provided in the event of engine pump failure. These were (a) by the hand pump and the normal hydraulic system, and (b) by the hand pump and a separate system of pipelines brought into use by operating the selector valve. Use of method (b) would presumably only be necessary if the normal hydraulic lines were shot away, in which event it would not be possible to operate the flaps. No emergency circuit for the flaps is however provided.

The switch layout was satisfactory and all switches were clearly labelled. Tumbler switches for the various services and the engine starter button were carried on a panel on the starboard side of the cockpit. The VHF selector box was positioned low on the port instrument panel.

4.4 *Instrument layout.* A standard blind flying panel was mounted centrally and a smaller panel underneath carried the three fuel contents gauges. These gauges were of the constant-reading type and were easily seen; they appeared to be reasonably accurate in level flight, but when climbing or diving became inaccurate. A reflector gunsight was mounted above the central panel and employed the windscreen as a reflector. It did not interfere with the forward view.

The port instrument panel contained the more important engine instruments (i.e. oil temperature, oil pressure, fuel pressure, engine speed indicator, rear bearing temperature, jet pipe temperature) and the undercarriage and flap position indicators.

The starboard panel contained the compass, oxygen supply indicator, suction gauge, pneumatic pressure gauge, and ammunition indicator.

In general the instrument layout was neatly arranged and satisfactory.

4.5 Emergency exit.

In the event of an emergency the hood could be jettisoned by pulling a release handle mounted forward of the normal hood operating gear on the starboard side of the cockpit. The release lever was painted red and was easily accessible, but before the lever could be pulled it would be necessary to extract a pin. It is considered that these two operations are unsatisfactory and it is suggested that the pin be replaced by wire of a gauge sufficiently heavy to prevent inadvertent release, but which would shear under a normal pull on the jettison lever.

With the hood jettisoned there should be ample space for the pilot to escape, but unless the aircraft were first inverted there would appear to be a danger of him hitting the tailplane.

In the event of a crash-landing the hood could be pushed back from outside by pressing a release button on the nacelle. Should the aircraft become inverted on the ground it would be impossible to release the pilot without first lifting the aircraft.

5. Ground handling and flying qualities.

5.1 *Taxying.* The taxying qualities of the aircraft were very satisfactory and remained so in winds of up to 20 mph (the highest encountered). The undercarriage possessed excellent shock-absorbing qualitites and on a rough airfield surface up to a speed of 110 mph the degree of comfort was outstanding, the action of the nose-wheel eliminating almost all pitching. The forward view when taxying was unobstructed and the brakes were smooth and effective in action. There was a slight tendency for the aircraft to swerve to the right and occasional slight application of the left wheel brake was necessary.

5.2 *Take-off and initial climb.* The manufacturer quoted the optimum flap setting for take-off as 30° and this angle was used throughout the tests, together with the elevator trimmer set in the neutral position. The normal procedure used for take-off was to run the engine up to take-off rpm holding the aircraft stationary by use of the brakes, and then to release the brakes when the desired engine speed was attained. There was no inherent tendency for the aircraft to swing, but occasionally a slight swing did develop at the start of the run due either to the nose wheel being slightly out of line or to unsymmetrical unbraking. Any such swing was easily checked by use of the brakes. Acceleration was smooth and reasonably good. In order to obtain the shortest ground run a definite 'pull-off' was required; the minimum speed at which this could be done was about 95 mph ASI. The run was moderately long by comparison with normal fighter standards. The aircraft left the ground cleanly and the initial clumb away was flat, the aircraft taking some time to attain the best climbing speed. The acceleration in flight could be assisted by retracting the undercarriage as soon as the aircraft was clear of the ground, retraction taking about 2 seconds. It was possible to raise the flaps immediately after the undercarriage, though a longer pause is advisable. There was no appreciable change of trim or sink when the wheels and flaps were raised.

The optimum climbing speed at low altitudes given by the manufacturers was about 220 mph ASI. The rate of climb was poor by comparison with other modern fighter aircraft. Sufficient elevator trim was available to trim out the stick load on the climb. The aircraft tended to yaw to starboard at climbing speeds, no rudder trimmer was fitted but action was taken by adjusting the geared balance tabs, though no further flying has been possible since this adjustment was made.

Should an engine failure occur during the initial climb away this aircraft would appear to be more advantageously placed than more conventional types, as the deceleration is small due to low drag and absence of propeller drag, thus giving the pilot more time to find a suitable landing space.

5.3 Controls.

(a) *Elevator.* The elevator was light and effective throughout the speed range, and was satisfactory. At high speed there was a slight buffeting of the elevator which caused a small amplitude vibration of the control column. Although this was somewhat unpleasant for the pilot it was not considered to be serious. It was noted that the elevator end skin in the rudder cut-away portion was dented and this may have accentuated the buffet.

(b) *Ailerons.* The ailerons were excellent and no improvement could be required except that the slight change of lateral trim which occurred with speed might be with advantage eliminated.

The ailerons were light and effective throughout the speed range and the general 'feel' of the control was excellent. There was a slight increase in heaviness with speed and angular deflection, but at diving speeds the ailerons were still pleasantly light. On this particular aircraft the ailerons were rigged so that the aircraft was slightly right wing low up to speeds of the order of 300 mph ASI, but above this figure the aircraft was laterally in trim. This feature was not particularly tiresome for general flying as only a light stick force was required to hold the aircraft level.

There was some loss in effectiveness in gliding flight but control was still considered to be adequate. These remarks are based on handling tests at moderate and low altitudes. On one flight made to 40,000 ft. it was reported that at that altitude there were slight signs of aileron overbalance, but it has not been possible in the limited amount of flying which has been done to substantiate or investigate this report.

(c) *Rudder.* The rudder was very light and effective over the first few degrees of its movement, then increasing suddenly in heaviness and having no further effect. At speeds above 250 mph ASI a buffet similar to that experienced on the elevator occurred, being slight at low speeds and increasing in intensity with speed. It is understood that the manufacturer is investigating this matter.

Considered as a control the rudder was poor and was the least satisfactory feature of the aircraft, but it had little effect on the general flying and manoeuvring qualities of the aircraft, since this control is normally little used.

(d) *Elevator trimmer.* The range of the elevator trim tab was sufficient for all conditions of flight tested. It was possible to move the trimmer quickly throughout its full range, but at altitude the circuit tended to stiffen up, due presumably to congealing of lubricants.

There was very little change of longitudinal trim with speed, the aircraft becoming slightly tail heavy as speed increased.

5.4 Stability characteristics.

(a) *Longitudinal.* It has not been possible to carry out a full assessment of the longitudinal stability characteristics of the aircraft but the following impressions were gained by the pilots.

The aircraft felt slightly unstable at low speeds, the stability improving with speed. For general flying and manoeuvres the stability characteristics were satisfactory, though the degree of stability was probably slightly below the required standard.

The manoeuvrability of the aircraft in the looping plane was good, and the light elevator forces and degree of stability seemed to combine to give the aircraft excellent manoeuvring qualities. The radius of turn was not assessed in comparison with other fighter aircraft but it did not appear to be very different.

(b) *Directional.* The directional characteristics of the aircraft were abnormal and require thorough investigation. When flying in calm air there was a slight oscillation about the axis of yaw, and in rough air this was aggravated until the aircraft was thrown sideways quite violently and the resulting oscillations required a considerable time to damp out, even when corrective control was applied. The oscillation persisted even longer if no control action was taken.

The behaviour would seem to indicate a deficiency of damping following a directional disturbance and also an inability to hold course when passing through small disturbances. If the aircraft were disturbed in calm air the amplitude of the resulting motion was reduced to a negligible amount in three oscillations, but the remaining slight oscillation or 'snake' did not always damp out without use of the controls. When the aircraft was disturbed directionally by a bump the first oscillation was rapid and of large amplitude, followed by a series of rapid and decaying oscillations. The motion could be brought to a small degree fairly quickly by use of the controls, but this required considerable concentration from the pilot. It is thought that the rate of yaw was faster than could be dealt with by the normal automatic reactions of the pilot, and it should also be noted that it was not possible to eradicate the oscillation by holding on rudder in one direction and then slowly straightening out.

Considering the aircraft from the point of view of a gun-platform, which is the essence of a fighter aircraft, the directional characteristics are not satisfactory, though considered as a pure flying machine the behaviour is only unsatisfactory in rough air. Quantitative measurements to determine the characteristics of this feature should be made.

5.5 *Stalling characteristics.* It was not possible to carry out full tests in accordance with AP.970, Chap.906 to investigate the control and stability characteristics at and near the stall. The following points were, however, noted.

With flaps and undercarriage up deceleration was very slow and considerable height was gained whilst reducing speed. The stall was not clearly defined as such but a condition and speed was reached when it was extremely difficult to maintain lateral control. As speed was reduced the rudders became completely ineffective without the aircraft showing any tendency to yaw and the elevator became very light and ineffective. At 100 mph ASI the stick force was light, and a heavy and marked aileron 'snatch' occurred which caused the port wing and the nose to drop. The wing could be picked up by use of the ailerons but lateral control was very poor and constant control manipulation was required to hold level flight. The nose was high and whenever speed fell to 100 mph ASI the aileron snatch occurred and the left wing dropped, making it impossible to reduce speed further.

With flaps and undercarriage down the stalling characteristics were similar to those described above with similar control column position and control behaviour. At 80 mph ASI 'snatching' of both ailerons occurred accompanied by a drop of either wing and the nose, and it was impossible to maintain steady level flight.

5.6 *Dives.* The aircraft was dived to a speed of 490 mph ASI when trimmed for high speed level flight, and at high speeds the buffet of the elevator and rudders previously mentioned in para. 5.3 became marked. The buffet was of small amplitude and appeared to the pilot as a control vibration. There was very little change of longitudinal trim with speed and apart from the slight directional oscillation the aircraft was steady in the dive and responsive to all controls. The acceleration in the dive was very quick. Recovery was easy and the stick force required was light.

5.7 *Aerobatics.* All normal fighter aerobatics and manoeuvres were carried out, and apart from the fact that the poor rudder control made precise rolling difficult, the behaviour of the aircraft was satisfactory.

5.8 *Approach and landing.* The best approach speed was found to be 110 mph ASI decreasing to 100 to 95 mph ASI when crossing the airfield boundary. The approach glide was flat and it is considered that more flap to steepen the angle of descent would be an advantage. However, the present arrangement is considered to be well within the limits of acceptability. The view was good and landing was straightforward and easy. The best method seemed to be to touch down on the two main wheels with the nose wheel just clear of the ground and then allow the aircraft to rock gently forward on to the nose wheel during the ground run. A landing with the tail well down is inadvisable as damage to the tail unit may be easily incurred. The brakes were smooth and powerful in operation and the aircraft showed no tendency to swing during the landing run.

No baulked landing tests were carried out.

6.   Operational assessment.

With the exception of the present directional behaviour which is unsatisfactory for gunnery, the flying characteristics of the de Havilland E6/41 compare very favourably with present day fighter aircraft. From the performance view-point, the flying done on the aircraft indicates that the speed is considerably greater at low altitudes though not much greater at height. However, the fuel consumption at low altitudes is very high and operation as a low altitude fighter would be difficult because of the resulting short duration. Also, the rate of climb is poor for a short range fighter which is an operational disadvantage.

It should also be noted that at present engine maintenance is more difficult than on conventional types because of the necessity of frequent inspections to the auxiliaries, but no doubt this will be overcome as more experience is gained. External starting equipment is necessary because of the high starting current required.

As the engine exists in its present form there is no equivalent of the normal boost control, and the throttle has to be progressively retracted as altitude is gained in order to prevent the engine speed becoming excessive. However, it is understood that a barostatic control is under development which will relieve the pilot of the necessity of constant attention to the throttle. Some such device is most desirable.

It is considered that formation flying would be rather more difficult than on other present-day Service types due to the less ready response to throttle movements.

7.   Conclusions.

The flying qualities of the de Havilland E6/41 compare very favourably with present day fighter aircraft; the most striking points are the excellent aileron control, the ease of manoeuvre in the looping plane, the comfortable and well laid-out cockpit, the extremely low noise level, and the high speed at low altitudes.

The chief points for consideration arising from these brief tests are:–

(i)   The thickness of the cockpit canopy framework detracts from the view sideways and the rearward view is also poor. Both these points require improvement.

(ii)   The substitution of a spade grip for the present type of control column grip would cater for a wider range of pilot's preference, and is considered desirable.

(iii)   The pin locking the hood jettison lever should be replaced by a wire locking which can be sheared easily in an emergency.

(iv)   A mechanical trip should be fitted in the undercarriage system in place of the present lock so that the undercarriage can be raised on the ground in the event of the brakes failing.

(v)   The directional characteristics are the most unsatisfactory feature of the aircraft and its directional unsteadiness may seriously impair the fighting efficiency of the aircraft in its present form.

(vi)   Acceleration in level flight did not appear to be so good as on other current fighter types. Due to its low drag the deceleration was also lower but it is understood that air brakes may be fitted in production to overcome this.

(vii) Difficulties in the tactical operation of the type may be caused by its short duration, relatively poor rate of climb and possible difficulties in formation flying.

(viii) As the engine exists at present frequent inspection of the engine auxiliaries is necessary.

Both the Meteor and the Vampire jets prototypes performed well enough considering they were the first of a totally new generation of aircraft which differed fundamentally from the preceding piston engined types, which had slowly been evolved and refined over forty years. That the test pilots at the A&AEE found points of criticism is hardly surprising; what is surprising is the almost casual way in which these revolutionary aircraft were first flown. Pilots from the A&AEE went to Moreton Valence, where they presumably talked to the Gloster Company's test pilots, then, without benefit of Pilot's Notes, dual control or ejector seats, each A&AEE pilot flew the first jet aircraft he had ever seen – indeed it is unlikely that they had even flown a high performance aircraft with a tricycle undercarriage before.

Later, not only were all four of the slightly different prototypes flown, the pilots also made a definitive evaluation: altogether a remarkable demonstration of the extremely high standard of the wartime A&AEE test flying – a performance soon to be repeated with the Vampire tests. It is pertinent here to remark that if average RAF squadron pilots, used to flying a proven service aircraft, found themselves in control of the first prototype, they would probably be astonished that it was the same type.

A&AEE handling trials of both Meteor and Vampire prototypes continued with mounting urgency in view of the numerous – and excellent – jet powered designs being used operationally by the Luftwaffe and being revealed by RAF photographic reconnaissance of the German factory airfields and the rough equivalent of Boscombe Down (and Farnborough) – Rechlin, where the secret prototypes were tested.

In the autumn of 1944, a Meteor I, EE212, powered by two Rolls-Royce W.2(B)/23-C centrifugal jets (in all but name Wellands), was subjected to further handling trials at Boscombe Down. The A&AEE report[4] noted that the aircraft had modified ailerons, fin and rudder (as a consequence of the earlier A&AEE test flights) and thus was no longer representative of the Mk I or the current production Mk IIIs. The aircraft was test flown at an AUW of 11,670 lb.

The pilots reported that EE212 was 'in general pleasant and easy to fly and had good stability characteristics about all axes. . . . [But] the stick forces to pull out from untrimmed dives, were too high for a fighter aircraft. At low speeds the elevator was light and effective. The ailerons were (deliberately) heavy, and the rudder heavy and rather ineffective. . . . The behaviour under asymmetric power and during slow speed flight was good. The worst feature was the directional oscillation, which is being further investigated.'

The report then makes one of the first references to that much misunderstood word: 'Mach Number' (post-war to become associated in the popular press with the so called 'Sound Barrier'). 'The critical Mach No. of 0.74 was . . . considered rather low for this type of aircraft.' That sentence is, in reality, an indictment of the dated aerodynamics of the Meteor airframe. Almost exactly three years earlier, the German rocket-powered Me 163 V1 Komet had attained 635.85 mph in level flight, which corresponded to Mach .84, the delta wing of the Messerschmitt enabling a high critical number to be achieved before the effects of compressibility were manifest. There was, after the war, to be ample evidence that the Germans were far ahead of any other country in the appreciation of the effect of transonic flight. They had, for example, constructed in the war years the first Mach 1 wind tunnel in the world.

The high speed trials of EE212 revealed the new problems being encountered as the 'sound barrier' – a purely journalistic invention, incidentally – was probed:

High Speed Flight. The aircraft gained speed rapidly in the dive and once a high speed had been reached it could be maintained for a considerable period in level flight.

Trimmed dives were made from both low and high altitudes. Change of longitudinal trim with speed was moderate up to the maximum speed reached of 470 mph ASI. There was no noticeable change of directional or lateral trim with speed.

At speeds above 400 mph the directional oscillation already referred to was present the whole time even in smooth air and was definitely uncomfortable.

In the first series of dives the aircraft was trimmed for level flight at 270 mph ASI at 12,000 ft and 15,700 rpm. The elevator force to hold the aircraft in the dive increased with speed up to 30 lb at 470 mph ASI . . . a stick force of 40 lb was required to hold the aircraft in the dive, the accelerometer reading on releasing the stick . . . being 3½ 'G'. . . . These stick forces were considered to be unduly high for a fighter aircraft.

The critical Mach No. of 0.74 could be very easily reached at high altitude, even with the engine throttled back. When this critical Mach No. was reached in an untrimmed dive [i.e. aircraft trimmed for 'hands off' level flight], there was a sudden easing of the forward pressure required on the control column. It was also noted that at this condition the ailerons appeared lighter than at the same ASI at lower altitudes. Recovery at this condition showed no dangerous characteristics.

At the other end of the flight envelope the Meteor had a satisfactory stall:

Flaps and undercarriage up. The stall was preceded by buffeting of the tailplane and elevator at about 5 mph above the stall . . . when the stall occurred, the nose fell straight to below the horizon. . . . The rate of sink during stalled flight was small.

Actual stalling speed at around 10,500 lb AUW were:

Flaps up and u/c up: 92 mph ASI
Flaps up and u/c down: 86 mph ASI

EE212, the subject of the above report, was destined to remain at the A&AEE for some time as part of the urgent work of investigating jet powered aircraft; it was to become, as a consequence, the first two-seater Meteor when, in April 1945, it was: 'to be used for the development of test techniques. In order to obtain reliable instrument readings, it is the intention to fit instruments and an observer's seat in the *ammunition compartment*.'*[5]

The instruments the observer had to read visually from his cramped billet – there were no 'black boxes' at that time to monitor them automatically – were:

Altimeter
Balanced bridge thermometer
Two flow meters (40–250 gph)
Two ESI (engine speed indicators) (0–20,000 rpm)
Two jet pipe total head pressure gauges
Two jet pipe thermometers (400–700°C)
Two fuel pressure gauges (0–500 lb/sq in)
Two compressor delivery pressure gauges (0–60 lb/sq in absolute)

As a concession, the last four items could 'if possible . . . be photographed by a camera controlled by the observer.'

The wartime A&AEE civilian flight observers certainly must have been dedicated men.

While the Meteor was undergoing trials with the A&AEE (it was, of course, by this time in squadron service with the RAF), the Vampire was progressing, though unlike the Meteor, it would be too late to see wartime service.

From July to October 1945, the first production Vampire, F.Mk 1, TG274, powered by a D.H. Goblin I, 2,700 lb s.t. (No. 1112 DGN 27-2), was based at Boscombe Down for handling trials. The European War was now over but the Japanese still were undefeated and the Allied air forces were still on a war footing, therefore the work of investigating jet powered flight went on unabated. The A&AEE report[6] noted:

The aircraft [TG274] was the first production Vampire I to be made by Messrs. English Electric [de Havillands were too committed to Mosquito and other production to undertake the Vampire at Hatfield]. . . . The salient external features of the aircraft were as follows: Plain unslotted air brake flaps were fitted at the trailing edge of the mainplane between the ailerons and the [tail] booms.
Engine air intakes in the leading edge of each wing root.

* Authors' italics

A sliding balloon non-rear view type hood was provided, with a flat bullet proof windscreen.

Carriers for drop tanks were fitted on the underside of both mainplanes.

The flight trials were made at typical service loading of 8,610 lb. The main object of the trials was to clear the type for squadron use.

The handling trials proved that the Vampire I was, in general, a pleasant aircraft to fly. The stick force in the looping plane was considered too low 'for a modern fighter'; also the A&AEE test pilot found that the aileron overbalance noted on the prototype was even more marked on the 1st production aircraft.

The combat level speed of this aircraft was found to be higher than that of the Meteor III, as reported by the A&AEE:[7]

The results of the tests showed that, using combat engine conditions of 10,000 rpm and a weight of 8,180 lb the maximum level speed which could be attained without exceeding the critical Mach number (0.76) was 526 mph TAS, at 25,500 ft. Above this height it was necessary to throttle back to avoid exceeding this limitation, which arose from a deterioration in handling qualities due to compressibility effects.

The normal engine limitations for the Vampire I were:

Max. rpm, take-off and combat:	10,000 rpm (5 min limit)
Max. rpm, take-off for climb:	9,500 rpm (30 min limit)
Max. rpm, take-off for cruise:	8,500 rpm continuous

Concurrent with the Vampire tests, a Meteor I, EE223, was also tested at Boscombe Down during February–March 1945,[8] to ascertain the maximum level speed attainable. This particular aircraft had been fitted at Hucknall with two experimental Rolls-Royce engines, W.2B/37s, which each offered a nominal maximum thrust of some 1,950 lb at ground level, at combat rpm. (The engine numbers were: Port 23/A.562283. Starboard 24/A.562284).

The aircraft was essentially similar to a normal production Meteor I, that is:

Normal short type engine nacelles.
Meteor I folding cockpit canopy.
Aerial mast on top of fuselage.
I.F.F. (Identification Friend or Foe) Aerial beneath fuselage.
4 × 20 mm Mk.V cannon with muzzles and ejection chutes unsealed.

The results of the test showed that at combat engine conditions of 16,850 rpm ... at a weight of 11,400 lbs the maximum level speed was 465 mph True airspeed (TAS) at 16,000 ft. The combat level speed varied between 458 and 465 mph TAS over the height range from sea level to 25,000 ft.

For comparison, one of the fastest contemporary piston engined fighters, the P 51D Mustang, achieved 437 mph at 25,000 ft and the production Vampire I, was over 60 mph faster than the Meteor III at 25,000 ft.

Once it became obvious to the Air Staff that the jet engine was to be the primary power plant of future military aircraft and not just an alternative, thought was given to the problem of operations in tropical climates, in particular the question of sand and dust ingestion which had been a cause for concern with piston engined fighters in the Western Desert. Clearly it would not be possible to fit air filters to a jet – that had been difficult enough with conventional engines. To discover the feasibility of operations in such an environment, between September and November 1945, a Meteor III, EE336, powered by a Rolls-Royce Derwent RB37 engine, took part in 'Intensive Flying Trials Under Tropical Conditions'. The relevant section of the subsequent A&AEE Report[9] is here reproduced:

1.1 *Tests Required.*   A programme of 300 hours intensive flying is being carried out at Khartoum on Meteor III EE.336 and this Report deals with the first 150 hours flying.

1.2 *Description of Aircraft at beginning of Tests.*   The aircraft was a standard production Meteor III, which had been crated and shipped to Port Sudan for erection. The aircraft was flown to Khartoum from Port Sudan making a total flying time of 3 hours 40 minutes before intensive flying commenced. The engines were Derwent RB.37 type fitted with Graviner fire extinguishers but were not fully tropicalised.

2.   Test Summary.

2.1 *General.*   The flying was done by two attached pilots with considerable operational experience on this type of aircraft. The ground maintenance was done by an attached ground crew from a Meteor Squadron under technical supervision of A.&.A.E.E. personnel. Representatives of both firms concerned were also available for advice and assistance.

The aircraft was flown between the 27th September and 1st November, 1945, for a total of 150 hours 30 minutes covering 148 flights mainly at an approximate take-off weight of 12,000 lb., c.g. 6" aft of datum. A 180 gallon fuselage drop tank was fitted for the last 30 hours flying but was not used as fittings were not available.

The Report continues:

4.   Assessment of Aircraft by Attached Operational Crews.

Nothing unusual was noted in the flying and handling characteristics under tropical conditions. The take-off run tended to be slightly longer than under temperate conditions but not appreciably so.

Cockpit comfort and layout were considered to be good and were favourably commented on by the two pilots who had each done 75 hours flying in the five week period of tests, often at midday and with the aircraft outside all day in the sun. The travel of the throttle levers was considered to be too long for convenient handling.

The cockpit heating system was not being used owing to the danger of cockpit contamination when the engine surges.

5.   Special Tests.

5.1 *Sand Trials.*   Three special sand trials were carried out at 86 hrs. 45 mins., 140 hrs. 45 mins., and 150 hrs. 30 mins. These sand trials consisted of running the Meteor engines 20 yards behind another aircraft with engines running, both aircraft being stationary and standing on the surface of the airfield. The arrangement of both aircraft can be seen and shows the intensity of the 'artificial sandstorm' so raised. [See photograph section.] The surface of the airfield where these tests were carried out consisted of loose fine sand with a fine covering of small stones of approximately pea size. It was noted that these small stones did not rise to the height of the Meteor engine nacelles and it is doubtful if any of these found their way into the engines.

After each sand trial the aircraft was examined for damage or effect, the following being noted:–

5.11 No damage could be seen to the turbine blades or guide vanes. There were no signs of the sand having scoured the blade edges or surfaces.

A large quantity of sand had obviously passed through the engines as the inside of the nacelles were thickly coated where fuel or oil had helped it to adhere and there was a coating of sand some .25 ins. thick at the bottom of the nacelle where it had 'drifted' against a former.

5.12 Very little sand was found on the fuselage, flying controls or undercarriage. This was due to the aircraft having been kept in a very clean condition throughout the trials with the minimum amount of lubricant used on all exposed moving parts.

5.13 A considerable amount of fine sand was found in the gun blast tubes. This sand was of a fine nature and did not contain any of the small stones found on the airfield surface. The guns had very little sand in them and the gun bays were very clean.

5.2 *Oil Consumption.*   The engine oil consumption was very low, throughout the tests. The port engine used 8 pints and the starboard engine 7 pints.

The gear box oil consumption was also very low, each engine consuming approximately 3 pints.

5.3 *Oil Cooling.*   The oil temperatures and pressures have remained within the limitations under all conditions of flight and during ground running and taxying.

6. Further Developments.

The trials are continuing on this aircraft at Khartoum to complete 300 hrs. flying under tropical conditions.

With those tropical trials, the Meteor and the Vampire pass from wartime to peace and thus beyond the scope of this present volume. Further testing and assessment of both these pioneer jet aircraft were, of course, made at Boscombe; indeed it could be said that they established the techniques of jet aircraft testing which have been developed to the high standards used today at A&AEE.

Post-war, the Meteor and the Vampire were to become the mainstay of RAF Fighter Command for a decade or more; Meteors served as front line fighters with some 26 RAF and RAFVR squadrons. Despite their conventional design, they were to prove to be tough and adaptable; later Meteor Mks (F4s) were powered by two Rolls-Royce Derwents offering 3,600 lb and a special Meteor F.4 (EE549) of the RAF High Speed Flight raised the world's speed record to 616 mph on 7 September 1946. A two-seater trainer, the T.7, was built, as were photographic reconnaissance and night fighter variants, the NF.11 to 14s. The last batch of single-seater Meteors, the F.8, were also Rolls-Royce Derwent powered. In all, 3,947 Meteors of all Mks had been built, many exported to foreign air forces, when production ceased in July 1954.

The de Havilland Vampire, too, was a success, 40 RAF and Royal Auxilliary Air Force squadrons at one time or another flying the type, excluding a number of Sea Vampires embarked on carriers with the Royal Navy's Fleet Air Arm, the first of which (LZ551) made a pioneer jet aircraft deck landing and performed subsequent carrier trials during December 1945. Like the Meteor, the Vampire was also developed into a two-seater for training (T.11) and as a night fighter (NF.10). In all 4,206 Vampires of all Mks had been delivered when production ceased in Britain in December 1953 – the largest number post-war of a single type. Vampires were a considerable export success; apart from ex-RAF aircraft flown by foreign air forces, Vampires were also licence built in Switzerland,

Austria and India. Though, in the 1970s, being supplanted in front line service, substantial numbers of Vampires are still operating around the world as trainers.

Although both these first generation British jet fighters were successful, they had their limitations, due in the main to a lack of appreciation on the part of their designers of the problems of transonic flight. In mitigation it must be pointed out that they were conceived at a time when – in Britain – no wind tunnel capable of simulating supersonic flight existed and the problems of high speed flight and its associated compressibility, the 'sound barrier', were then purely theoretical.

Post-war, there is little doubt that the British aircraft industry was to exhibit a curiously Luddite attitude to the work into transonic flight made by the Germans. The Americans and Russians had no such inhibitions, with the result that the United States saved themselves ten years of research and billions of dollars to get into space and the Russians, helped, it must be said, by Sir Stafford Cripps' free gift of the best of the early jets, the Rolls-Royce Nene, lost no time in using that unlicenced built engine to power their swept wing MiG-15. This aircraft came as a distinct surprise to United Nations pilots during the Korean war, so much so that the RAF declined to field any British jets at all, only the US North American F-86E and Fs Sabres, swept wing fighters of roughly the same high performance (maximum speed around 670 mph) as the Chinese and Korean piloted MiG-15Gs (NATO code name Fagot).

Whatever their shortcomings, in the 1950s the Meteor and Vampire played a major, indeed a vital, role in getting the RAF's Fighter Command into the jet age. The Vampire (with its later development, the D.H. Venom) remains the only single-engined jet fighter to be used by the RAF. The RAF Historical Flight retain two immaculate airworthy examples of these aircraft: Vampire (XH304) and Meteor (WA669), which, as the 'vintage pair', continue to delight the public at the many summer airshows.

Notes for Chapter One

1   22nd Part of Report No. A&AEE/760a: 'General review of Halifax II' Part 3 'Trials of Halifax II DG221'.
2   Ibid. Appendix C.
3   Ibid.
4   DG221 was one of four Halifax IIs tested at Boscombe Down. Another of the quartet, W7776 was noted in the report (22nd Part A&AEE/760) as having been 'treated with a very rough special night black finish. The finish beneath the body, where congealed masses of oil and paint had formed in places, was particularly bad. There was evidence of poor workmanship – some of the fuselage plating was warped and the bomb doors were fitting badly. Engine cowlings were also in bad condition'.
5   This report is referred to in the summary of the 22nd Part of Report No. A&AEE/760a: 'General review of Halifax II Performance', October 1942. The relevant report of the results of 'cleaning up' L9515 do not seem to have survived.
6   The accident report on Halifax II, W7917, is contained in PRO File AIR29–897, A&AEE Operation Record Book 1939–44 – Appendix A.
7   32nd Part of Report No. A&AEE/760a: 'Further Investigation of the Behaviour of Halifax subsequent to rudder overbalance'. S/Ldr. J. W. Truran, 20 May 1942.
8   Ibid.
9   Ibid.
10 Ibid.
11 Ibid.
12 3rd Part of Report No. A&AEE/760c: Halifax V DK145, 'Handling trials with large D type fins', 8 August 1943.

Notes for Chapter Two

1   See Appendix 1 to 2nd Part of Report No. A&AEE/751: 'History of Manchester Trials at Boscombe Down'.
2   Contained, *inter alia*, in a letter dated 22 January 1940 (ref. A&AEE/4475/ 35) from E. T. Jones, Chief Technical Officer, A&AEE, to Air Ministry Dept. ZA, Harrogate.
3   Ibid.
4   This figure of +9 lb/sq inch should be treated with reserve since it appears to exceed the limitations of the early Vulture engine.
5   Appendix I. 2nd Part of Report No. A&AEE/751.
6   2nd Part of Report No. A&AEE/751, 3 December 1940.

7 *Aircraft of The Royal Air Force*, 1918–58 (p. 54), Owen Thetford, Putnam, London, 1958.

8 For a detailed history of all Manchesters (and Lancasters) see *Lancaster – The Story of a Famous Bomber*, Bruce Robertson, Harleyford, Letchworth, 1964. p. 145 et seq.

9 Ibid.

10 Instrument Trials contained in 1st Part/751, issued 13 September 1940.

11 'U/S' was current RAF slang, being the usual abbreviation for 'unserviceable'. It was not a disparaging reflection on American equipment.

12 8th Part of Report No. A&AEE/751, 27 May 1941.

13 In 1940 the concept of a 'Safety Speed' meant the minimum at which an aircraft could be controlled by the pilot without regard to performance.

14 8th Part /751.

15 12th Part of Report No. A&AEE/751, 14 November 1941, 'Tail Structure Vibration'.

16 13th Part of Report No. A&AEE/751, 30 December 1941.

17 In a 1981 letter to the authors.

18 'The Strategic Air Offensive Against Germany'.

Notes for Chapter Three

1 1st Part of Report No. A&AEE/766. BT308 (Four Merlin XXs) 'Preliminary Handling Trials', 3 March 1941.

2 2nd Part of Report No. A&AEE/766. BT308 'Maximum level speed'.

3 3rd Part of Report No. A&AEE/766. 'Further investigations in flight with one and two engines cut', 16 April 1941.

4 20th Part of Report No. A&AEE/766. DG595 'Level speed trials', 4 April 1942.

5 30th Part of Report No. A&AEE/766. Lancaster Is R5539 and R5546, 'Diving Trials', 17 December 1942.

6 41st Part of Report No. A&AEE/766. Lancaster I W4963, 'Take-off, climb and level speed performance at 63,000 lbs', 19 October 1943.

7 Standard Day: 15°C at a sea level pressure of 1,013.2 millibars and a lapse rate of 1.98° per 1,000 ft up to 36,090 ft, temperature constant at −57.5°C above that height.

8 42nd Part of Report No. A&AEE/766. DV297, 'Performance and Handling of Production Aircraft', 21 October 1943.

9 7th Part of Report No. A&AEE/766a. 'Fuel consumption range and operation of a Lancaster II, DT810, fitted with four Hercules VI engines', issued 7 September 1942.

10 Fuel flow for a given height and engine setting is proportional to $1/\sqrt{}$ absolute air temperature.

11 13th Part of Report No. A&AEE/766d. 'Level Speeds', 20 November 1942.

12 56th Part of Report No. A&AEE/766. Lancaster I W4963 (Merlin 22s), 'The effect of H_2S blister on performance', 6 June 1944.

13 71st Part of Report No. A&AEE/766. W9408, 'Handling with enlarged H_2S blister', 13 May 1945.

14 50th Part of Report No. A&AEE/766. Lancaster I, JB127 (Four Merlin 24s), 'Climb and Level Speed performance', 30 April 1944.

15 54th Part of Report No. A&AEE/766. Lancaster I, JB127, 'Fuel consumption trials', 8 January 1944.

16 See 36th Part of Report No. A&AEE/766.

17 57th Part of Report No. A&AEE/766. JB127 (Merlin 24s), 'Climb and level speed performance with Paddle Blade propellers', 28 June 1944.

18 The modifications were the deletion of oil grooves in the governor control valve and the fitting of a new distribution valve assembly and larger oil feeds in the propeller. (See 63rd Part of Report No. A&AEE/766, 11 November 1944.

19 67th Part of Report No. A&AEE/766. Lancaster I PB592/G, 'Brief handling trials with and without 22,000 lb bombs'.

20 68th Part of Report No. A&AEE/766. Lancaster I PB592/G, 'Brief climb performance and determination of s.a.r. [Specific Air Range] with 22,000 lb bomb fitted', 28 March 1945.

21 82nd Part of Report No. A&AEE/766. Lancaster I, PB592, 'Further handling with 22,000 lb and 12,000 lb DP bombs in modified bomb bay fittings', 27 June 1945.

22 75th Part of Report No. A&AEE/766. Lancaster I, PB592/G, 'Performance with and without 22,000 lb bomb after modification to aircraft', 7 September 1945.

23 82nd Part of Report No. A&AEE/766. Lancaster I, PB995, 'Determination of s.a.r. with 22,000 lb bomb', 30 July 1945.

24 84th Part of Report No. A&AEE/766. 'Overload trials in India to determine operational capability of the Lancaster under high temperature conditions'. A. S. Crouch and H. G. Newbigin, June 1945.

25 The A&AEE test results (except for take-off) were converted to ICAN + 19°C, as data from the Met. Office showed the mean maximum temperature above 10,000 ft in the proposed area of operations to be closer to that value than the full tropical standard of ICAN + 26°C. Take-off data was corrected to ICAN +26°C. See 84th Part of Report No. A&AEE/766.

26 86th Part of Report No. A&AEE/766. LL813, 'Tests of reversible pitch propellers as a landing brake'.

27 To be strictly accurate, although RF355 was the last RAF operational Lancaster, there is (1982) an airworthy Lancaster on RAF charge: PA474, which forms part of the RAF Historical Flight based at Coningsby and which continues to delight airshow crowds throughout the summer months. One might also mention R5868 – the famous 'S' Sugar – a veteran of some 137 operations, preserved in the excellent RAF Museum at Hendon.

28 70th Part of Report No. A&AEE/766. Lancaster I, PB731 (Four Merlin 22s), 'Handling trials of an alleged rogue aircraft'.

29 29th Part of Report No. A&AEE/766. Lancaster II, DS670 (Four Hercules XVIs), 'Brief handling trials of an alleged rogue aircraft'.

Notes for Chapter Four

1 *Aircraft of the Fighting Powers*, Vol. 4, p. 8. Harborough, Leicester, 1944.
2 4th Part of Report No. A&AEE/768, 1 October 1941.
3 This figure is quoted (with all performance details) in *The Book of Westland Aircraft*, Aircraft and Technical Publications, Leicester, 1944.
4 A&AEE Report M.4/4493/36 – AM46, 'Note on Handling of Short Half Scale Model B.12/36 Stirling', 24 November 1938.
5 1st Part of Report A&AEE/812, 25 August 1943, 'Boulton Paul P92/2 V3142'.
6 For an excellent and detailed history of the Martin-Baker aircraft see 'The Martin-Baker Aircraft', Parts 1 and 2 by Bill Gunston, published in *Aeroplane Monthly*, October and November 1973
   See also 'Mr. Martin's Memorable M.B.5'., published in *Air International*, February 1979.
   See also *Engineering for Life*, the story of Martin-Baker, by John Jewell, published 1979 privately by the Martin-Baker Aircraft Co. Ltd., Denham, Buckinghamshire.
7 A&AEE (Martlesham Heath) Report No. M/730/Q1, 'Martin-Baker PV.F5/34, Ease of Maintenance'.
8 A&AEE Reference: M.H/4487/27-AS62, 7 December 1938. The letter was addressed to N. E. Rowe Esq., Air Ministry (A.D./R.D.A.), Berkeley Square, London, W.1.
9 A&AEE Ref: AS62, 'Decisions made at Conference on Martin-Baker Aeroplane,' Internal Memorandum dated 31 December 1938.
10 A&AEE Report M/730/2, 'Martin-Baker F3/34 P9594 (Dagger Special), Handling trials after Modification', 17 July 1939.
11 'The Martin-Baker Aircraft', by Bill Gunston (quoted above).
12 Ibid.

Notes for Chapter Five

1 Report No. A&AEE/749, 13 November 1939.
2 8th Part of Report No. A&AEE/749a, 5 April 1941.
3 *Famous Bombers of the Second World War* (Second Series). William Green. Macdonald, London 1960.
4 Report No. A&AEE/752. Douglas DB7. 'Report on inspection and handling flights', 22 April 1940.
5 Ibid, Appendix A.
6 Interim Report No. A&AEE/752a. Douglas Boston AE758, 'Preliminary performance and operational data', 16 September 1940.
7 5th Part of Report No. A&AEE/762. Martlet 1, AX826 'Handling trials', 22 August 1941.
8 8th Part of Report No. A&AEE/762a. 'Martlet II Brief Performance Trials.'
9 Quoted by James Gilbert, p. 117 *The World's Worst Aircraft*. M. J. Hobbs and Michael Joseph Ltd, London 1975.

10 1st Part of Report No. A&AEE/762. Brewster 339B Buffalo, 22 September 1941.

11 2nd Part of Report No. A&AEE/722. Brewster 339s 'Brief Handling trials with C of G extended aft', 13 July 1941.

12 *United States Navy Aircraft Since 1911* (2nd Edition), p. 73. Gordon Swanborough & Peter M. Bowen. Putnam, London 1976.

13 2nd and 3rd Parts of Report No. A&AEE/765. 'Maryland I Performance Trials', 3 April 1941.

14 1st Part of Report No. A&AEE/773. Chesapeake I, AL909 and AL913. 'The determination of the maximum weight and most aft CG position', 26 September 1941.

15 2nd Part of Report No. A&AEE/773. 'Chesapeake I AL913 performance tests and fuel consumption', 4 November 1941.

16 The armament is quoted from a copy of A.P.2064A: 'Pilot's notes, The Airacobra I Aeroplane', 1st Issue, March 1941. This early publication (printed before the aircraft arrived in the UK) was valid only up to aircraft AH629. Commencing AH630, certain changes were made which might have included an anglicisation of the armament to .303 Browning guns, which some Airacobras carried.

17 7th Part of Report No. A&AEE/774. 'Airacobra AH574, Climb and Level Speed Performance', 9 July 1942.

18. 9th Part of Report No. A&AEE/774, 25 August 1942.

19 3rd Part of Report No. A&AEE/781 Mustang I, AG351. 'Brief handling trials', 19 May, 1942.

20 The reference to 'sideslip' when making a cross wind landing means the pilots adopted the usual wartime practice of making a cross wind approach with 'one wing low' technique; this enables a pilot to align his aircraft with the runway and sideslip off the drift caused by the cross wind. Today it would be usual to employ the 'crabbing' technique, whereby the aircraft is crabbed down to the runway to compensate for the drift, the pilot, 'kicking off the drift', with the rudder, just prior to touchdown.

21 11th Part of Report No. A&AEE/781. Mustang I, AG351, 'Fuel consumption trials'.

22 Report No. A&AEE/769/F1. Liberator AM912, 'Accident during landing trials', 18 May 1941.

23 Ibid.

24 2nd Part of Report No. A&AEE/769. Liberator I AM929. 'Acceptance trials with ASV installation', 26 August 1941.

25 5th Part of Report No. A&AEE/769. 'Diving trials', 7 November 1941.

26 9th Part of Report No. A&AEE/769. Liberators II AL505 and AL506. 'Comparative trials of English and American compass installation', 19 January 1942.

27 Ibid.

28 Quoted by Roger A. Freeman in his book p.12 *B-17 Fortress at War*, Ian Allan, Shepperton, Surrey, 1977.

29 2nd Part of Report No. A&AEE/770. Boeing B-17C AN531, 'Noise measurement', 30 June 1941.

30   3rd Part of Report No. A&AEE/770. 'Handling, 2 and 3 engine flight and diving trial', 13 August 1941.
31   4th Part of Report No. A&AEE/770. 'Brief performance trials', 13 August 1941.
32   Ibid.
33   1st Part of Report No. A&AEE/758. 'Lightning I AF106, Brief Handling trials', 26 September 1942.
34   4th Part of Report No. A&AEE/811. 'Seamew FN475, Brief Handling trials', 22 September 1943.
35   Performance data from Owen Thetford: *British Naval Aircraft 1912–58*, p. 96, Putnam, London, 1958.

Notes for Chapter Six

1   2nd Part of Report No. A&AEE/703h. 'Wellington VI, W5795, Night Flying Trials'.
2   4th Part of Report No. A&AEE/703h. 'Wellington VI. Pressure Cabin. Assessment of Pilots' Domes.' April 1942.
3   Ibid.
4   Ibid.
5   5th Part of Report No. A&AEE/703h. 'Full load climb'.
6   Ibid.
7   Source: Form 540 Appendix 'F' 765c in PRO File AIR29/897.
8   8th Part of Report No. A&AEE/703h. DR484 'Brief performance trials and estimate of range', December 1942.
9   'Merlin 62s' are given as DR484's engines, though other sources give Merlin 60s.
10   As note 8 above.
11   10th Part of Report No. A&AEE/703h. DR484 'Brief handling trials'.
12   11th Part of Report No. A&AEE/703h. DR482 'Performance in climb and level flight', December 1942, January 1943.

Notes for Chapter Seven

1   Report No. A&AEE/751. 'Messerschmitt 109 Fighter, Brief handling trials', 10 June 1940.
2   Flt. Lt. G. H. Stainforth was a member of the victorious Schneider Trophy team. After the contest in 1931, Stainforth, piloting the Supermarine S6B S1596, achieved a world speed record of 379.05 mph on 13 September 1931.
3   Original source unknown. Report quoted to be found in Royal Air Force Museum, Aviation Records Department, Hendon, London. RAF Museum ref: AC/78/2.
4   Alfred Price, *Spitfire*, published by Macdonald & Jane's, London, 1977. 'Spitfire I Versus Messerschmitt 109', pp 65–67.

5 Ibid.

6 1st Part of Report No. A&AEE/799a. 'Special York LV633 (Merlin 22s) Acceptance Trials'. 27 May 1943.

7 Report No. A&AEE/Tech/51. 'The American Brodie System. Erection and Operation of Suspended Runway', 20 November 1946.

8 41st and 44th Part of Report A&AEE/777a. P9795/G. 'Brief handling trials with Cuda floats and containers'. (The writer was one of the joint present authors, Terry Heffernan).

9 Report No. A&AEE/Res/189. 'Anomalous deviations of the P4 compass in the Beaufighter produced by gun firing, the non-decay of the deviations and the practical cure'. Snowall & Preiss, August 1943.

Notes for Chapter Eight

1 The original letter is contained in PRO file AVIA 15/4.

2 Ibid. 'De Havilland's proposal for Bomber of Wooden construction'.

3 1st Part of Report No. A&AEE/767. 'Mosquito W4050 (2 Merlin XX1 engines). Preliminary Performance and Handling Trials'. 3 March 1941.

4 Ibid (Part II). 5 March 1941.

5 Ibid.

6 1st Part of Report No. A&AEE/767a. 'Mosquito II W4052. Longitudinal Stability'. 23 May 1941.

7 3rd Part of Report No. A&AEE/767a. 'Mosquito II W4052 Brief performance and handling trials'. 18 September 1941.

8 6th Part of Report No. A&AEE/767a. 'Longitudinal Stability tests with two different sizes of tailplane'. 13 February 1942.

9 8th Part of Report No. A&AEE/767a. 'Mosquito II W4070 (Merlin 21). Level speed measurements with matt and smooth black finish'. 28 April 1942.

10 12th Part of Report No. A&AEE/767a. 'Mosquito F. Mk II W4052 (2 Merlin 21s). Test with airbrake fitted round the fuselage'. 24 September 1942.

11 2nd Part of Report No. A&AEE/767e. 'Mosquito Mk VI HJ662/G (2 Merlin 21s). Brief handling and diving trials of Intruder version'. 1 October 1942.

12 6th Part of Report No. A&AEE/767e. 'Mosquito B Mk IV, DK290/G (2 Merlin 21s). Brief handling trials with stores in situ'. May 1943.

Notes for Chapter Nine

1 1st part of Report No. A&AEE/817: 'Gloster F9/40 2 W2B/23 engines. Preliminary handling trials', February 1944.

2 The original of this letter is in the form of an appendix attached to the A&AEE Meteor reports (A&AEE/817) contained in the Boscombe Down archives.

3   1st part of Report No. A&AEE/819: 'De Havilland E6/41 MP838/G, Handling trials', June 1944.
4   5th part of Report No. A&AEE/817: 'Meteor I EE212 (2 Rolls-Royce W2(B)/23-C) Handling trials', November 1944.
5   Memorandum from Superintendent of Performance dated 23 April 1945, A&AEE Ref. 5711,n/2, 'Meteor I EE212 Performance Test Instruction No. 13: Development of test techniques'.
See also A&AEE Note from D. Fraser: 'Meteor I. EE212 Instrumentation for development of test techniques', memo. dated 4 April 1945. (Original A&AEE Ref. Illegible.)
6   3rd part of Report No. A&AEE/819a: 'Vampire I TG274 (Goblin I) Preliminary handling trials of first production aircraft', June 1945.
7   4th part of Report No. A&AEE/819a: 'Vampire I TG274 (Goblin) Level Speed and Position Error Trials', October 1945.
8   16th part of Report No. A&AEE/817: 'Meteor I EE223 (Two Rolls-Royce W2B/37 engines) Maximum level speed performance', March 1945.
9   8th part of Report No. A&AEE/817: 'Meteor III EE336 (2 Derwent RB.37 engines) Intensive Flying Trials Under Tropical Conditions: Interim Report', November 1945.

APPENDIX A

Aircraft on Charge, September 1939

A Flt. Per T Section (Performance Testing)

Defiant	K8620	Magister	P2381
Defiant	L6053	Magister	U6
Defiant	L6950	Master	N7409
Gloster F5/34	K5604	Mentor	L4393
Heston	L7706	Pup T1/37	P6326
Hurricane	L1547	Spitfire	K9793
Lysander	L4739	Whirlwind	L6845

B Flt. Per T Section

Blenheim	L1348	Wellington	L4213
Blenheim	L4835	Wellington	N2865
Hampden	L4032	Wellington	R2700
Hardy	K5919	Whitley III	K8936
Hudson	N7205	Whitley V	N1345
Hudson	N7206		

C Flt. Per T Section

Blenheim	L1222	Hereford	L6003
Botha	L6105	Oxford	N4720
Cunliffe Owen	G-AMF B	Roc	L3057
Gladiator	K6129	Skua	L2667
Harvard	N7001	Skua	L2888
Hereford	L6002		

A Flt. Arm T Section (Armament Testing)

Battle	K9231	Hurricane	L1574
Defiant	K8310	Hurricane	L1695
Demon	K3764	Hurricane	L1750
Fantôme	L7045	Monospar	K8307
Gladiator	K7964	Roc	L3069
Gordon	K2749	Spitfire	L1007
Henley	L3247	Tiger Moth	K4281

B Flt. Arm T Section

Battle	K9221	Bombay	L3812
Battle	K9223	Hampden	L4035
Blenheim	L1253	Hampden	P1169
Blenheim	L1495	Hind	K2915
Blenheim	L8662	Skua	L2868
Blenheim	L8689	Wellington	N2874
Blenheim	K7044	Whitley	N1349

APPENDIX B

Aircraft on Charge, 10 May 1945

A Squadron No. 1 Flt.

Boston	BZ315	Spitfire	LA211		
Boston	BZ320	Spitfire	MD114		
Firefly	MB465	Spitfire	MD190		
Hawker F2/43	NX798	Spitfire	MF124		
Meteor	EE214	Spitfire	MV247		
Mosquito	RG182	Spitfire	RB146		
Mosquito	RG183	Spitfire	RM784		
Mustang	FX953	Spitfire	TB232		
Mustang	TK589	Thunderbolt	FL844		
Spitfire	EN397	Typhoon	MN290		
Spitfire	LA187				

A Squadron No. 2 Flt.

Hornet	RR919	Tempest	JN740
Hurricane	LE525	Tempest	JN798
Hurricane	LB743	Tempest	JN799
Mustang	KH766	Tempest	MW736
Mustang	TK586	Tempest	NV732
Spitfire	EE611	Tempest	NV946
Spitfire	RR238	Thunderbolt	FL849
Spitfire	TA822	Typhoon	MN861
Spitfire	RR238	Typhoon	SW535
Tempest	EJ891		

B Squadron No. 1 Flt.

Halifax	LV838	Lancaster	W4963
Halifax	LW125	Liberator	EW126
Halifax	NP849	Liberator	KG902
Halifax	NP924	Liberator (IX)	JT778
Halifax	PP225	Lincoln	RE232
Lancaster	HK541	Warwick	PN697
Lancaster	PD435	York	MW132

183

B Squadron No. 2 Flt.

Halifax	LV999/G	Lancaster	ND794/G
Lancaster	HK543	Lancaster	NN801
Lancaster	JB456	Lincoln	PW929
Lancaster	JB457	Lincoln	RE227
Lancaster	LL619	Stirling	EF517

C Squadron

Avenger	FN895	Firefly	Z1970
Avenger	JZ634	Hellcat	JX901
Barracuda	LS708	Helldriver	JW115
Barracuda	LS923	Seafire	PR314
Barracuda (VI)	P9976	Seafire	PX921
Corsair	KD834	Seafire	SR446
Firebrand	DK373	Seafire	SR448
Firebrand	DK396	Tigercat	TT349
Firefly	DT985	Wildcat	JV431
Firefly	MB576	Wildcat	JV528
Firefly	Z1844	Wildcat	JV875
Firefly	Z1909		

Communications & Special Duties Flt.

Albemarle	V1743	Magister	N3782
Anson	LT764	Martinet	JN303
Auster	NJ630	Mitchell	FV922
Auster	NJ631	Mitchell	FW151
Boston	W8315	Reliant	FK818
Defiant	N1579	Swordfish	LS364
Hudson	AM553	Tempest	SN219
Hurricane	KZ381	Traveller	FT461
Magister	L8253	Traveller	FT466

D Squadron No. 1 Flt.

Anson	NL171	Mosquito	HR303
Boston	BZ401	Mosquito	KB352
Boston	B2580	Mosquito	KB471
Buckingham	KV322	Mosquito	ML994
Buckingham	KV337	Mosquito	NS624
Buckmaster	RP122	Mosquito	RG176
Marauder	HD412	Mosquito	RG178
Mitchell	FV984	Mosquito	RG194
Mitchell	HD361	Warwick	HG215

D Squadron No. 2 Flt.

Beaufighter	EL393	Mitchell	FW143
Beaufighter	JL955	Mitchell	HD347
Mitchell	FJ904		

ETPS (Empire Test Pilots School)

Boston	BZ252	Mosquito	RF648
Boston	BZ346	Oxford	AS658
Harvard	FS718	Oxford	PG935
Harvard	FX229	Spitfire	LA192
Harvard	FX354	Spitfire	ML174
Hudson	V9222	Spitfire	NH194
Lancaster	ED491	Swordfish	HS642
Lancaster	ME830	Tempest	JN732
Lancaster	R5842	Tempest	JN739
Meteor	EE213	Tempest	JN770
Mosquito	KB552	Tiger Moth	T6831
Mosquito	RF644		

IFDF (Intensive Flying Development Flight)

Barracuda	LS837	Tempest	MW801
Buckingham	KV358	Tempest	MW802
Lincoln	RE228	Tempest	MW803
Lincoln	RE230	Tempest	MW804
Reliant	FK894	Tempest	MW805
Spitfire	LV674	Tempest	MW806

INDEX

Typhoon 66

Unwin, J. J. 6, 35

V1s 156
  deviation problems 134
Vickers 104, 112
  Foxwarren factory 105
Vickers Wellesley 104
Vindicator 90
Vokert, G. R. 1
Vought-Sikorsky Chesapeake 88–90
  A&AEE report 89–90
  French orders transferred to Britain 89
  in USN service 88–9
  performance 90

Walker, C. C. 136
Wallis, Barnes
  designs Wellington 103, 104
  'Grand Slam' bomb design 33, 40
Wasp, USS 89
Wellington 14, 103
  high-altitude 103
    A&AEE report 106–12
    crash during test 1942 113

performance 114
pilots' domes for 112–13
pressurisation 104
production of 113–14, 115
prototypes 104, 105
tests of production aircraft 114–15
nicknamed 'Wimpey' 103
numbers built 103
wartime service 103
Westland Co. 55
Westland Lysander 55
  numbers built 55
  tandem winged version 55–6
Whitley bomber 14
Whittle, Wing Cdr. (later Sir) Frank 149, 150
Wildcat, *see* Martlet I
Wilkes, S. B. 150
Wolverhampton Dreadnought 59–60
Wright Cyclone engine 86

Yamamoto, Adm.
  shot down by P-38 Lightning 101

Zero fighter 79
Zurakowski, Sqn. Ldr. Jan 75

193